PLANE AND SPHERICAL TRIGONOMETRY

BOOKS BY
C. I. PALMER

(Published by the McGraw-Hill Book Company, Inc.)

PALMER AND BIBB'S
Practical Mathematics

    Part I—Arithmetic with Applications

    Part II—Algebra with Applications

    Part III—Geometry with Applications

    Part IV—Trigonometry and Logarithms

PALMER'S
Practical Mathematics for Home Study

PALMER'S
Practical Calculus for Home Study

PALMER AND LEIGH'S
Plane and Spherical Trigonometry with Tables

PALMER AND KRATHWOHL'S
Analytic Geometry

PALMER AND MISER'S
College Algebra

(Published by Scott, Foresman and Company)

PALMER, TAYLOR, AND FARNUM'S
Plane Geometry

PALMER, TAYLOR, AND FARNUM'S
Solid Geometry

PALMER, TAYLOR, AND FARNUM'S
Plane and Solid Geometry

PLANE AND SPHERICAL TRIGONOMETRY

BY

CLAUDE IRWIN PALMER

Late Professor of Mathematics and Dean of Students, Armour Institute of Technology; Author of a Series of Mathematics Texts

AND

CHARLES WILBER LEIGH

Professor Emeritus of Analytic Mechanics, Armour Institute of Technology, Author of Practical Mechanics

FOURTH EDITION
SEVENTEENTH IMPRESSION

McGRAW-HILL BOOK COMPANY, Inc.

NEW YORK AND LONDON

1934

THE MAPLE PRESS COMPANY, YORK, PA.

PREFACE TO THE FOURTH EDITION

This edition presents a new set of problems in Plane Trigonometry. The type of problem has been preserved, but the details have been changed. The undersigned acknowledges indebtedness to the members of the Department of Mathematics at the Armour Institute of Technology for valuable suggestions and criticisms. He is especially indebted to Profs. S. F. Bibb and W. A. Spencer for their contribution of many new identities and equations and also expresses thanks to Mr. Clark Palmer, son of the late Dean Palmer, for assisting in checking answers to problems and in proofreading and for offering many constructive criticisms.

CHARLES WILBER LEIGH.

CHICAGO,
  June, 1934.

PREFACE TO THE FIRST EDITION

This text has been written because the authors felt the need of a treatment of trigonometry that duly emphasized those parts necessary to a proper understanding of the courses taken in schools of technology. Yet it is hoped that teachers of mathematics in classical colleges and universities as well will find it suited to their needs. It is useless to claim any great originality in treatment or in the selection of subject matter. No attempt has been made to be novel only; but the best ideas and treatment have been used, no matter how often they have appeared in other works on trigonometry.

The following points are to be especially noted:

(1) The measurement of angles is considered at the beginning.

(2) The trigonometric functions are defined at once for any angle, then specialized for the acute angle; not first defined for acute angles, then for obtuse angles, and then for general angles. To do this, use is made of Cartesian coordinates, which are now almost universally taught in elementary algebra.

(3) The treatment of triangles comes in its natural and logical order and is not *forced* to the first pages of the book.

(4) Considerable use is made of the line representation of the trigonometric functions. This makes the proof of certain theorems easier of comprehension and lends itself to many useful applications.

(5) Trigonometric equations are introduced early and used often.

(6) Anti-trigonometric functions are used throughout the work, not placed in a short chapter at the close. They are used in the solutions of equations and triangles. Much stress is laid upon the principal values of anti-trigonometric functions as used later in the more advanced subjects of mathematics.

(7) A limited use is made of the so-called "laboratory method" to impress upon the student certain fundamental ideas.

(8) Numerous carefully graded practical problems are given and an abundance of drill exercises.

(9) There is a chapter on complex numbers, series, and hyperbolic functions.

(10) A very complete treatment is given on the use of logarithmic and trigonometric tables. This is printed in connection with the tables, and so does not break up the continuity of the trigonometry proper.

(11) The tables are carefully compiled and are based upon those of Gauss. Particular attention has been given to the determination of angles near 0 and 90°, and to the functions of such angles. The tables are printed in an unshaded type, and the arrangement on the pages has received careful study.

The authors take this opportunity to express their indebtedness to Prof. D. F. Campbell of the Armour Institute of Technology, Prof. N. C. Riggs of the Carnegie Institute of Technology, and Prof. W. B. Carver of Cornell University, who have read the work in manuscript and proof and have made many valuable suggestions and criticisms.

THE AUTHORS.

CHICAGO,
September, 1914.

CONTENTS

CHAPTER I

INTRODUCTION

CHAPTER II

TRIGONOMETRIC FUNCTIONS OF ONE ANGLE

CHAPTER III

RELATIONS BETWEEN TRIGONOMETRIC FUNCTIONS

CHAPTER IV

RIGHT TRIANGLES

CHAPTER V

FUNCTIONS OF LARGE ANGLES

CHAPTER VI

GRAPHICAL REPRESENTATION OF TRIGONOMETRIC FUNCTIONS

CHAPTER VII

PRACTICAL APPLICATIONS AND RELATED PROBLEMS

CHAPTER VIII

FUNCTIONS INVOLVING MORE THAN ONE ANGLE

CHAPTER IX

OBLIQUE TRIANGLES

CHAPTER XII

SPHERICAL TRIGONOMETRY

The contents for the Logarithmic and Trigonometric Tables and Explanatory Chapter is printed with the tables.

GREEK ALPHABET

A, α	. . . . *Alpha*		N, ν	. . . . *Nu*
B, β	. . . . *Beta*		Ξ, ξ	. . . . *Xi*
Γ, γ	. . . . *Gamma*		O, o	. . . . *Omicron*
Δ, δ	. . . . *Delta*		Π, π	. . . . *Pi*
E, ε	. . . . *Epsilon*		P, ρ	. . . . *Rho*
Z, ζ	. . . . *Zeta*		Σ, σ	. . . . *Sigma*
H, η	. . . . *Eta*		T, τ	. . . . *Tau*
Θ, θ	. . . . *Theta*		Υ, υ	. . . . *Upsilon*
I, ι	. . . . *Iota*		Φ, φ	. . . . *Phi*
K, κ	. . . . *Kappa*		X, χ	. . . . *Chi*
Λ, λ	. . . . *Lambda*		Ψ, ψ	. . . . *Psi*
M, μ	. . . . *Mu*		Ω, ω	. . . . *Omega*

PLANE AND SPHERICAL TRIGONOMETRY

CHAPTER I

INTRODUCTION

GEOMETRY

1. Introductory remarks.—The word trigonometry is derived from two Greek words, τριγωνον (trigonon), meaning triangle, and μετρια (metria), meaning measurement. While the derivation of the word would seem to confine the subject to triangles, the measurement of triangles is merely a part of the general subject which includes many other investigations involving angles.

Trigonometry is both geometric and algebraic in nature. Historically, trigonometry developed in connection with astronomy, where distances that could not be measured directly were computed by means of angles and lines that could be measured. The beginning of these methods may be traced to Babylon and Ancient Egypt.

The noted Greek astronomer Hipparchus is often called the founder of trigonometry. He did his chief work between 146 and 126 B. C. and developed trigonometry as an aid in measuring angles and lines in connection with astronomy. The subject of trigonometry was separated from astronomy and established as a distinct branch of mathematics by the great mathematician Leonhard Euler, who lived from 1707 to 1783.

To pursue the subject of trigonometry successfully, the student should know the subjects usually treated in algebra up to and including quadratic equations, and be familiar with plane geometry, especially the theorems on triangles and circles.

Frequent use is made of the protractor, compasses, and the straightedge in constructing figures.

While parts of trigonometry can be applied at once to the solution of various interesting and practical problems, much of

1

it is studied because it is very frequently used in more advanced subjects in mathematics.

ANGLES

2. Definitions.—The definition of an angle as given in geometry admits of a clear conception of small angles only. In trigonometry, we wish to consider *positive* and *negative* angles and these of any size whatever; hence we need a more comprehensive definition of an angle.

If a line, starting from the position OX (Fig. 1), is revolved about the point O and always kept in the same plane, we say the line **generates** an angle. If it revolves from the position OX to the position OA, in the direction indicated by the arrow, the angle XOA is generated.

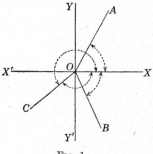

Fig. 1.

The original position OX of the generating line is called the **initial side,** and the final position OA, the **terminal side** of the angle.

If the rotation of the generating line is *counterclockwise*, as already taken, the angle is said to be **positive.** If OX revolves in a *clockwise* direction to a position, as OB, the angle generated is said to be **negative.**

In reading an angle, the letter on the initial side is read first to give the proper sense of direction. If the angle is read in the opposite sense, the negative of the angle is meant.

Thus, $\angle AOX = -\angle XOA.$

It is easily seen that this conception of an angle makes it possible to think of an angle as being of any size whatever. Thus, the generating line, when it has reached the position OY, having made a quarter of a revolution in a counterclockwise direction, has generated a right angle; when it has reached the position OX' it has generated two right angles. A complete revolution generates an angle containing four right angles; two revolutions, eight right angles; and so on for any amount of turning.

The right angle is divided into 90 equal parts called degrees (°), each degree is divided into 60 equal parts called minutes ('), and each minute into 60 equal parts called seconds ('').

Starting from any position as initial side, it is evident that for each position of the terminal side, there are two angles less than 360°, one positive and one negative. Thus, in Fig. 1, *OC* is the terminal side for the positive angle *XOC* or for the negative angle *XOC*.

3. Quadrants.—It is convenient to divide the plane formed by a complete revolution of the generating line into four parts by the two perpendicular lines *X'X* and *Y'Y*. These parts are called **first, second, third,** and **fourth quadrants,** respectively. They are placed as shown by the Roman numerals in Fig. 2.

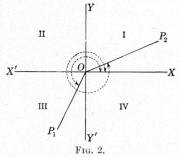

FIG. 2.

If *OX* is taken as the initial side of an angle, the angle is said to lie in the quadrant in which its terminal side lies. Thus, *XOP*₁ (Fig. 2) lies in the third quadrant, and *XOP*₂, formed by more than one revolution, lies in the first quadrant.

An angle lies between two quadrants if its terminal side lies on the line between two quadrants.

4. Graphical addition and subtraction of angles.—Two angles are added by placing them in the same plane with their vertices together and the initial side of the second on the terminal side of the first. The sum is the angle from the initial side of the first to the terminal side of the second.

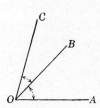

FIG. 3.

Subtraction is performed by adding the negative of the subtrahend to the minuend. Thus, in Fig. 3,

$\angle AOB + \angle BOC = \angle AOC.$
$\angle AOC - \angle BOC = \angle AOC + \angle COB = \angle AOB.$
$\angle BOC - \angle AOC = \angle BOC + \angle COA = \angle BOA.$

EXERCISES

Use the protractor in laying off the angles in the following exercises:

1. Choose an initial side and lay off the following angles. Indicate each angle by a circular arrow. 75°; 145°; 243°; 729°; 456°; 976°. State the quadrant in which each angle lies.

2. Lay off the following angles and state the quadrant that each is in: −40°; −147°; −295°; −456°; −1048°.

3. Lay off the following pairs of angles, using the same initial side for each pair: 170° and −190°; −40° and 320°; 150° and −210°.

4. Give a positive angle that has the same terminal side as each of the following: 30°; 165°; −90°; −210°; −45°; 395°; −390°.

5. Show by a figure the position of the revolving line when it has generated each of the following: 3 right angles; $2\frac{1}{2}$ right angles; $1\frac{1}{3}$ right angles; $4\frac{2}{3}$ right angles.

Unite graphically, using the protractor:

6. 40° + 70°; 25° + 36°; 95° + 125°; 243° + 725°.

7. 75° − 43°; 125° − 59°; 23° − 49°; 743° − 542°; 90° − 270°.

8. 45° + 30° + 25°; 125° + 46° + 95°; 327° + 25° + 400°.

9. 45° − 56° + 85°; 325° − 256° + 400°.

10. Draw two angles lying in the first quadrant but differing by 360°. Two negative angles in the fourth quadrant and differing by 360°.

11. Draw the following angles and their complements: 30°; 210°; 345°; −45°; −300°; −150°.

5. Angle measurement.—Several systems for measuring angles are in use. The system is chosen that is best adapted to the purpose for which it is used.

(1) *The right angle.*—The most familiar unit of measure of an angle is the right angle. It is easy to construct, enters frequently into the practical uses of life, and is almost always used in geometry. It has no subdivisions and does not lend itself readily to computations.

(2) *The sexagesimal system.*—The **sexagesimal system** has for its fundamental unit the degree, which is defined to be the angle formed by $\frac{1}{360}$ part of a revolution of the generating line. This is the system used by engineers and others in making practical numerical computations. The subdivisions of the degree are the minute and the second, as stated in **Art. 2.** The word "sexagesimal" is derived from the Latin word *sexagesimus,* meaning one-sixtieth.

(3) *The centesimal system.*—Another system for measuring angles was proposed in France somewhat over a century ago. This is the **centesimal system.** In it the right angle is divided into 100 equal parts called **grades,** the grade into 100 equal parts called minutes, and the minute into 100 equal parts called seconds. While this system has many admirable features, its use could not become general without recomputing with a great expenditure of labor many of the existing tables.

(4) *The circular or natural system.*—In the **circular** or **natural system** for measuring angles, sometimes called **radian measure** or **π-measure,** the fundamental unit is the radian.

The radian is defined to be the *angle which, when placed with its vertex at the center of a circle, intercepts an arc equal in length to the radius of the circle.* Or it is defined as *the positive angle generated when a point on the generating line has passed through an arc equal in length to the radius of the circle being formed by that point.*

In Fig. 4, the angles AOB, BOC, $\cdots$ FOG are each 1 radian, since the sides of each angle intercept an arc equal in length to the radius of the circle.

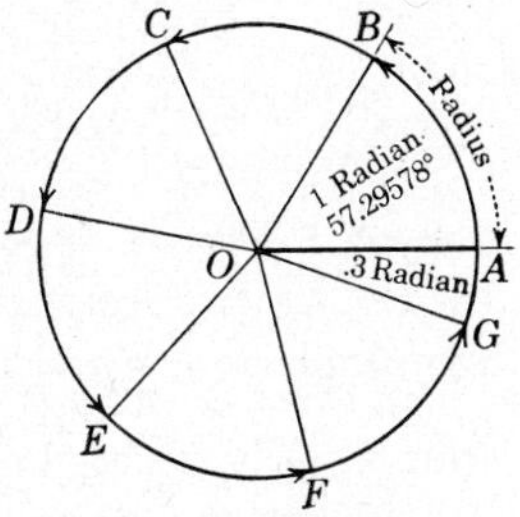

The circular system lends itself naturally to the measurement of angles in many theoretical considerations. It is used almost exclusively in the calculus and its applications.

(5) *Other systems.*—Instead of dividing the degree into minutes and seconds, it is sometimes divided into tenths, hundredths, and thousandths. This decimal scale has been used more or less ever since decimal fractions were invented in the sixteenth century.

FIG. 4.

The **mil** is a unit of angle used in artillery practice. The mil is $\frac{1}{6400}$ revolution, or very nearly $\frac{1}{1000}$ radian; hence its name. The scales by means of which the guns in the United States Field Artillery are aimed are graduated in this unit.

6. The radian.—That the circular measure is the natural system to use in measuring an angle is apparent from a consideration of the geometrical basis for the definition of the radian.

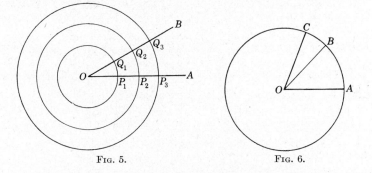

FIG. 5. FIG. 6.

(1) Given several concentric circles and an angle AOB at the center as in Fig. 5, then

$$\frac{\text{arc } P_1Q_1}{OP_1} = \frac{\text{arc } P_2Q_2}{OP_2} = \frac{\text{arc } P_3Q_3}{OP_3}, \text{ etc.}$$

That is, the ratio of the intercepted arc to the radius of that arc is a constant for all circles when the angle is the same. *The angle at the center which makes this ratio unity is then a convenient unit for measuring angles. This is* 1 *radian.*

(2) In the same or equal circles, two angles at the center are in the same ratio as their intercepted arcs. That is, in Fig. 6,

$$\frac{\angle AOB}{\angle AOC} = \frac{\text{arc } AB}{\text{arc } AC}.$$

Here, if $\angle AOC$ is unity when arc $AC = r$, $\angle AOB = \dfrac{\text{arc } AB}{r}$, or,

in general, $\theta = \dfrac{s}{r}$, where θ is the angle at the center measured in radians, s the arc length, and r the radius of the circle.

7. Relations between radian and degree.—The relations between a degree and a radian can be readily determined from their definitions. Since the circumference of a circle is 2π times the radius,

$$2\pi \text{ radians} = 1 \text{ revolution.}$$
Also $\qquad\qquad 360° = 1 \text{ revolution.}$
Then $\qquad\qquad 2\pi \text{ radians} = 360°.$

$$\therefore 1 \text{ radian} = \frac{360°}{2\pi} = \frac{180°}{\pi} = 57.29578° -$$

$$= 206264.8'' + = 57° \; 17' \; 44.8'' +.$$

For less accurate work 1 radian is taken as 57.3°.
Conversely, **180° = π radians.**

$$\therefore 1° = \frac{\pi}{180} = 0.0174533 - \text{ radian.}$$

To convert radians to degrees, multiply the number of radians by $\dfrac{180}{\pi}$, *or* 57.29578 −.

To convert degrees to radians, multiply the number of degrees by $\dfrac{\pi}{180}$, *or* 0.017453 +.

In writing an angle in degrees, minutes, and seconds, the signs °, ′, ″ are always expressed. In writing an angle in circular measure, usually no abbreviation is used. Thus, the angle 2 means an angle of 2 radians, the angle $\frac{1}{2}\pi$ means an angle of $\frac{1}{2}\pi$ radians. One should be careful to note that $\frac{1}{2}\pi$ does not denote an angle, it simply tells how many radians the angle contains. Sometimes radian is abbreviated as follows: 3^r, $3^{(r)}$, 3ρ, or 3 rad. When the word "radians" is omitted, the student should be careful to supply it mentally.

Many of the most frequently used angles are conveniently expressed in radian measure by using π. In this manner the values are expressed accurately and long decimals are avoided. Thus, $180° = \pi$ radians, $90° = \frac{1}{2}\pi$ radians, $60° = \frac{1}{3}\pi$ radians, $135° = \frac{3}{4}\pi$ radians, $30° = \frac{1}{6}\pi$ radians. These forms are more convenient than the decimal form. For instance, $\frac{1}{3}\pi$ radians = 1.0472 radians.

Example 1.—Reduce 2.5 radians to degrees, minutes, and seconds.

Solution.—1 radian = 57.29578°.

Then 2.5 radians = $2.5 \times 57.29578° = 143.2394°$.

To find the number of minutes, multiply the decimal part of the number of degrees by 60.

$$0.2394° = 60 \times 0.2394 = 14.364'.$$

Likewise, $0.364' = 60 \times 0.364 = 21.8''$.

$$\therefore 2.5 \text{ radians} = 143° 14' 22''.$$

Example 2.—Reduce 22° 36′ 30″ to radians.

Solution.—First, change to degrees and decimal of degree.

This gives $\quad 22° 36' 30'' = 22.6083°$.

$$1° = 0.017453 \text{ radian.}$$

$$22.6083° = 22.6083 \times 0.017453 = 0.3946 \text{ radian.}$$
$$\therefore 22° 36' 30'' = 0.3946 \text{ radian.}$$

EXERCISES

The first eight exercises are to be done orally.

1. Express the angles of the following numbers of radians in degrees: $\frac{1}{2}\pi$; $\frac{2}{3}\pi$; $\frac{3}{2}\pi$; $\frac{5}{6}\pi$; $\frac{4}{3}\pi$; $\frac{3}{4}\pi$; $\frac{1}{6}\frac{1}{6}\pi$; $\frac{7}{6}\pi$.

2. Express the following angles as some number of π radians: 30°; 90°; 180°; 135°; 120°; 240°; 270°; 330°; 225°; 315°; 81°; 360°; 720°.

3. Express the angles of the following numbers of right angles in radians, using π; 2; $\frac{1}{2}$; $\frac{1}{3}$; $\frac{4}{3}$; $3\frac{1}{2}$; $2\frac{1}{3}$; $1\frac{2}{3}$; $3\frac{1}{3}$.

4. Express in radians each angle of an equilateral triangle. Of a regular hexagon. Of an isosceles triangle if the vertex angle is a right angle.

5. How many degrees does the minute hand of a watch turn through in 15 min.? In 20 min.? How many radians in each of these angles?

6. What is the measure of 90° when the right angle is taken as the unit of measure? Of 135°? Of 60°? Of 240°? Of 540°? Of −270°? Of −360°? Of −630°?

7. What is the measure of each of the angles of the previous exercise when the radian is taken as the unit of measure?

8. What is the angular velocity of the second hand of a watch in radians per minute? What is the angular velocity of the minute hand?

Reduce the following angles to degrees, minutes and integral seconds:

9. 2.3 radians.   *Ans.* 131° 46′ 49″.

10. 1.42 radians.   *Ans.* 81° 21′ 36″.

11. 3.75 radians.   *Ans.* 214° 51′ 33″.

12. 0.25 radian.   *Ans.* 14° 19′ 26″.

13. $\frac{3}{16}\pi$ radian.   *Ans.* 33° 45′.

14. $\frac{11}{4}\pi$ radians.   *Ans.* 495°.

15. 0.0074 radian.   *Ans.* 25′ 16″.

16. 6.28 radians.   *Ans.* 359° 49′ 3″.

Reduce the following angles to radians correct to four decimals, using **Art. 7** :

17. 55°.   **18.** 103°.   **19.** 265°.   **20.** 17°.

21. 24° 37′ 27″.   *Ans.* 0.4298.

22. 285° 28′ 56″.   *Ans.* 4.9825.

23. 416° 48′ 45″.   *Ans.* 7.2746.

Reduce the following angles to radians, using **Table V**, of **Tables.**

24. 25° 14′ 23″.   *Ans.* 0.4405162.

25. 175° 42′ 15″.   *Ans.* 3.0666162.

26. 78° 15′ 30″.   *Ans.* 1.3658655.

27. 243° 35′ 42″.   *Ans.* 4.2515348.

28. 69° 25′ 8″.   *Ans.* 1.2115882.

29. 9° 9′ 9″.   *Ans.* 0.1597412.

30. Compute the equivalents given in **Art. 7.**

31. Show that 1 mil is very nearly 0.001 radian, and find the per cent of error in using 1 mil = 0.001 radian.   *Ans.* 1.86 per cent.

32. What is the measure of each of the following angles when the right angle is taken as the unit of measure: 1 radian, 2π radians, 650°, 2.157 radians?   *Ans.* 0.6366; 4; 7.222; 1.373.

33. An angular velocity of 10 revolutions per second is how many radians per minute?   *Ans.* 3769.91.

34. An angular velocity of 30 revolutions per minute is how many π radians per second?   *Ans.* One-π radians.

35. An angular velocity of 80 radians per minute is how many degrees per second?   *Ans.* 76.394°.

36. Show that nine-tenths the number of grades in an angle is the number of degrees in that angle.

37. The angles of a triangle are in the ratio of 2:3:7. Express the angles in radians.   *Ans.* $\frac{1}{6}\pi$; $\frac{1}{4}\pi$; $\frac{7}{12}\pi$.

38. Express an interior angle of each of the following regular polygons in radians: octagon, pentagon, 16-gon, 59-gon.

39. Express 48° 22′ 25″ in the centesimal system in grades, minutes, and seconds.   *Ans.* 53 grades 74 min. 84 sec.

ANGLE AT CENTER OF CIRCLE

8. Relations between angle, arc, and radius.—In **Art. 6,** it is shown that, if the central angle is measured in radians and the arc length and the radius are measured in the same linear unit, then

$$\text{angle} = \frac{\text{arc}}{\text{radius}}.$$

That is, if θ, s, and r are the measures, respectively, of the angle, arc, and radius (Fig. 7),

$$\theta = s \div r,$$

Solving this for s and then for r,

$$s = r\theta,$$

and
$$r = s \div \theta.$$

These are the simplest geometrical relations between the angle at the center of a circle, the intercepted arc, and the radius. They are of frequent use in mathematics and its applications, and should be remembered.

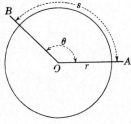

FIG. 7.

Example 1.—The diameter of a graduated circle is 10 ft., and the graduations are 5′ of arc apart; find the length of arc between the graduations in fractions of an inch to three decimal places.

Solution.—By formula, $s = r\theta$.

From the example, $r = 12 \times 5 = 60$ in.,

and $\qquad \theta = 0.01745 \times \frac{5}{60} = 0.00145$ radian.

Substituting in the formula, $s = 60 \times 0.00145 = 0.087$.

∴ length of 5′ arc is 0.087 in.

Example 2.—A train is traveling on a circular curve of $\frac{1}{2}$-mile radius at the rate of 30 miles per hour. Through what angle would the train turn in 45 sec.?

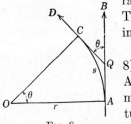

FIG. 8.

Solution.—When at the position A (Fig. 8), the train is moving in the direction AB. After 45 sec. it has reached C, and is then moving in the direction CD. It has then turned through the angle BQC.

But $\angle BQC = \angle AOC = \theta$.   Why?

The train travels the arc $s = \frac{3}{8}$ mile in 45 sec.

To find value of θ, use formula

$$\theta = s \div r.$$
$$\therefore \theta = \tfrac{3}{8} \div \tfrac{1}{2} = 0.75 \text{ radian} = 42° 58′ 19″.$$

9. Area of circular sector.—In Fig. 9, the area *BOC*, bounded by two radii and an arc of a circle, is a sector.   In geometry it is shown that *the area of a sector of a circle equals one-half the arc length times the radius.*

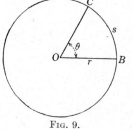

That is, $A = \frac{1}{2}rs$.

But $s = r\theta$.

Hence, $A = \frac{1}{2}r^2\theta$.

Example.—Find the area of the sector of a circle having a radius 8 ft. if the central angle is 40°.

Solution.—

$40° = 40 \times 0.01745 = 0.698$ radian.

FIG. 9.

Using the formula $A = \frac{1}{2}r^2\theta$,

$$A = \frac{1}{2} \times 8^2 \times 0.698 = 22.34.$$

∴ area of sector = 22.34 sq. ft.

ORAL EXERCISES

1. How many radians are there in the central angle intercepting an arc of 20 in. on a circle of 5-in. radius?

2. The minute hand of a clock is 4 in. long.   Find the distance moved by the outer end when the hand has turned through 3 radians.   When it has moved 20 min.

3. A wheel revolves with an angular velocity of 8 radians per second. Find the linear velocity of a point on the circumference if the radius is 6 ft.

4. The velocity of the rim of a flywheel is 75 ft. per second.   Find the angular velocity in radians per second if the wheel is 8 ft. in diameter.

5. A pulley carrying a belt is revolving with an angular velocity of 10 radians per second.   Find the velocity of the belt if the pulley is 5 ft. in diameter.

6. An angle of 3 mils will intercept what length of arc at 1000 yd.?

7. A freight car 30 ft. in length at right angles to the line of sight intercepts an angle of 2 mils.   What is its distance from the observer?

8. A train is traveling on a circular curve of $\frac{1}{2}$-mile radius at the rate of 30 miles an hour.   Through what angle does it turn in 15 sec.?

9. A belt traveling 60 ft. per second runs on a pulley 3 ft. in diameter. What is the angular velocity of the pulley in radians per second?

10. A circular target at 3000 yd. subtends an angle of 1 mil at the eye. How large is the target?

WRITTEN EXERCISES

1. The diameter of the drive wheels of a locomotive is 72 in.   Find the number of revolutions per minute they make when the engine is going 45 miles per hour.   *Ans.* 210.08 r.p.m.

2. A flywheel is revolving at the rate of 456 r.p.m. What angle does a radius of the wheel generate in 1 sec.? Express in degrees and radians. How many π radians are generated in 2.5 sec.?

Ans. 2736°; 47.752 radians; 38.

3. A flywheel 6 ft. in diameter is revolving at an angular velocity of 30 radians per second. Find the rim velocity in miles per hour.

Ans. 61.36 miles per hour.

4. The angular velocity of a flywheel is 10π radians per second. Find the circumferential velocity in feet per second if the radius of the wheel is 6 ft. *Ans.* 188.5 ft. per second.

5. A wheel is revolving at an angular velocity of $\frac{5\pi}{3}$ radians per second. Find the number of revolutions per minute. Per hour.

Ans. 50 r.p.m.; 3000 r.p.h.

6. In a circle of 9-in. radius, how long an arc will have an angle at the center of 2.5 radians? An angle of 155° 36'? *Ans.* 22.5 in.; 24.44 in.

7. An automobile wheel 2.5 ft. in outside diameter rolls along a road, the axle moving at the rate of 45 miles per hour; find the angular velocity in π radians per second. *Ans.* 16.81 π radians.

8. Chicago is at north latitude 41° 59'. Use 3960 miles as the radius of the earth and find the distance from Chicago to the equator.

Ans. 2901.7 miles.

9. Use 3960 miles as the radius of the earth and find the length in feet of 1″ of arc of the equator. *Ans.* 101.37 ft.

10. A train of cars is running at the rate of 35 miles per hour on a curve of 1000 ft. radius. Find its angular velocity in radians per minute.

Ans. 3.08 radians per minute.

11. Find the length of arc which at 1 mile will subtend an angle of 1′. An angle of 1″. *Ans.* 1.536 ft.; 0.0253 ft.

12. The radius of the earth's orbit around the sun, which is about 92,700,000 miles, subtends at the star Sirius an angle of about 0.4″. Find the approximate distance of Sirius from the earth. *Ans.* 48 (10^{12}) miles.

13. Assume that the earth moves around the sun in a circle of 93,000,000-mile radius. Find its rate per second, using $365\frac{1}{4}$ days for a revolution.

Ans. 18.5 miles per second.

14. The earth revolves on its axis once in 24 hours. Use 3960 miles for the radius and find the velocity of a point on the equator in feet per second. Find the angular velocity in radians per hour. In seconds of angle per second of time. *Ans.* 1520.6 ft. per second; 0.262 radian per hour.

15. The circumferential speed generally advised by makers of emery wheels is 5500 ft. per minute. Find the angular velocity in radians per second for a wheel 16 in. in diameter. *Ans.* 137.5 radian per second.

16. Find the area of a circular sector in a circle of 12 in. radius, if the angle is π radians. If 135°. If 5 radians.

Ans. 226.2 sq. in.; 169.7 sq. in.

17. The perimeter of a sector of a circle is equal to two-thirds the circumference of the circle. Find the angle of the sector in circular measure and in sexagesimal measure. *Ans.* 2.1888 radians; 125° 24.5'.

10. General angles.—In Fig. 10, the angle XOP_1 is 30°; or if the angle is thought of as formed by one complete revolution and 30°, it is 390°; if by two complete revolutions and 30°, it is 750°. So an angle having OX for initial side and OP_1 for terminal side is 30°, 360° + 30°, 2 × 360° + 30°, or, in general, $n \times 360° + 30°$, where n takes the values 0, 1, 2, 3, · · · , that is, n is any integer, zero included.

In radian measure this is $2n\pi + \frac{1}{6}\pi$.

The expression $n \times 360° + 30°$, or $2n\pi + \frac{1}{6}\pi$, is called the **general measure** of all the angles having OX as initial side and OP_1 as terminal side.

If the angle XOP_2 is 30° less than 180°, then the general measure of the angles having OX as initial side and OP_2 as terminal

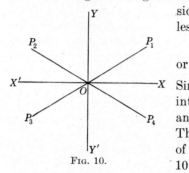

FIG. 10.

side is an odd number times 180° less 30°; and may be written

$$(2n + 1)180° - 30°,$$
or $\quad (2n + 1)\pi - \frac{1}{6}\pi.$

Similarly, $n\pi \pm \frac{1}{6}\pi$ means an integral number of times π is taken and then $\frac{1}{6}\pi$ is added or subtracted. This gives the terminal side in one of the four positions shown in Fig. 10 by OP_1, OP_2, OP_3, and OP_4.

It is evident that throughout this article n may have negative as well as positive values, and that any angle θ might be used instead of 30°, or $\frac{1}{6}\pi$.

EXERCISES

1. Use the same initial side for each and draw angles of 50°; 360° + 50°; $n \cdot 360° + 50°$.

2. Use the same initial side for each and draw angles of 40°; 180° + 40°; $2 \cdot 180° + 40°$; $3 \cdot 180° + 40°$; $n \cdot 180° + 40°$.

3. Use the same initial side for each and draw angles of 30°; 90° + 30°; $2 \cdot 90° + 30°$; $3 \cdot 90° + 30°$; $n \cdot 90° + 30°$.

4. Draw the terminal sides for all the angles whose general measure is $2n \cdot 90°$. For all the angles whose general measure is $(2n + 1)90°$.

5. Draw the following angles: $2n\pi$; $(2n + 1)\pi$; $(2n + 1)\frac{1}{2}\pi$; $(4n + 1)\frac{1}{2}\pi$; $(4n + 3)\frac{1}{2}\pi$.

6. Draw the following angles: $2n \times 180° \pm 60°$; $(2n + 1)180° \pm 60°$; $(2n + 1)\pi \pm \frac{1}{3}\pi$; $2n\pi + \frac{1}{3}\pi$; $(2n + 1)\frac{\pi}{2} \pm \frac{\pi}{3}$; $n\pi \pm \frac{1}{4}\pi$; $(4n + 1)\frac{\pi}{2} \pm \frac{\pi}{6}$; $(4n - 1)\frac{\pi}{2} \pm \frac{\pi}{6}$.

7. Give the general measure of all the angles having the lines that bisect the four quadrants as terminal sides. Those that have the lines that trisect the four quadrants as terminal sides.

COORDINATES

11. Directed lines and segments.—For certain purposes in trigonometry it is convenient to give a line a property not often used in plane geometry. This is the property of having *direction*.

In Fig. 11, RQ is a directed straight line if it is thought of as traced by a point moving without change of direction from R toward Q or from Q toward R. The direction is often shown by an arrow.

Let a fixed point O on RQ be taken as a point from which to measure distances. Choose a fixed length as a unit and lay it off on the line RQ beginning at O. The successive points located in this manner will be 1, 2, 3, 4, $\cdots$ times the unit distance

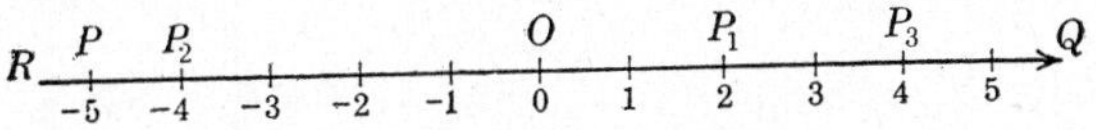

Fig. 11.

from O. These points may be thought of as representing the numbers, or the numbers may be thought of as representing the points.

Since there are two directions from O in which the measurements may be made, it is evident that there are two points equally distant from O. Since there are both positive and negative numbers, we shall *agree* to represent the points to the *right* of O by positive numbers and those to the *left* by negative numbers.

Thus, a point 2 units to the right of O represents the number 2; and, conversely, the number 2 represents a point 2 units to the right of O. A point 4 units to the left of O represents the number -4; and, conversely, the number -4 represents a point 4 units to the left of O.

The point O from which the measurements are made is called the **origin**. It represents the number zero.

A **segment** of a line is a definite part of a directed line.

The segment of a line is read by giving its initial point and its terminal point. Thus, in Fig. 11, OP_1, OP_2, and P_1P_3 are segments. In the last, P_1 is the **initial point** and P_3 the **terminal point.**

The **value** of a segment is determined by its length and direction, and it is defined to be *the number which would represent the terminal point of the segment if the initial point were taken as origin.*

It follows from this definition that the value of a segment read in one direction is the negative of the value if read in the opposite direction.

In Fig. 12, taking O as origin, the values of the segments are as follows:

$$OP_1 = 3, OP_3 = 8, OP_5 = -5, P_2P_3 = 3, P_3P_1 = -5.$$
$$P_4P_6 = -6, P_6P_5 = 3, P_1P_2 = -P_2P_1 = 2.$$

Two segments are equal if they have the same direction and the same length, that is, the same value.

If two segments are so placed that the initial point of the second is on the terminal point of the first, the **sum of the two segments**

$$
\begin{array}{ccccccc}
P_6 & P_5 & P_4 & O & P_1 & P_2 & P_3
\end{array}
$$

-10 -9 -8 -7 -6 -5 -4 -3 -2 -1 0 1 2 3 4 5 6 7 8 9 10

Fig. 12.

is the segment having as initial point the initial point of the first, and as terminal point the terminal point of the second.

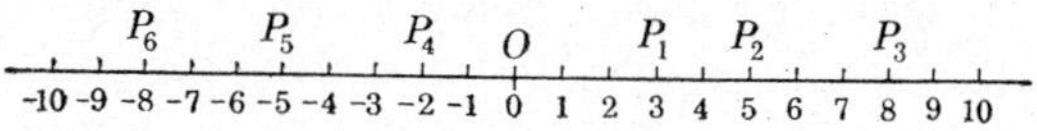

The segments are subtracted by reversing the direction of the subtrahend and adding.

Thus, in Fig. 12,

$$P_5P_4 + P_4P_1 = P_5P_1 = 8.$$
$$P_2P_4 + P_4P_6 = P_2P_6 = -13.$$
$$P_1P_3 - P_2P_3 = P_1P_3 + P_3P_2 = P_1P_2 = 2.$$
$$P_2P_3 - P_1P_3 = P_2P_3 + P_3P_1 = P_2P_1 = -2.$$

12. Rectangular coordinates.—Let $X'X$ and $Y'Y$ (Fig. 13) be two fixed directed straight lines, perpendicular to each other and intersecting at the point O. Choose the positive direction towards the right, when parallel to $X'X$; and upwards, when parallel to $Y'Y$. Hence the negative directions are towards the left, and downwards.

The two lines $X'X$ and $Y'Y$ divide the plane into four quadrants, numbered as in **Art. 3.**

Any point P_1 in the plane is located by the segments NP_1 and MP_1 drawn parallel to $X'X$ and $Y'Y$ respectively, for the values of these segments tell how far and in what direction P_1 is from the two lines $X'X$ and $Y'Y$.

It is evident that for any point in the plane there is *one pair of values and only one;* and, conversely, for every pair of values there is *one point and only one.*

The value of the segment NP_1 or OM is called the **abscissa** of the point P_1, and is usually represented by x. The value of the segment MP_1 or ON is called the **ordinate** of the point P_1, and is usually represented by y. Taken together the abscissa x and the ordinate y are called the **coordinates** of the point P_1. They are written, for brevity, within parentheses and separated by a comma, the abscissa always being first, as (x, y).

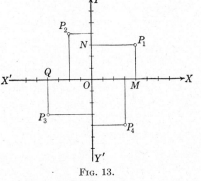

Fig. 13.

The line $X'X$ is called the **axis of abscissas** or the **x-axis**. The line $Y'Y$ is called the **axis of ordinates** or the **y-axis**. Together, these lines are called the **coordinate axes**.

It is evident that, in the first quadrant, both coordinates are positive; in the second quadrant, the abscissa is negative and the ordinate is positive; in the third quadrant, both coordinates are negative; and, in the fourth quadrant, the abscissa is positive and the ordinate is negative. This is shown in the following table:

Quadrant	I	II	III	IV
Abscissa..................................	$+$	$-$	$-$	$+$
Ordinate..................................	$+$	$+$	$-$	$-$

Thus, in Fig. 13, P_1, P_2, P_3, and P_4 are, respectively, the points $(4, 3)$, $(-2, 4)$, $(-4, -3)$, and $(3, -4)$. The points M, O, N, and Q are, respectively, $(4, 0)$, $(0, 0)$, $(0, 3)$, and $(-4, 0)$.

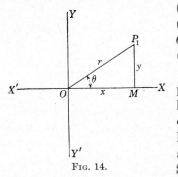

Fig. 14.

13. Polar coordinates.—The point P_1 (Fig. 14) can also be located if the angle θ and the length of the line OP_1 are known. The line OP_1 is called the **radius vector** and is usually represented by r. Since r denotes the distance of the point P_1 from O, it is always considered positive.

Point O is called the pole. The corresponding values of r and θ taken together are called the *polar coordinates* of the point P.

It is seen that r is the hypotenuse of a right triangle of which x and y are the legs; hence $r^2 = x^2 + y^2$, no matter in what quadrant the point is located.

EXERCISES

1. Plot the points (4, 5), (2, 7), (0, 4), (5, 5), (7, 0), (−2, 4), (−4, 5), (−6, −2), (0, −7), (−6, 0), (3, −4), (7, −6).

2. Find the radius vector for each of the points in Exercise 1. Plot in each case.   *Ans.* 6.40; 7.28; 4; 7.07.

3. Where are all the points whose abscissas are 5? Whose ordinates are 0? Whose abscissas are −2? Whose *radius vectors* are 3?

4. The positive direction of the x-axis is taken as the initial side of an angle of 60°. A point is taken on the terminal side with a radius vector equal to 12. Find the ordinate and the abscissa of the point.

5. In Exercise 4, what is the ratio of the ordinate to the abscissa? The ratio of the radius vector to the ordinate? Show that you get the same ratios if any other point on the terminal side is taken.

6. With the positive x-axis as initial side, construct angles of 30°, 135°, 240°, 300°. Take a point on the terminal side so that the radius vector is $2a$ in each case, and find the length of the ordinate and the abscissa of the point.

7. The hour hand of a clock is 2 ft. long. Find the coordinates of its outer end when it is twelve o'clock; when three; nine; half-past ten. Use perpendicular and horizontal axes intersecting where the hands are fastened
                    Ans. (0, 2); (2, 0); (−2, 0); (−1.414, 1.414).

CHAPTER II

TRIGONOMETRIC FUNCTIONS OF ONE ANGLE

14. Functions of an angle.—Connected with any angle there are six ratios that are of fundamental importance, as upon them is founded the whole subject of trigonometry. They are called **trigonometric ratios** or **trigonometric functions of the angle.**

One of the first things to be done in trigonometry is to investigate the properties of these ratios, and to establish relations

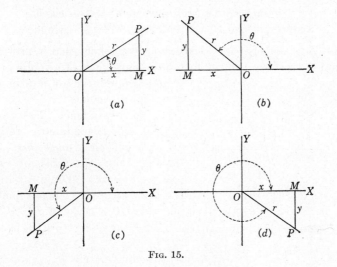

(a)   (b)

(c)   (d)

Fɪɢ. 15.

between them, as they are the tools by which we work all sorts of problems in trigonometry.

15. Trigonometric ratios.—Draw an angle θ in each of the four quadrants as shown in Fig. 15, each angle having its vertex at the origin and its initial side coinciding with the positive part of the x-axis. Choose any point P (x, y) in the terminal side of such angle at the distance r from the origin. Draw $MP \perp OX$, forming the coordinates $OM = x$ and $MP = y$, and the radius vector, or distance, $OP = r$. Then in whatever quadrant θ is found, the functions are defined as follows:

17

$$\text{sine } \theta \text{ (written sin } \theta) = \frac{\text{ordinate}}{\text{distance}} = \frac{MP}{OP} = \frac{y}{r}.$$

$$\text{cosine } \theta \text{ (written cos } \theta) = \frac{\text{abscissa}}{\text{distance}} = \frac{OM}{OP} = \frac{x}{r}.$$

$$\text{tangent } \theta \text{ (written tan } \theta) = \frac{\text{ordinate}}{\text{abscissa}} = \frac{MP}{OM} = \frac{y}{x}.$$

$$\text{cotangent } \theta \text{ (written cot } \theta) = \frac{\text{abscissa}}{\text{ordinate}} = \frac{OM}{MP} = \frac{x}{y}.$$

$$\text{secant } \theta \text{ (written sec } \theta) = \frac{\text{distance}}{\text{abscissa}} = \frac{OP}{OM} = \frac{r}{x}.$$

$$\text{cosecant } \theta \text{ (written csc } \theta) = \frac{\text{distance}}{\text{ordinate}} = \frac{OP}{MP} = \frac{r}{y}.$$

Two other functions frequently used are:

$$\text{versed sine } \theta \text{ (written vers } \theta) = 1 - \cos \theta.$$
$$\text{coversed sine } \theta \text{ (written covers } \theta) = 1 - \sin \theta.$$

The trigonometric functions are pure numbers, that is, abstract numbers, and are subject to the ordinary rules of algebra, such as addition, subtraction, multiplication, and division.

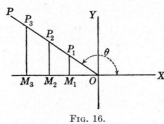

16. Correspondence between angles and trigonometric ratios. *To each and every angle there corresponds but one value of each trigonometric ratio.* Draw any angle

FIG. 16.

θ as in Fig. 16. Choose points P_1, P_2, P_3, etc. on the terminal side OP. Draw M_1P_1, M_2P_2, M_3P_3, etc. perpendicular to OX. From the geometry of the figure,

$$\frac{M_1P_1}{OP_1} = \frac{M_2P_2}{OP_2} = \frac{M_3P_3}{OP_3} = \text{etc.} = \sin \theta,$$

$$\frac{OM_1}{OP_1} = \frac{OM_2}{OP_2} = \frac{OM_3}{OP_3} = \text{etc.} = \cos \theta,$$

$$\frac{M_1P_1}{OM_1} = \frac{M_2P_2}{OM_2} = \frac{M_2P_3}{OM_3} = \text{etc.} = \tan \theta,$$

and similarly for the other trigonometric ratios. Hence, the six ratios remain unchanged as long as the value of the angle is unchanged.

It is this exactness of relations between angles and certain lines connected with them that makes it possible to consider a great variety of questions by means of trigonometry which cannot be handled by methods of geometry. Geometry gives but few relations between angles and lines that can be used in computations, as most of these relations are stated in a comparative manner—for instance, in a triangle, the greater side is opposite the greater angle.

Definition.—When one quantity so depends on another that for every value of the first there are one or more values of the second, the second is said to be a **function** of the first.

Since to every value of the angle there corresponds a value for each of the trigonometric ratios, the ratios are called **trigonometric functions.**

They are also called **natural trigonometric functions** in order to distinguish them from logarithmic trigonometric functions.

A table of natural trigonometric functions for angles 0 to 90° for each minute is given on pages 112 to 134 of **Tables.*** An explanation of the table is given on page 29 of **Tables.**

17. Signs of the trigonometric functions.—The sine of an angle θ has been defined as the ratio of the ordinate to the distance of any point in the terminal side of the angle. Since the distance r is always positive (**Art. 13**), $\sin \theta$ will have the same algebraic sign as the ordinate of the point. Therefore, $\sin \theta$ is positive when the angle is in the first or second quadrant, and negative when the angle is in the third or fourth quadrant.

In a similar manner the algebraic signs of the remaining functions of θ are determined. The student should verify the following table:

Quadrant	$\sin \theta$	$\cos \theta$	$\tan \theta$	$\cot \theta$	$\sec \theta$	$\csc \theta$
I.........................	+	+	+	+	+	+
II........................	+	−	−	−	−	+
III.......................	−	−	+	+	−	−
IV........................	−	+	−	−	+	−

It is very important that one should be able to tell immediately the sign of any trigonometric function in any quadrant. The signs may be remembered by memorizing the table given; but, for most students, they may be more readily remembered by discerning relations between the signs of the functions. One

* The reference is to "Logarithmic and Trigonometric Tables" by the authors.

good scheme is to fix in mind the signs of the sine and cosine. Then if the sine and cosine have like signs, the tangent is plus; and if they have unlike signs, the tangent is negative. The signs of the cosecant, secant, and cotangent always agree respectively with the sine, cosine, and tangent. The scheme shown in Fig. 17 may help in remembering the signs.

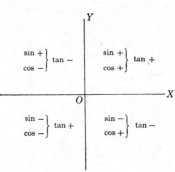

FIG. 17.

EXERCISES

Answer Exercises 1 to 27 orally.

In what quadrant does the terminal side of the angle lie in each of the following cases:

1. When all the functions are positive?

2. When sin θ is positive and cos θ negative?

3. When sin θ is positive and tan θ negative?

4. When cos θ is positive and tan θ negative?

5. When sin θ is negative and tan θ positive?

6. When sin θ is negative and cos θ negative?

7. When sec θ is negative and csc θ negative?

Give the sign of each of the trigonometric functions of the following angles:

8. 120°.	**12.** $\frac{1}{3}\pi$.	**16.** $\frac{27}{4}\pi$.	**20.** $2n\pi + \frac{1}{3}\pi$.
9. 230°.	**13.** $\frac{3}{4}\pi$.	**17.** $-27°$.	**21.** $2n\pi - \frac{1}{4}\pi$.
10. 340°.	**14.** $1\frac{1}{6}\pi$.	**18.** $-213°$.	**22.** $(2n + 1)\pi - \frac{1}{6}\pi$.
11. 520°.	**15.** $\frac{5}{4}\pi$.	**19.** $-700°$.	**23.** $(2n + 1)\pi + \frac{1}{3}\pi$.

24. Show that neither the sine nor the cosine of an angle can be greater than $+1$ or less than -1.

25. Show that neither the secant nor the cosecant of an angle can have a value between -1 and $+1$.

26. Show that the tangent and the cotangent of an angle may have any real value whatever.

27. Is there an angle whose tangent is positive and whose cotangent is negative? Whose secant is positive and whose cosine is negative? Whose secant is positive and whose cosecant is negative?

Construct and measure the following acute angles:

28. Whose sine is $\frac{2}{5}$.   **31.** Whose cotangent is 3.

29. Whose tangent is $\frac{2}{5}$.   **32.** Whose secant is $\frac{4}{3}$.

30. Whose cosine is $\frac{2}{3}$.   **33.** Whose cosecant is $\frac{5}{3}$.

COMPUTATIONS OF TRIGONOMETRIC FUNCTIONS

18. Calculation from measurements. *Example.*—Determine the approximate values of the functions of 25°. By means of the protractor draw angle $XOP = 25°$ (Fig. 18). Choose P in the terminal side, say, $2\frac{3}{16}$ in. distant from the origin. Draw $MP \perp OX$. By measurement, $OM = 2$ in. and $MP = \frac{15}{16}$ in. From the definitions we have:

$$\sin 25° = \frac{MP}{OP} = \frac{\frac{15}{16}}{2\frac{3}{16}} = 0.43. \quad \cos 25° = \frac{OM}{OP} = \frac{2}{2\frac{3}{16}} = 0.91.$$

$$\tan 25° = \frac{MP}{OM} = \frac{\frac{15}{16}}{2} = 0.47. \quad \cot 25° = \frac{OM}{MP} = \frac{2}{\frac{15}{16}} = 2.13.$$

$$\sec 25° = \frac{OP}{OM} = \frac{2\frac{3}{16}}{2} = 1.09. \quad \csc 25° = \frac{OP}{MP} = \frac{2\frac{3}{16}}{\frac{15}{16}} = 2.33.$$

$$\text{vers } 25° = 1 - \cos 25° = 1 - 0.91 = 0.09.$$
$$\text{covers } 25° = 1 - \sin 25° = 1 - 0.43 = 0.57.$$

In a similar manner any angle can be constructed, measurements taken, and the functions computed; but the results will be only approximate because of the inaccuracy of measurement.

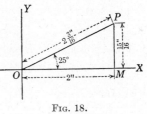

FIG. 18.

EXERCISE

In the same figure construct angles of 10°, 20°, 30°, · · · 80°, with their vertices at the origin and their initial sides on the positive part of the x-axis. Choose the same distance on the terminal side of each angle, draw and measure the coordinates, and calculate the trigonometric functions of each angle to two decimal places. Tabulate the results and compare with **Table IV**.

19. Calculations from geometric relations.—There are two right triangles for which geometry gives definite relations between sides and angles. These are the right isosceles triangle whose acute angles are each 45°, and the right triangles whose acute angles are 30 and 60°. The functions of any angle for which the abscissa, ordinate, and distance form one of these triangles can readily be computed to any desired degree of accuracy. All such angles, together with 0, 90, 180, 270, and 360°, with their functions are tabulated on page 24. These are very important for future use.

20. Trigonometric functions of 30°.—Draw angle $XOP = 30°$ as in Fig. 19. Choose P in the terminal side and draw $MP \perp OX$. By geometry, MP, the side opposite the 30°-angle, is one-half the hypotenuse OP. Take $y = MP = 1$ unit. Then $r = OP = 2$ units, and $x = OM = \sqrt{3}$. By definition, then, we have:

$$\sin 30° = \frac{y}{r} = \frac{1}{2}. \qquad\qquad \cot 30° = \frac{x}{y} = \frac{\sqrt{3}}{1} = \sqrt{3}.$$

$$\cos 30° = \frac{x}{r} = \frac{\sqrt{3}}{2} = \frac{1}{2}\sqrt{3}. \qquad \sec 30° = \frac{r}{x} = \frac{2}{\sqrt{3}} = \frac{2}{3}\sqrt{3}.$$

$$\tan 30° = \frac{y}{x} = \frac{1}{\sqrt{3}} = \frac{\sqrt{3}}{3} = \frac{1}{3}\sqrt{3}. \quad \csc 30° = \frac{r}{y} = \frac{2}{1} = 2.$$

21. Trigonometric functions of 45°.—Draw angle $XOP = 45°$ as in Fig. 20. Choose the point P in the terminal side and draw its coordinates OM and MP, which are necessarily equal. Then

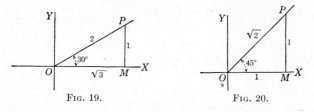

Fig. 19. Fig. 20.

the coordinates of P may be taken as $(1, 1)$, and $r = \sqrt{2}$. By definition, then, we have:

$$\sin 45° = \frac{y}{r} = \frac{1}{\sqrt{2}} = \frac{1}{2}\sqrt{2}. \qquad \cot 45° = \frac{x}{y} = \frac{1}{1} = 1.$$

$$\cos 45° = \frac{x}{r} = \frac{1}{\sqrt{2}} = \frac{1}{2}\sqrt{2}. \qquad \sec 45° = \frac{r}{x} = \frac{\sqrt{2}}{1} = \sqrt{2}.$$

$$\tan 45° = \frac{y}{x} = \frac{1}{1} = 1. \qquad\qquad \csc 45° = \frac{r}{y} = \frac{\sqrt{2}}{1} = \sqrt{2}.$$

22. Trigonometric functions of 120°.—Draw angle $XOP = 120°$ as in Fig. 21. Choose any point P in the terminal side and draw its coordinates OM and MP. Triangle MOP is a right triangle with $\angle MOP = 60°$. Then, as in computing the functions of 30°, we may take $OP = 2$, $MO = 1$, and $MP = \sqrt{3}$. But the abscissa of P is $OM = -1$. Then the coordinates of P are $(-1, \sqrt{3})$, and $r = 2$. By definition, then, we have:

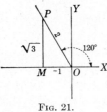

Fig. 21.

$$\sin 120° = \frac{y}{r} = \frac{\sqrt{3}}{2} = \frac{1}{2}\sqrt{3}.$$

$$\cos 120° = \frac{x}{r} = \frac{-1}{2} = -\frac{1}{2}.$$

$$\tan 120° = \frac{y}{x} = \frac{\sqrt{3}}{-1} = -\sqrt{3}.$$

$$\cot 120° = \frac{x}{y} = \frac{-1}{\sqrt{3}} = -\frac{1}{3}\sqrt{3}.$$

$$\sec 120° = \frac{r}{x} = \frac{2}{-1} = -2.$$

$$\csc 120° = \frac{r}{y} = \frac{2}{\sqrt{3}} = \frac{2}{3}\sqrt{3}.$$

In forming the ratios for the angles whose terminal sides lie on the lines between the quadrants, such as 0, 90, 180, 270, and 360°, the denominator is frequently zero. Strictly speaking, this gives rise to an impossibility for division by zero is meaningless. In all such cases we say that the function has become infinite.

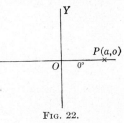

FIG. 22.

23. Trigonometric functions of 0°.— The initial and terminal sides of 0° are both on OX. Choose the point P on OX as in Fig. 22, at the distance of a from O. Then the coordinates of P are $(a, 0)$, and $r = a$. By definition, then, we have:

$$\sin 0° = \frac{y}{r} = \frac{0}{a} = 0. \qquad \tan 0° = \frac{y}{x} = \frac{0}{a} = 0.$$

$$\cos 0° = \frac{x}{r} = \frac{a}{a} = 1. \qquad \sec 0° = \frac{r}{x} = \frac{a}{a} = 1.$$

$\cot 0°$ and $\csc 0°$ have no meaning.*

24. Trigonometric functions of 90°.—Draw angle $XOY = 90°$ as in Fig. 23. Choose any point P in the terminal side at

---

* By the expression $\frac{a}{0} = \infty$ is understood the value of $\frac{a}{x}$ as x approaches zero as a limit. For example, $\frac{a}{1} = a$; $\frac{a}{0.1} = 10a$; $\frac{a}{0.01} = 100a$; $\frac{a}{0.001} = 1000a$; $\frac{a}{0.0000001} = 10,000,000a$; etc. That is, as x gets nearer and nearer to zero $\frac{a}{x}$ gets larger and larger, and can be made to become larger than any number N. The value of $\frac{a}{x}$ is then said to become infinite as x approaches zero. The symbol is ∞ usually read infinity. It should be carefully noted that a is not divided by 0, for division by 0 is meaningless.

Whenever the symbol " ∞ " is used it should be read "has no meaning."

FREQUENTLY USED ANGLES AND THEIR FUNCTIONS

$\theta°$	θ in radians	$\sin \theta$	$\cos \theta$	$\tan \theta$	$\cot \theta$	$\sec \theta$	$\csc \theta$
0°	0	0	1	0	∞	1	∞
30°	$\dfrac{\pi}{6}$	$\dfrac{1}{2}$	$\dfrac{\sqrt{3}}{2}$	$\dfrac{\sqrt{3}}{3}$	$\sqrt{3}$	$\dfrac{2\sqrt{3}}{3}$	2
45°	$\dfrac{\pi}{4}$	$\dfrac{\sqrt{2}}{2}$	$\dfrac{\sqrt{2}}{2}$	1	1	$\sqrt{2}$	$\sqrt{2}$
60°	$\dfrac{\pi}{3}$	$\dfrac{\sqrt{3}}{2}$	$\dfrac{1}{2}$	$\sqrt{3}$	$\dfrac{\sqrt{3}}{3}$	2	$\dfrac{2\sqrt{3}}{3}$
90°	$\dfrac{\pi}{2}$	1	0	∞	0	∞	1
120°	$\dfrac{2\pi}{3}$	$\dfrac{\sqrt{3}}{2}$	$-\dfrac{1}{2}$	$-\sqrt{3}$	$-\dfrac{\sqrt{3}}{3}$	-2	$\dfrac{2\sqrt{3}}{3}$
135°	$\dfrac{3\pi}{4}$	$\dfrac{\sqrt{2}}{2}$	$-\dfrac{\sqrt{2}}{2}$	-1	-1	$-\sqrt{2}$	$\sqrt{2}$
150°	$\dfrac{5\pi}{6}$	$\dfrac{1}{2}$	$-\dfrac{\sqrt{3}}{2}$	$-\dfrac{\sqrt{3}}{3}$	$-\sqrt{3}$	$-\dfrac{2\sqrt{3}}{3}$	2
180°	π	0	-1	0	∞	-1	∞
210°	$\dfrac{7\pi}{6}$	$-\dfrac{1}{2}$	$-\dfrac{\sqrt{3}}{2}$	$\dfrac{\sqrt{3}}{3}$	$\sqrt{3}$	$-\dfrac{2\sqrt{3}}{3}$	-2
225°	$\dfrac{5\pi}{4}$	$-\dfrac{\sqrt{2}}{2}$	$-\dfrac{\sqrt{2}}{2}$	1	1	$-\sqrt{2}$	$-\sqrt{2}$
240°	$\dfrac{4\pi}{3}$	$-\dfrac{\sqrt{3}}{2}$	$-\dfrac{1}{2}$	$\sqrt{3}$	$\dfrac{\sqrt{3}}{3}$	-2	$-\dfrac{2\sqrt{3}}{3}$
270°	$\dfrac{3\pi}{2}$	-1	0	∞	0	∞	-1
300°	$\dfrac{5\pi}{3}$	$-\dfrac{\sqrt{3}}{2}$	$\dfrac{1}{2}$	$-\sqrt{3}$	$-\dfrac{\sqrt{3}}{3}$	2	$-\dfrac{2\sqrt{3}}{3}$
315°	$\dfrac{7\pi}{4}$	$-\dfrac{\sqrt{2}}{2}$	$\dfrac{\sqrt{2}}{2}$	-1	-1	$\sqrt{2}$	$-\sqrt{2}$
330°	$\dfrac{11\pi}{6}$	$-\dfrac{1}{2}$	$\dfrac{\sqrt{3}}{2}$	$-\dfrac{\sqrt{3}}{3}$	$-\sqrt{3}$	$\dfrac{2\sqrt{3}}{3}$	-2
360°	2π	0	1	0	∞	1	∞

the distance a from the origin. Then the coordinates of P are $(0, a)$, and $r = a$. By definition, then, we have:

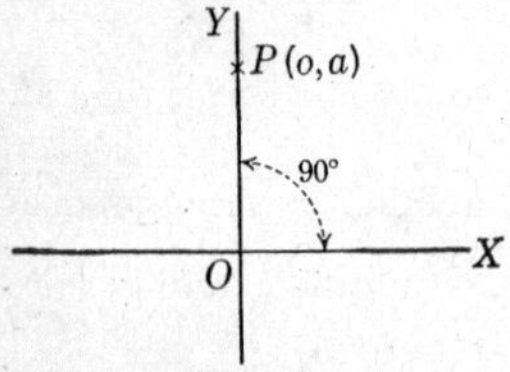

FIG. 23.

$$\sin 90° = \frac{y}{r} = \frac{a}{a} = 1.$$

$$\cot 90° = \frac{x}{y} = \frac{0}{a} = 0.$$

$$\cos 90° = \frac{x}{r} = \frac{0}{a} = 0. \qquad \csc 90° = \frac{r}{y} = \frac{a}{a} = 1.$$

tan 90° and sec 90° have no meaning.

EXERCISES

Construct the figure and compute the functions for each of the following angles.

1. 60°	**3.** 150°.	**5.** 240°.	**7.** 270°.
2. 135°.	**4.** 180°.	**6.** 330°.	**8.** 315°.

25. Exponents of trigonometric functions.—When the trigonometric functions are to be raised to powers, they are written $\sin^2 \theta$, $\cos^3 \theta$, $\tan^4 \theta$, etc., instead of $(\sin \theta)^2$, $(\cos \theta)^3$, $(\tan \theta)^4$, etc., except when the exponent is -1. Then the function is enclosed in parentheses. Thus, $(\sin \theta)^{-1} = \dfrac{1}{\sin \theta}$ (see **Art. 35**).

EXERCISES

Find that the numerical values of each of the Exercises 1 to 10 is unity.

1. $\sin^2 30° + \cos^2 30°$.	**6.** $\sec^2 30° - \tan^2 30°$.
2. $\sin^2 60° + \cos^2 60°$.	**7.** $\sec^2 150° - \tan^2 150°$.
3. $\sin^2 120° + \cos^2 120°$.	**8.** $\sec^2 330° - \tan^2 330°$.
4. $\sin^2 135° + \cos^2 135°$.	**9.** $\csc^2 45° - \cot^2 45°$.
5. $\sin^2 300° + \cos^2 300°$.	**10.** $\csc^2 240° - \cot^2 240°$.

Find the numerical values of the following expressions correct to three decimal places:

11. $\sin 45° + 3 \cos 60°$.   *Ans.* 2.207.
12. $\cos^2 60° + \sin^3 90°$.   *Ans.* 1.250.
13. $10 \cos^4 30° + \sec 45°$.   *Ans.* 7.039.
14. $\sec 0° \cdot \cos 60° + \csc 90° \sec^2 45°$.   *Ans.* 2.500.
15. $\cos 120° \cos 270° - \sin 90° \tan^3 135°$.   *Ans.* 1.000.

In the following expressions, show that the left-hand member is equal to the right, by using the table on page 24:

16. $\sin 60° \cos 30° + \cos 60° \sin 30° = \sin 90°$.
17. $\cos 45° \cos 135° - \sin 45° \sin 135° = \cos 180°$.
18. $\sin 60° \cos 30° - \cos 60° \sin 30° = \sin 30°$.
19. $\cos 210° \cos 30° - \sin 210° \sin 30° = \cos 240°$.
20. $\sin 300° \cos 30° - \cos 300° \sin 30° = \sin 270°$.
21. $\dfrac{\tan 240° + \tan 60°}{1 - \tan 240° \tan 60°} = \tan 300°$.
22. $\dfrac{\tan 120° - \tan 60°}{1 + \tan 120° \tan 60°} = \tan 60°$.

26. Given the function of an acute angle, to construct the angle. *Example 1.*—Given $\sin \theta = \frac{4}{5}$. Construct angle θ and find the other functions.

Solution.—By definition, $\sin \theta = \dfrac{y}{r} = \dfrac{4}{5}$. Since we are concerned only with the ratios of the lines, we may take $y = 4$, and $r = 5$ units of any size. Draw AB parallel to OX and 4 units above (Fig. 24), intersecting OY at N. With the origin as a center and

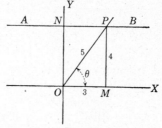

FIG. 24.

a radius of 5 units, draw an arc intersecting AB in the point P. Draw OP forming $\angle XOP$, and draw $MP \perp OX$. Then $OP = 5$, $MP = 4$, and

$$OM = \sqrt{\overline{OP^2} - \overline{MP^2}} = \sqrt{25 - 16} = 3.$$

$\therefore \angle XOP = \theta$ is the required angle since $\sin \theta = \dfrac{MP}{OP} = \dfrac{4}{5}$.

The remaining functions may be written as follows:

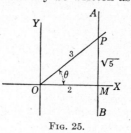

FIG. 25.

$$\cos \theta = \frac{OM}{OP} = \frac{3}{5}, \ \tan \theta = \frac{MP}{OM} = \frac{4}{3}, \ \cot \theta = \frac{OM}{MP} = \frac{3}{4},$$
$$\sec \theta = \frac{OP}{OM} = \frac{5}{3}, \ \csc \theta = \frac{OP}{MP} = \frac{5}{4}.$$

Example 2.—Given $\cos \theta = \frac{2}{3}$. Construct angle θ and find the other functions.

Solution.—By definition, $\cos \theta = \dfrac{x}{r} = \dfrac{2}{3}$. Choose $x = 2$ and $r = 3$. Draw $AB \parallel OY$ and 2 units to the right (Fig. 25), intersecting OX at M. With the origin as a center and a radius of 3 units, draw an arc cutting AB at P. Join O and P, forming $\angle XOP$. Then $OP = 3$, $OM = 2$, and

$$MP = \sqrt{\overline{OP^2} - \overline{OM^2}} = \sqrt{5}.$$

$\therefore \angle XOP = \theta$ is the required angle since $\cos \theta = \dfrac{OM}{OP} = \dfrac{2}{3}.$

The remaining functions are as follows:

$$\sin \theta = \frac{MP}{OP} = \frac{\sqrt{5}}{3}, \ \tan \theta = \frac{MP}{OM} = \frac{\sqrt{5}}{2}, \ \cot \theta = \frac{OM}{MP} = \frac{2}{\sqrt{5}},$$

$$\sec \theta = \frac{OP}{OM} = \frac{3}{2}, \ \csc \theta = \frac{OP}{MP} = \frac{3}{\sqrt{5}}.$$

Example 3.—Given $\tan \theta = \frac{2}{5}$. Construct angle θ and find the other functions.

Solution.—By definition, $\tan \theta = \dfrac{y}{x} = \dfrac{2}{5}.$ Choose $y = 2$ and $x = 5$. Draw $AB \parallel OY$ and 5 units to the right (Fig. 26), intersecting OX at M; also draw $CD \parallel OX$ and 2 units above intersecting AB at P. Then $OM = 5$, $MP = 2$, and $OP = \sqrt{29}.$

$\therefore \angle XOP = \theta$ is the required angle since $\tan \theta = \dfrac{MP}{OM} = \dfrac{2}{5}.$

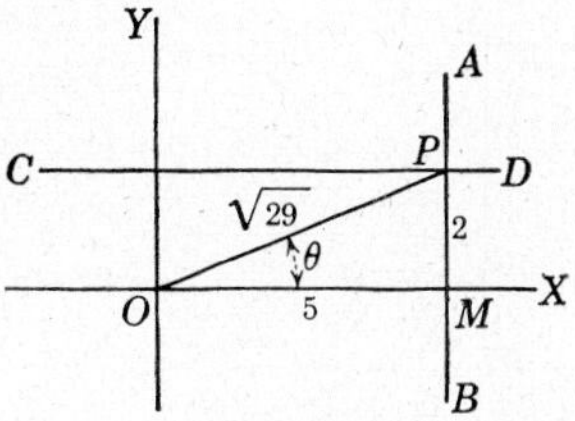

Fig. 26

The other functions are as follows:

$$\sin \theta = \frac{2}{\sqrt{29}}, \quad \cos \theta = \frac{5}{\sqrt{29}}, \quad \cot \theta = \frac{5}{2}, \quad \sec \theta = \frac{\sqrt{29}}{5},$$

$$\csc \theta = \frac{\sqrt{29}}{2}.$$

EXERCISES

In Exercises 1 to 12, construct θ from the given function and find the other functions of θ when in the first quadrant.

1. $\sin \theta = \frac{3}{5}.$

2. $\cos \theta = \frac{3}{4}.$

3. $\tan \theta = 3.$

4. $\cot \theta = 2.5.$

5. $\sin \theta = \frac{1}{2}.$

6. $\cos \theta = \frac{1}{2}\sqrt{3}.$

7. $\tan \theta = \dfrac{a}{b}.$

8. $\cos \theta = \dfrac{a}{r}.$

9. $\sec \theta = \sqrt{2}.$

10. $\csc \theta = \frac{4}{3}.$

11. $\tan \theta = 4.$

12. $\cot \theta = \frac{3}{2}.$

13. Find the value of $\sqrt{\dfrac{\sin \theta \cos \theta}{\sec \theta \csc \theta}}$, when $\tan \theta = \dfrac{1}{5}$, and θ is an acute angle. *Ans.* $\frac{5}{26}.$

14. Find the value of $\dfrac{\sec \theta + \tan \theta}{\cos \theta + \text{vers } \theta}$, when $\cos \theta = \dfrac{3}{5}$, and θ is an acute angle. *Ans.* 3.

15. Find the value of $\dfrac{\csc\theta + \sec\theta}{\sin\theta + \cos\theta}$, when $\cos\theta = \dfrac{\sqrt{10}}{10}$, and θ is an acute angle.

Ans. $1\frac{9}{3}$.

16. Find the value of $\dfrac{\sin\theta\cot\theta + \cos\theta}{\sec\theta\cot\theta}$, when $\cot\theta = \sqrt{5}$, and θ is an acute angle.

Ans. 0.745.

17. Find the value of $\dfrac{\sin\theta}{\cos\theta} + \dfrac{\sin^2\theta\sec\theta}{\cos^2\theta\tan^2\theta}$, when $\csc\theta = 3$ and θ is an acute angle.

Ans. 1.414.

27. Trigonometric functions applied to right triangles.—When the angle θ is acute, the abscissa, ordinate, and distance for any point in the terminal side form a right triangle, in which the given angle θ is one of the acute angles.   On account of the many applications of the right triangle in trigonometry, the definitions of the trigonometric functions will be stated with special reference to the right triangle. These definitions are very important and are frequently the first ones taught, but it should be carefully noted that they are not general because they apply only to *acute* angles.

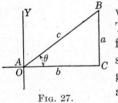

Fig. 27.

Draw the right triangle ABC (Fig. 27), with the vertex A at the origin, and AC on the initial line.   Then AC and CB are the coordinates of B in the terminal side AB. Let $AC = b$, $CB = a$, and $AB = c$.

By definition:

$$\sin A = \frac{\text{ordinate}}{\text{distance}} = \frac{a}{c} = \frac{\text{side opposite}}{\text{hypotenuse}}.$$

$$\cos A = \frac{\text{abscissa}}{\text{distance}} = \frac{b}{c} = \frac{\text{side adjacent}}{\text{hypotenuse}}.$$

$$\tan A = \frac{\text{ordinate}}{\text{abscissa}} = \frac{a}{b} = \frac{\text{side opposite}}{\text{side adjacent}}.$$

$$\cot A = \frac{\text{abscissa}}{\text{ordinate}} = \frac{b}{a} = \frac{\text{side adjacent}}{\text{side opposite}}.$$

$$\sec A = \frac{\text{distance}}{\text{abscissa}} = \frac{c}{b} = \frac{\text{hypotenuse}}{\text{side adjacent}}.$$

$$\csc A = \frac{\text{distance}}{\text{ordinate}} = \frac{c}{a} = \frac{\text{hypotenuse}}{\text{side opposite}}.$$

Again, suppose the triangle ABC placed so that $\angle B$ has its vertex at the origin, BC for the initial side, and BA for the terminal side, as in Fig. 28. The coordinates of A are $BC = a$ and $CA = b$.

By definition:

$$\sin B = \frac{b}{c} = \frac{\text{side opposite}}{\text{hypotenuse}}. \qquad \cot B = \frac{a}{b} = \frac{\text{side adjacent}}{\text{side opposite}}.$$

$$\cos B = \frac{a}{c} = \frac{\text{side adjacent}}{\text{hypotenuse}}. \qquad \sec B = \frac{c}{a} = \frac{\text{hypotenuse}}{\text{side adjacent}}.$$

$$\tan B = \frac{b}{a} = \frac{\text{side opposite}}{\text{side adjacent}}. \qquad \csc B = \frac{c}{b} = \frac{\text{hypotenuse}}{\text{side opposite}}.$$

Then, no matter where the right triangle is found, the functions of the acute angles may be written in terms of the legs and the hypotenuse of the right triangle.

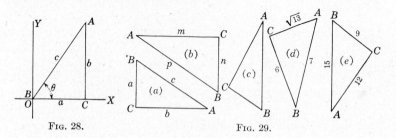

FIG. 28.   FIG. 29.

EXERCISES

1. Give orally the six trigonometric ratios of each of the acute angles of the right triangles in Fig. 29.

In the right triangle ABC, find the six trigonometric ratios from the following data:

2. $a = \frac{1}{4}c$. **3.** $b = \frac{1}{3}c$. **4.** $a = 4b$.

5. In a right triangle find a if $\sin A = \frac{3}{5}$, and $c = 4.28$.

Ans. a = 2.568.

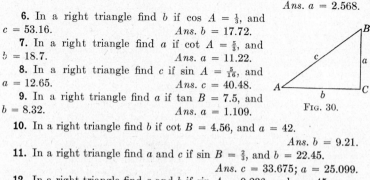

6. In a right triangle find b if $\cos A = \frac{1}{3}$, and $c = 53.16$.   *Ans. b = 17.72.*

7. In a right triangle find a if $\cot A = \frac{5}{3}$, and $b = 18.7$.   *Ans. a = 11.22.*

8. In a right triangle find c if $\sin A = \frac{5}{16}$, and $a = 12.65$.   *Ans. c = 40.48.*

9. In a right triangle find a if $\tan B = 7.5$, and $b = 8.32$.   *Ans. a = 1.109.*

FIG. 30.

10. In a right triangle find b if $\cot B = 4.56$, and $a = 42$.

Ans. b = 9.21.

11. In a right triangle find a and c if $\sin B = \frac{2}{3}$, and $b = 22.45$.

Ans. c = 33.675; a = 25.099.

12. In a right triangle find a and b if $\sin A = 0.236$, and $c = 45$.

Ans. a = 10.62; b = 43.73.

The following refer to a right triangle:

13. $c = r + s$, $a = \sqrt{2rs}$; find $\tan A$.   *Ans.* $\tan A = \sqrt{\dfrac{2rs}{r^2 + s^2}}$.

14. $b = \sqrt{r^2 + s^2}$, $c = r + s$; find $\sin A$.   *Ans.* $\sin A = \dfrac{\sqrt{2rs}}{r + s}$.

15. $a = 2rs$, $b = r^2 - s^2$; find $\cos B$.   *Ans.* $\cos B = \dfrac{2rs}{r^2 + s^2}$.

16. Construct a right triangle in which $\sin A = 2 \sin B$. In which $\sin A = 3 \cos A$. In which $\tan A = 3 \tan B$.

Construct the angle θ from each of the following data:

17. $\tan \theta = 2 \cot \theta$.   **19.** $\sin \theta = 3 \cos \theta$.   **21.** $\cot \theta = 3 \tan \theta$.

18. $\cos \theta = 2 \sin \theta$.   **20.** $\sec \theta = 2 \csc \theta$.   **22.** $\sin \theta = \cos \theta$.

28. Relations between the functions of complementary angles.

—From the formulas of **Art. 27,** the following relations are evident:

$$\sin A = \cos B = \frac{a}{c}. \qquad\qquad \cot A = \tan B = \frac{b}{a}.$$

$$\cos A = \sin B = \frac{b}{c}. \qquad\qquad \sec A = \csc B = \frac{c}{b}.$$

$$\tan A = \cot B = \frac{a}{b}. \qquad\qquad \csc A = \sec B = \frac{c}{a}.$$

But angles A and B are complementary; therefore, *the sine, cosine, tangent, cotangent, secant, and cosecant of an angle are, respectively, the cosine, sine, cotangent, tangent, cosecant, and secant of the complement of the angle. They are also called cofunctions.*

For example, $\cos 75° = \sin (90° - 75°) = \sin 15°$;
$$\tan 80° = \cot (90° - 80°) = \cot 10°.$$

Note.—The term cosine was not used until the beginning of the seventeenth century. Before that time the expression, sine of the complement (Latin, *complementi sinus*) was used instead. Cosine is a contraction of the Latin expression. Similarly, cotangent and cosecant are contractions of *complementi tangens* and *complementi secans* respectively.

The abbreviations, sin, cos, tan, cot, sec, and csc did not come into general use until the middle of the eighteenth century.

EXERCISES

1. Express the following functions as functions of the complements of these angles: $\sin 60°$; $\cos 25°$; $\tan 15°$; $\cot 65°$; $\sec 10°$; $\csc 42°$; $\sin \theta$; $\sin 3\theta$; $\cos (\theta - 90°)$.

2. If $\sin 40° = \cos \theta$, find θ.   **6.** If $\sin 2\theta = \cos 4\theta$, find θ.

3. If $\tan 50° = \cot 2\theta$, find θ.   **7.** If $\tan \theta = \cot 5\theta$, find θ.

4. If $\csc 20° = \sec 2\theta$, find θ.   **8.** If $\csc 6\theta = \sec 4\theta$, find θ.

5. If $\cos \theta = \sin 2\theta$, find θ.   **9.** If $\cos \tfrac{1}{3}\theta = \sin \theta$, find θ.

10. If $\cot \tfrac{1}{4}\theta = \tan \theta$, find θ.   *Ans.* $67\tfrac{1}{2}°$.

11. If $\cos \theta = \sin (45° - \frac{1}{2}\theta)$, find θ. *Ans.* 90°.

12. If $\cot \alpha = \tan (45° + \alpha)$, find α. *Ans.* 22° 30′.

13. If $\csc (60° - \alpha) = \sec (15° + 3\alpha)$, find α. *Ans.* 7° 30′.

14. If $\sin (35° + \beta) = \cos (\beta - 15°)$, find β. *Ans.* 35°.

15. Express each of the following functions as functions of angles less than 45°: sin 68°; cot 88°; sec 75°; csc 47° 58′ 12″; cos 71° 12′ 56″.

29. Given the function of an angle in any quadrant, to construct the angle. *Example* 1.—Given $\sin \theta = \frac{3}{5}$. Construct angle θ and find all the other functions.

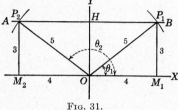

Solution.—By definition, $\sin$ $\theta = \frac{y}{r}$. Take $y = 3$ units and $r = 5$ units. Draw $AB \parallel OX$ and 3 units above it as in Fig. 31. Construct the arc of a circle with

Fig. 31.

center at O and radius 5 units, intersecting AB at P_1 and P_2. Then for P_1, $x = 4$, $y = 3$, and $r = 5$; for P_2, $x = -4$, $y = 3$, and $r = 5$. Now OP_1 and OP_2 are terminal sides, respectively of $\angle XOP_1 = \theta_1$ and $\angle XOP_2 = \theta_2$, each of which has its sine equal to $\frac{3}{5}$. Then from the definitions of the trigonometric functions we have the following:

Quadrant	Angle	$\sin \theta$	$\cos \theta$	$\tan \theta$	$\cot \theta$	$\sec \theta$	$\csc \theta$
I...........	θ_1	$\frac{3}{5}$	$\frac{4}{5}$	$\frac{3}{4}$	$\frac{4}{3}$	$\frac{5}{4}$	$\frac{5}{3}$
II...........	θ_2	$\frac{3}{5}$	$-\frac{4}{5}$	$-\frac{3}{4}$	$-\frac{4}{3}$	$-\frac{5}{4}$	$\frac{5}{3}$

Example 2.—Given $\cos \theta = -\frac{2}{3}$. Construct θ and find all the other functions.

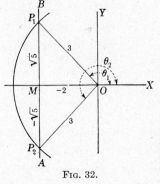

Fig. 32.

Solution.—By definition, $\cos \theta = \frac{x}{r} = -\frac{2}{3}$. Since r is always positive, we take $x = -2$ units and $r = 3$ units. Draw $AB \parallel OY$ and 2 units to the left as in Fig. 32. Construct a circle of radius 3, with its center at O, and intersecting AB at P_1 and P_2. Draw OP_1 and OP_2. As in Example 1, it may be shown that $\angle XOP_1 = \theta_1$ and $\angle XOP_2 = \theta_2$ are the required angles. The functions are as follows:

Quadrant	Angle	$\sin \theta$	$\cos \theta$	$\tan \theta$	$\cot \theta$	$\sec \theta$	$\csc \theta$
II...........	θ_1	$\dfrac{\sqrt{5}}{3}$	$-\dfrac{2}{3}$	$-\dfrac{\sqrt{5}}{2}$	$-\dfrac{2}{\sqrt{5}}$	$-\dfrac{3}{2}$	$\dfrac{3}{\sqrt{5}}$
III..........	θ_2	$-\dfrac{\sqrt{5}}{3}$	$-\dfrac{2}{3}$	$\dfrac{\sqrt{5}}{2}$	$\dfrac{2}{\sqrt{5}}$	$-\dfrac{3}{2}$	$-\dfrac{3}{\sqrt{5}}$

Example 3.—Given $\tan \theta = \frac{3}{4}$. Construct angle θ and find all the other functions.

Solution.—By definition, $\tan \theta = \dfrac{y}{x}$. Hence $\dfrac{y}{x} = \dfrac{3}{4} = \dfrac{-3}{-4}$, and we may take $y = \pm 3$ and $x = \pm 4$. Then

$$r = \sqrt{(\pm 4)^2 + (\pm 3)^2} = 5.$$

With O as a center and 5 as a radius, construct a circle as in Fig. 33. Draw AB and $CD \parallel OY$ and 4 units to the right and left

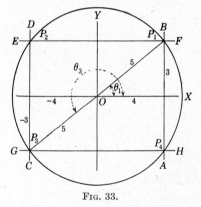

Fig. 33.

respectively of OY. Also draw EF and $GH \parallel OX$ and 3 units above and below OX respectively. These lines and the circle intersect at the points P_1, P_2, P_3, and P_4. Since x and y must both be positive or both negative, the required points must be P_1 and P_3 located in the first and third quadrants. Draw OP_1 and OP_3 forming the angles $XOP_1 = \theta_1$ and $XOP_3 = \theta_3$. The functions are as follows:

Quadrant	Angle	$\sin \theta$	$\cos \theta$	$\tan \theta$	$\cot \theta$	$\sec \theta$	$\csc \theta$
I.............	θ_1	$\frac{3}{5}$	$\frac{4}{5}$	$\frac{3}{4}$	$\frac{4}{3}$	$\frac{5}{4}$	$\frac{5}{3}$
III...·.......	θ_3	$-\frac{3}{5}$	$-\frac{4}{5}$	$\frac{3}{4}$	$\frac{4}{3}$	$-\frac{5}{4}$	$-\frac{5}{3}$

EXERCISES

Draw the angles less than 360° and tabulate the six trigonometric ratios determined by each of the following:

1. $\cos \theta = -\frac{4}{5}$.　　**5.** $\cos \theta = 0.6$.　　**9.** $\csc \theta = -\frac{2}{\sqrt{3}}$.

2. $\sin \theta = -\frac{5}{13}$.　　**6.** $\cot \theta = 3$.　　**10.** $\sin \theta = -\frac{4}{7}$.

3. $\tan \theta = -\frac{1}{4}$.　　**7.** $\tan \theta = -\sqrt{3}$.　　**11.** $\tan \theta = \frac{5}{2}$.

4. $\sin \theta = \frac{7}{25}$.　　**8.** $\sec \theta = -4$.　　**12.** $\csc \theta = 2.4$.

13. What is the greatest value that the sine of an angle may have? The least value? How does the value of the sine change as the angle changes from 0° to 90°? From 90° to 180°? From 180° to 270°? From 270° to 360°?

14. Answer the questions of Exercise 13 for the cosine. For the tangent.

In Exercises 15, 18, and 21 show by substitution that the right-hand member is equal to the left.

15. $(1 + \tan^2 \theta)(1 - \cot^2 \theta) = \sec^2 \theta - \csc^2 \theta$, when $\sin \theta = \frac{4}{5}$ and θ is in the second quadrant.

16. Find the value of $\dfrac{\sin \theta \tan \theta}{\sec \theta}$, when $\cot \theta = -\dfrac{2}{3}$ and θ is in the fourth quadrant.　　　　　　　　　　　　　　　　　　*Ans.* $\frac{9}{13}$.

17. Find the value of $\dfrac{\sin \theta + \tan \theta}{\cos \theta + \text{vers } \theta}$, when $\csc \theta = -\dfrac{5}{4}$ and θ is in the fourth quadrant.　　　　　　　　　　　　　*Ans.* -2.133.

18. $\cos \theta \tan \theta + \sin \theta \cot \theta = \sin \theta + \cos \theta$, when $\sec \theta = 2$ and θ is in the fourth quadrant.

19. Find the value of $\dfrac{\sec \theta - \csc \theta}{\sec \theta + \csc \theta}$, when $\tan \theta = -2$ and θ is in the second quadrant.　　　　　　　　　　　　　　*Ans.* **3.**

20. Find the value of $\dfrac{\sin \theta + \cot \theta}{\cos \theta + \csc \theta}$, when $\cot \theta = 2\sqrt{2}$ and $\sin \theta = -\dfrac{1}{3}$.

　　　　　　　　　　　　　　　　　　　　　Ans. -0.6328.

21. $\cot \theta + \dfrac{\sin \theta}{1 + \cos \theta} = \csc \theta$, when $\sin \theta = -\dfrac{\sqrt{3}}{2}$ and θ is in the third quadrant.

CHAPTER III

RELATIONS BETWEEN TRIGONOMETRIC FUNCTIONS

30. Fundamental relations between the functions of an angle.—In handling questions that occur in mathematics a great deal of use is made of relations that exist between trigonometric functions of angles. These relations are numerous, but it is necessary to memorize only a few of them. In this chapter are considered only those relations that exist between functions of one angle. In a later chapter will be found relations where different angles are involved.

From the figures of **Art. 15,** it is evident that for an angle in any quadrant

(1) $$x^2 + y^2 = r^2.$$

Dividing (1) by r^2, $\dfrac{x^2}{r^2} + \dfrac{y^2}{r^2} = \dfrac{r^2}{r^2} = \mathbf{1.}$

But $\dfrac{x}{r} = \cos \theta$ and $\dfrac{y}{r} = \sin \theta.$

[1] $$\therefore \ \mathbf{sin^2 \ \theta + cos^2 \ \theta = 1.}$$

Dividing (1) by x^2, $1 + \dfrac{y^2}{x^2} = \dfrac{r^2}{x^2}.$

But $\tan \theta = \dfrac{y}{x}$ and $\sec \theta = \dfrac{r}{x}.$

[2] $$\therefore \ \mathbf{1 + tan^2 \ \theta = sec^2 \ \theta.}$$

Dividing (1) by y^2, $\dfrac{x^2}{y^2} + 1 = \dfrac{r^2}{y^2}.$

But $\cot \theta = \dfrac{x}{y}$ and $\csc \theta = \dfrac{r}{y}.$

[3] $$\therefore \ \mathbf{1 + cot^2 \ \theta = csc^2 \ \theta.}$$

Also, from the definitions of the trigonometric functions, the following reciprocal relations are evident:

[4] $$\mathbf{csc \ \theta = \dfrac{1}{sin \ \theta}} \quad \text{and} \quad \mathbf{sin \ \theta = \dfrac{1}{csc \ \theta}.}$$

[5] $$\mathbf{sec \ \theta = \dfrac{1}{cos \ \theta}} \quad \text{and} \quad \mathbf{cos \ \theta = \dfrac{1}{sec \ \theta}.}$$

[6] $$\cot \theta = \frac{1}{\tan \theta} \quad \text{and} \quad \tan \theta = \frac{1}{\cot \theta}.$$

The following formulas are easily derived:

[7] $$\tan \theta = \frac{\sin \theta}{\cos \theta}.$$

[8] $$\cot \theta = \frac{\cos \theta}{\sin \theta}.$$

The eight formulas of this article are **identities,** for they are true for any angle whatever. They are often spoken of as **fundamental identities,** or **formulas.** They should be carefully memorized as they are frequently used.

It will be noted that throughout the book the important formulas are printed in bold-faced type and numbered in square brackets for ready reference.

The following examples make use of the fundamental formulas in computing the other trigonometric functions when one function is given. Compare the work with that of the previous articles where the angles were first constructed.

Example 1.—Given tan $\theta = \frac{4}{3}$, and θ in the first quadrant, determine the other functions by means of the fundamental formulas.

Solution.—By [2], sec $\theta = \sqrt{1 + \tan^2 \theta} = \sqrt{1 + \frac{16}{9}} = \frac{5}{3}$.

By [6], $\quad \cot \theta = \dfrac{1}{\tan \theta} = \dfrac{1}{\frac{4}{3}} = \dfrac{3}{4}.$

By [3], $\quad \csc \theta = \sqrt{1 + \cot^2 \theta} = \sqrt{1 + \frac{9}{16}} = \frac{5}{4}.$

By [4], $\quad \sin \theta = \dfrac{1}{\csc \theta} = \dfrac{1}{\frac{5}{4}} = \dfrac{4}{5}.$

By [5], $\quad \cos \theta = \dfrac{1}{\sec \theta} = \dfrac{1}{\frac{5}{3}} = \dfrac{3}{5}.$

Example 2.—Given sin $\theta = \frac{1}{2}$, and θ in the second quadrant, determine the other functions by means of the fundamental formulas.

Solution.—By [1], cos $\theta = -\sqrt{1 - \sin^2 \theta} = -\sqrt{1 - \frac{1}{4}} = -\frac{1}{2}\sqrt{3}.$

By [7], $\quad \tan \theta = \dfrac{\sin \theta}{\cos \theta} = \dfrac{\frac{1}{2}}{-\frac{1}{2}\sqrt{3}} = -\dfrac{1}{3}\sqrt{3}.$

By [6], $\quad \cot \theta = \dfrac{1}{\tan \theta} = \dfrac{1}{-\frac{1}{3}\sqrt{3}} = -\sqrt{3}.$

By [**5**], $\sec \theta = \dfrac{1}{\cos \theta} = \dfrac{1}{-\frac{1}{2}\sqrt{3}} = -\dfrac{2}{3}\sqrt{3}.$

By [**4**], $\csc \theta = \dfrac{1}{\sin \theta} = \dfrac{1}{\frac{1}{2}} = 2.$

Note.—The proper algebraic sign is determined by **Art. 17**.

EXERCISES

In Exercises 1 to 10 determine the remaining functions from the given functions by means of the fundamental identities and check by constructing the angle and computing the functions.

1. Given $\sin \theta = -\frac{4}{5}$, and θ in the third quadrant.

2. Given $\tan \theta = -\frac{5}{12}$, and θ in the fourth quadrant.

3. Given $\sec \theta = \sqrt{2}$, and θ in the first quadrant.

4. Given $\cos \theta = \dfrac{\sqrt{3}}{2}$, and θ in the fourth quadrant.

5. Given $\tan \theta = \frac{3}{2}$, and θ in the third quadrant.

6. Given $\cot \theta = 5$, and θ in the first quadrant.

7. Given $\sec \alpha = -\frac{5}{4}$, and α in the third quadrant.

8. Given $\tan \beta = \frac{24}{7}$, and β in the third quadrant.

9. Given $\csc \theta = -\frac{17}{8}$, and θ in the fourth quadrant.

10. Given $\sin \alpha = -\frac{9}{41}$, and α in the third quadrant.

11. If $\cos \frac{1}{2}\alpha = \sqrt{\dfrac{s(s-a)}{bc}}$, where $s = \dfrac{a+b+c}{2}$, show that $\sin \frac{1}{2}\alpha$
$= \sqrt{\dfrac{(s-b)(s-c)}{bc}}.$

12. If $\cos \frac{1}{2}\gamma = \sqrt{\dfrac{s(s-c)}{ab}}$, where $s = \dfrac{a+b+c}{2}$, show that $\tan \frac{1}{2}\gamma$
$= \sqrt{\dfrac{(s-a)(s-b)}{s(s-c)}}.$

13. If $\tan \beta = c$, show that $\csc \beta$ is real for all values of **c**.

14. Given $\sin \gamma = \dfrac{2mn}{m^2 + n^2}$; show that $\tan \gamma = \pm \dfrac{2mn}{m^2 - n^2}.$

31. To express one function in terms of each of the other functions.—Any trigonometric function can readily be expressed in terms of any other function by means of the fundamental formulas. While the work cannot be carried out so rapidly as by the method of the following article, it gives needed drill in the use of the formulas.

Example.—Express $\sin \theta$ in terms of each of the other functions.

By [**1**], $\sin \theta = \sqrt{1 - \cos^2 \theta}.$

By [**5**], $\cos \theta = \dfrac{1}{\sec \theta}.$

$$\therefore \sin \theta = \sqrt{1 - \cos^2 \theta} = \sqrt{1 - \frac{1}{\sec^2 \theta}} = \frac{\sqrt{\sec^2 \theta - 1}}{\sec \theta}.$$

By [2], $\qquad \sec^2 \theta = 1 + \tan^2 \theta.$

$$\therefore \sin \theta = \frac{\sqrt{\sec^2 \theta - 1}}{\sec \theta} = \frac{\sqrt{\tan^2 \theta}}{\sqrt{1 + \tan^2 \theta}} = \frac{\tan \theta}{\sqrt{1 + \tan^2 \theta}}.$$

Also $\sin \theta = \dfrac{\tan \theta}{\sqrt{1 + \tan^2 \theta}} = \dfrac{\dfrac{1}{\cot \theta}}{\sqrt{1 + \dfrac{1}{\cot^2 \theta}}} = \dfrac{1}{\sqrt{1 + \cot^2 \theta}}.$

By [4], $\qquad \sin \theta = \dfrac{1}{\csc \theta}.$

The algebraic sign of $\sin \theta$ is determined from the quadrant in which θ is found.

32. To express all the functions of an angle in terms of one function of the angle, by means of a triangle.—The scheme outlined in this article can be carried out rapidly and will be found of very great use in future work.

Example 1.—Express all the functions of θ in terms of $\sin \theta$.

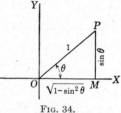

FIG. 34.

Solution.—Construct angle θ in the first quadrant (Fig. 34) and choose the point P in the terminal side with coordinates OM and MP. Then, by definition, $\sin \theta = \dfrac{MP}{OP}$, and, if OP is taken equal to 1, $MP = \sin \theta$, and $OM = \sqrt{OP^2 - MP^2} = \sqrt{1 - \sin^2 \theta}.$

The remaining functions may then be written as follows:

$\cos \theta = \dfrac{OM}{OP} = \sqrt{1 - \sin^2 \theta}.$ $\quad \sec \theta = \dfrac{OP}{OM} = \dfrac{1}{\sqrt{1 - \sin^2 \theta}}.$

$\tan \theta = \dfrac{MP}{OM} = \dfrac{\sin \theta}{\sqrt{1 - \sin^2 \theta}}.$ $\quad \csc \theta = \dfrac{OP}{MP} = \dfrac{1}{\sin \theta}.$

$\cot \theta = \dfrac{OM}{MP} = \dfrac{\sqrt{1 - \sin^2 \theta}}{\sin \theta}.$

Example 2.—Express all the functions in terms of $\cos \theta$.

Solution.—Construct angle θ in the first quadrant (Fig. 35) and choose the point P in the terminal side with coordinates

OM and MP. Then, by definition, $\cos \theta = \dfrac{OM}{OP}$, and, if OP is

FIG. 35.

taken equal to 1, $OM = \cos \theta$, and $MP = \sqrt{\overline{OP}^2 - \overline{OM}^2} = \sqrt{1 - \cos^2 \theta}$.

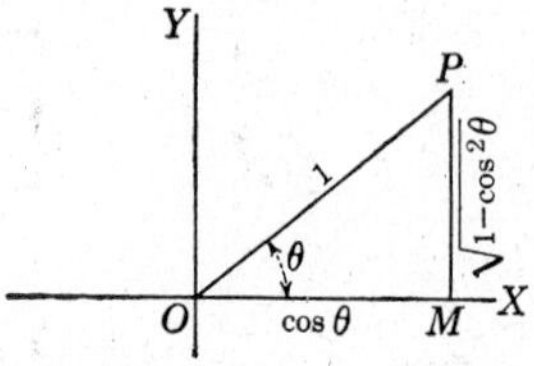

The remaining functions may then be written as follows:

$$\sin \theta = \frac{MP}{OP} = \sqrt{1 - \cos^2 \theta}.$$

$$\tan \theta = \frac{MP}{OM} = \frac{\sqrt{1 - \cos^2 \theta}}{\cos \theta}. \quad \sec \theta = \frac{OP}{OM} = \frac{1}{\cos \theta}.$$

$$\cot \theta = \frac{OM}{MP} = \frac{\cos \theta}{\sqrt{1 - \cos^2 \theta}}. \quad \csc \theta = \frac{OP}{MP} = \frac{1}{\sqrt{1 - \cos^2 \theta}}.$$

In the following table, the student is asked to show that each function in the first column is equal to every expression found in the same row with the function:

$\sin \theta$	$\sin \theta$	$\sqrt{1 - \cos^2 \theta}$	$\dfrac{\tan \theta}{\sqrt{1 + \tan^2 \theta}}$	$\dfrac{1}{\sqrt{1 + \cot^2 \theta}}$	$\dfrac{\sqrt{\sec^2 \theta - 1}}{\sec \theta}$	$\dfrac{1}{\csc \theta}$
$\cos \theta$	$\sqrt{1 - \sin^2 \theta}$	$\cos \theta$	$\dfrac{1}{\sqrt{1 + \tan^2 \theta}}$	$\dfrac{\cot \theta}{\sqrt{1 + \cot^2 \theta}}$	$\dfrac{1}{\sec \theta}$	$\dfrac{\sqrt{\csc^2 \theta - 1}}{\csc \theta}$
$\tan \theta$	$\dfrac{\sin \theta}{\sqrt{1 - \sin^2 \theta}}$	$\dfrac{\sqrt{1 - \cos^2 \theta}}{\cos \theta}$	$\tan \theta$	$\dfrac{1}{\cot \theta}$	$\sqrt{\sec^2 \theta - 1}$	$\dfrac{1}{\sqrt{\csc^2 \theta - 1}}$
$\cot \theta$	$\dfrac{\sqrt{1 - \sin^2 \theta}}{\sin \theta}$	$\dfrac{\cos \theta}{\sqrt{1 - \cos^2 \theta}}$	$\dfrac{1}{\tan \theta}$	$\cot \theta$	$\dfrac{1}{\sqrt{\sec^2 \theta - 1}}$	$\sqrt{\csc^2 \theta - 1}$
$\sec \theta$	$\dfrac{1}{\sqrt{1 - \sin^2 \theta}}$	$\dfrac{1}{\cos \theta}$	$\sqrt{1 + \tan^2 \theta}$	$\dfrac{\sqrt{1 + \cot^2 \theta}}{\cot \theta}$	$\sec \theta$	$\dfrac{\csc \theta}{\sqrt{\csc^2 \theta - 1}}$
$\csc \theta$	$\dfrac{1}{\sin \theta}$	$\dfrac{1}{\sqrt{1 - \cos^2 \theta}}$	$\dfrac{\sqrt{1 + \tan^2 \theta}}{\tan \theta}$	$\sqrt{1 + \cot^2 \theta}$	$\dfrac{\sec \theta}{\sqrt{\sec^2 \theta - 1}}$	$\csc \theta$

The table has been prepared under the assumption that θ is an acute angle. Should θ be in any other quadrant, the proper sign for each function may then be determined.

33. Transformation of trigonometric expressions.—In all transformations, avoid radicals if possible. Usually, this can best be done by changing to sines and cosines and then simplifying. It will be noticed that, if there are no radicals in an expression, it can be changed to sines and cosines without using radicals. If the expression is in a factored form, it is often desirable to reduce each factor separately and multiply the results.

Example 1.—Express $\dfrac{\cos \theta}{\sin \theta \cot^2 \theta}$ in terms of $\tan \theta$.

Solution.—$\cot \theta = \dfrac{\cos \theta}{\sin \theta}$, then $\dfrac{\cos \theta}{\sin \theta \cdot \cot^2 \theta}$

$$= \frac{\cos \theta}{\sin \theta \cdot \dfrac{\cos^2 \theta}{\sin^2 \theta}} = \frac{\sin \theta}{\cos \theta} = \tan \theta.$$

Example 2.—Express $1 - 2(1 - \text{covers } \theta)^2 + \dfrac{\tan^4 \theta}{(1 + \tan^2 \theta)^2}$ in terms of $\cos \theta$.

Solution.—By definition and formulas, $\text{covers } \theta = 1 - \sin \theta$, $\tan \theta = \dfrac{\sin \theta}{\cos \theta}$, $1 + \tan^2 \theta = \sec^2 \theta$, and $\cos \theta = \dfrac{1}{\sec \theta}$.

Substituting these values, we have

$$1 - 2[1 - (1 - \sin \theta)]^2 + \frac{\dfrac{\sin^4 \theta}{\cos^4 \theta}}{\sec^4 \theta} = 1 - 2 \sin^2 \theta + \frac{\dfrac{\sin^4 \theta}{\cos^4 \theta}}{\dfrac{1}{\cos^4 \theta}}$$

$$= 1 - 2 \sin^2 \theta + \sin^4 \theta = (1 - \sin^2 \theta)^2 = (\cos^2 \theta)^2 = \cos^4 \theta.$$

EXERCISES

Transform the following expressions as indicated:

1. $\sin \theta \cot \theta \sec \theta$ to 1.
2. $\cos \theta \tan \theta \csc \theta$ to 1.
3. $(1 - \sin^2 \phi)(1 + \tan^2 \phi)$ to 1.
4. $(1 + \cos \theta) \text{ vers } \theta + \text{covers } \theta (1 + \sin \theta)$ to 1.
5. $\dfrac{1 - \sec^2 \phi}{1 - \csc^2 \phi}$ to $\tan^4 \phi$.
6. $\sec \theta - \tan \theta \sin \theta$ to $\cos \theta$.
7. $\sin^2 \phi(1 + \sec^2 \phi)$ to $\sec^2 \phi - \cos^2 \phi$.
8. $\dfrac{\sin \theta}{1 - \cos \theta}$ to $\cot \theta + \csc \theta$.
9. $\sin^4 \phi - \cos^4 \phi$ to $1 - 2 \cos^2 \phi$.
10. $\sin^4 \theta + \cos^4 \theta$ to $1 - 2 \sin^2 \theta \cos^2 \theta$.
11. $\dfrac{\sin^2 \phi \sec \phi}{1 + \sec \phi} + \cos \phi$ to 1.
12. $\dfrac{\cos \theta}{2} \sqrt{\dfrac{1 + \sin^2 \theta}{\cos \theta}} \left[\sqrt{\dfrac{\cos^3 \theta}{1 + \sin^2 \theta}} + \sqrt{\dfrac{1 + \sin^2 \theta}{\cos \theta}} \right]$ to 1.
13. $\sqrt{\dfrac{\sec^2 \phi - 1}{\sec^2 \phi(1 + \cot^2 \phi)}} + \dfrac{\cot^2 \phi}{\csc \phi} \sqrt{\dfrac{\csc^2 \phi - 1}{\csc^2 \phi}}$ to $(1 + \cot \phi)(1 - \sin \phi \cos \phi)$.
14. $7 \sec^2 \phi - 6 \tan^2 \phi + 9 \cos^2 \phi$ to $\dfrac{(1 + 3 \cos^2 \phi)^2}{\cos^2 \phi}$.
15. $\dfrac{\sin^2 \phi \cos^2 \phi + \cos^4 \phi + 2 \cos^2 \phi + \sin^2 \phi}{1 - \tan^2 \phi}$ to $\dfrac{3 + \tan^2 \phi}{1 - \tan^4 \phi}$.
16. $\dfrac{(1 - \text{vers}^2 \theta)^2 - (1 - \text{covers}^2 \theta)^2}{\cos \theta - \sin \theta}$ to $5(\cos \theta + \sin \theta) - 4(1 + \sin \theta \cos \theta)$.

34. Identities.—When two expressions in some letter x are equal for all values of that letter they are said to be **identically equal.**

The equation formed by equating the two expressions is called an **identity.**

The symbol denoting identity is $\equiv$. When there can be no misunderstanding as to the meaning, the sign of equality is often used to denote identity. The symbol $\equiv$ is read "identically equals," or "is identically equal to."

Thus, $x^2 - 1 \equiv (x - 1)(x + 1)$ because the equation is true for all values of x.

Since the fundamental formulas are true for all values of θ, they are identities.

In showing that one trigonometric expression is identically equal to another, we either transform both expressions to the same form, or transform one expression into the other, by means of the fundamental formulas. That is, if A is to be proved identically equal to B, it can be done by

(1) *Changing A to B,*

(2) *Changing B to A, or*

(3) *Changing both A and B to a third form C.*

In the applications of this part of trigonometry, however, one usually knows exactly into what form a certain expression must be transformed. For this reason it is usual to require the student to change the first member of an identity into the second.

It is usually best, especially for the beginner, to express all the functions of the expression which is to be transformed in terms of sine and cosine before attempting to simplify.

Avoid radicals whenever possible.

When the expression that is to be transformed is given in a factored form, it is usually best to simplify each factor separately before multiplying them together.

Example 1.—By transforming the first member into the second prove the identity $\tan \theta \sin \theta + \cos \theta = \sec \theta$.

Proof.—Substituting $\dfrac{\sin \theta}{\cos \theta}$ for $\tan \theta$, we have

$$\frac{\sin \theta}{\cos \theta} \cdot \sin \theta + \cos \theta = \frac{\sin^2 \theta + \cos^2 \theta}{\cos \theta} = \frac{1}{\cos \theta} = \sec \theta.$$

Example 2.—By transforming the first member into the second prove the identity $\dfrac{\cot \alpha \cos \alpha}{\cot \alpha + \cos \alpha} = \dfrac{\cot \alpha - \cos \alpha}{\cot \alpha \cos \alpha}$.

Proof.—Substituting $\dfrac{\cos \alpha}{\sin \alpha}$ for cot α, we have

$$\frac{\cot \alpha \cos \alpha}{\cot \alpha + \cos \alpha} = \frac{\dfrac{\cos \alpha}{\sin \alpha} \cdot \cos \alpha}{\dfrac{\cos \alpha}{\sin \alpha} + \cos \alpha} = \frac{\dfrac{\cos^2 \alpha}{\sin \alpha}}{\dfrac{\cos \alpha(1 + \sin \alpha)}{\sin \alpha}}$$

$$= \frac{\cos^2 \alpha}{\cos \alpha(1 + \sin \alpha)} = \frac{1 - \sin^2 \alpha}{\cos \alpha(1 + \sin \alpha)} = \frac{1 - \sin \alpha}{\cos \alpha}.$$

Now multiply the numerator and denominator by cot α, and we have

$$\frac{1 - \sin \alpha}{\cos \alpha} \cdot \frac{\cot \alpha}{\cot \alpha} = \frac{\cot \alpha - \sin \alpha \cot \alpha}{\cos \alpha \cot \alpha} = \frac{\cot \alpha - \cos \alpha}{\cos \alpha \cot \alpha}.$$

EXERCISES

Prove the following identities by transforming the first member of the identity into the second:

1. $\dfrac{\cos \theta \csc \theta}{\cot \theta} = 1.$

2. $\tan \theta \cos \theta = \sin \theta.$

3. $\sec \theta \cot \theta = \csc \theta.$

4. $\dfrac{\sin \theta \sec \theta}{\tan \theta} = 1.$

5. $(1 - \cos^2 \phi) \sec^2 \phi = \tan^2 \phi.$

6. $\sec^2 \phi + \csc^2 \phi = \sec^2 \phi \csc^2 \phi.$

7. $\dfrac{1}{\cot^2 \phi} - \sin^2 \phi = \left(\dfrac{1}{\cot^2 \phi}\right) \sin^2 \phi.$

8. $\cot^2 \phi - \cos^2 \phi = \cos^2 \phi \cot^2 \phi.$

9. $(\sec^2 \theta - 1)\csc^2 \theta = \sec^2 \theta.$

10. $\cot \theta + \tan \theta = \cot \theta \sec^2 \theta.$

11. $(\tan \phi + \cot \phi)^2 = \sec^2 \phi \csc^2 \phi.$

12. $(\cos \theta - \sin \theta)^2 + 2 \sin \theta \cos \theta = 1.$

13. $\sec^4 \phi - \tan^4 \phi = (\sec^2 \phi)(2 \sin^2 \phi + \cos^2 \phi).$

14. $\tan \theta(\sin \theta + \cos \theta)^2 \cot \theta - 2 \sin \theta \cos \theta = 1.$

15. $\dfrac{1 + \csc \theta}{\csc \theta - 1} = \dfrac{1 + \sin \theta}{1 - \sin \theta}.$

16. $\dfrac{\sin \beta}{\sec \phi} \dfrac{\sqrt{\sec^2 \phi - 1}}{\sqrt{1 - \sin^2 \beta}} \cdot (1 - \sin^2 \phi)^{-\frac{1}{2}} = \tan \phi \tan \beta.$

17. $\dfrac{\cos \theta}{1 - \sin \theta} - \dfrac{1 - \sin \theta}{\cos \theta} = 2 \tan \theta.$

18. $\dfrac{(1 - \tan \phi)^2}{\sec^2 \phi} + 2 \sin \phi \cos \phi = 1.$

19. $\dfrac{\sin \theta + \sin \phi}{\sin \theta - \sin \phi} = \dfrac{\csc \phi + \csc \theta}{\csc \phi - \csc \theta}.$

20. $\dfrac{(1 + \sin \phi)}{2 \cos \phi}\left[\sqrt{\dfrac{1 - \sin \phi}{1 + \sin \phi}} + \sqrt{\dfrac{1 + \sin \phi}{1 - \sin \phi}}\right]\sqrt{\dfrac{1 - \sin \phi}{1 + \sin \phi}} = \sec \phi.$

21. $(\tan^2 \theta + 1)\cot^2 \theta = \csc^2 \theta.$

22. $\sin^2 \phi \sec \phi (\sin^2 \theta \sec \theta + \cos \theta) + \cos \phi (\sin^2 \theta \sec \theta + \cos \theta) = \sec \phi \sec \theta.$

23. $2 \sin \phi \cos \phi + \sin^2 \phi \tan \phi + \cos^2 \phi \cot \phi = \sec \phi \csc \phi.$

24. $\sin \phi \cos \phi [2 + (\sec^2 \phi - 1) + (\csc^2 \phi - 1)] = \sec \phi \csc \phi.$

25. $\cos \theta (\sec \theta + \csc \theta) + \sin \theta (\sec \theta - \csc \theta) = \sec \theta \csc \theta.$

26. $\sqrt{\dfrac{1 + \cos \phi}{1 - \cos \phi}} = \csc \phi + \cot \phi.$

27. $\dfrac{\sec^2 \phi (1 + \cos \phi \tan \phi)}{(\tan \phi + \sec \phi)^2 + 1} = \dfrac{1}{2}.$

28. $2 \tan^2 \theta + 2 \tan \theta \sec \theta + 1 = \sec^2 \theta (1 + \sin \theta)^2.$

29. $1 - 3 \cos^2 \phi \sin^2 \phi + 2 \sin^3 \phi \cos^3 \phi = (\sin^3 \phi + \cos^3 \phi)^2.$

30. $\operatorname{covers} B(1 - \cos^3 B) - \operatorname{vers} B(1 - \sin^3 B) =$
$$\operatorname{vers} B \operatorname{covers} B(\cos B - \sin B)(1 + \sin B + \cos B).$$

31. $(2 \sin^2 \theta - \cos^2 \theta)^2 - 9(2 \sin^2 \theta - 1)^2 =$
$$(2 - 3 \sin^2 \theta)(2 + 3 \sin \theta)(3 \sin \theta - 2).$$

32. $\dfrac{\tan^2 \phi (\sec \phi - 1)}{\sec \phi + 1} - \sec^2 \phi = 1 - 2 \sec \phi.$

33. $\dfrac{\sqrt{1 - \sin \phi \cos \phi}}{\sin \phi \cos \phi} \left[\sqrt{\dfrac{1 + \cot \phi}{\sin^2 \phi + \dfrac{\cos^2 \phi}{\tan \phi}}} - \sqrt{\dfrac{1 + \cot^3 \phi}{\csc^2 \phi (1 + \cot \phi)}} \right] = 1.$

34. $\dfrac{\sin^2 \theta [\cos^4 \theta - \sin^2 \theta] + \cos^6 \theta}{\cos^2 \theta [2 \cos^2 \theta - 1]} = \sec^2 \theta.$

35. $\dfrac{\tan \alpha + \tan \beta}{\sec \alpha - \sec \beta} = \dfrac{\sec \alpha + \sec \beta}{\tan \alpha - \tan \beta}.$

35. Inverse trigonometric functions.—The equation

$$\sin \theta = a$$

means that θ is an angle whose sine is a. The expression $\sin^{-1} a$ is an abbreviation for the expression *"an angle whose sine is a."* Then we may write

$$\theta = \sin^{-1} a.$$

The form $\sin^{-1} a$ is also read *"anti-sine a," "inverse-sine a," "arc sine a."* It is also written invsin a and arc sin a.

Analogous forms with analogous meanings are given for the other functions.

Illustrations.—$\sin^{-1} \frac{1}{2} = 30$ or $150°$. $\cos^{-1} 1 = 0°$. $\tan^{-1} 1 = 45$ or $225°$.

The notations $\sin^{-1} a$, $\cos^{-1} a$, etc. have the advantage that they are the forms most frequently used in other branches of mathematics and its applications; but they have the disadvantage of conflicting with the customary notation for exponents, and so tend to cause confusion. Thus, $\sin^2 \theta$ is usually written for

$(\sin \theta)^2$ and x^{-1} for $\dfrac{1}{x}$, and so the symbol $\sin^{-1} a$ might consistently

be taken to mean $\dfrac{1}{\sin a} = \csc a$, which is something entirely differ-

ent from our meaning of $\sin^{-1} a$ as explained at the beginning of this article.

Example.—Show that $\sin \cos^{-1} \frac{15}{17} = \frac{8}{17}$,

Solution.—Let $\theta = \cos^{-1} \frac{15}{17}$.

Then from the definitions of the inverse functions,

$$\cos \theta = \tfrac{15}{17},$$

By [1], $\sin \theta = \sqrt{1 - \cos^2 \theta} = \sqrt{1 - (\tfrac{15}{17})^2} = \tfrac{8}{17}.$

$$\therefore \sin \cos^{-1} \tfrac{15}{17} = \tfrac{8}{17}.$$

This could also be solved by constructing the angle.

EXERCISES

Answer Exercises 1 to 12 orally, considering only angles that are less than 90°.

1. $\sin \cos^{-1} \dfrac{\sqrt{2}}{2}$.   5. $\cos \sec^{-1} 5$.   9. $\sin \sec^{-1} \frac{13}{12}$.

2. $\sin \sin^{-1} \frac{7}{25}$.   6. $\tan \sin^{-1} \frac{24}{25}$.   10. $\csc \cot^{-1} \frac{1}{3}$.

3. $\tan \sec^{-1} 2$.   7. $\sin \cos^{-1} 0$.   11. $\sin \cos^{-1} \frac{3}{8}$.

4. $\cos \csc^{-1} 3$.   8. $\sin \tan^{-1} \sqrt{3}$.   12. $\cos \sec^{-1} 5$.

Prove the relations in Exercises 13 to 22.

13. $\sin \cos^{-1} a = \pm \sqrt{1 - a^2}$.   18. $\cos \sin^{-1} a = \pm \sqrt{1 - a^2}$.

14. $\sin \tan^{-1} a = \pm \dfrac{a}{\sqrt{1 + a^2}}$.   19. $\cos \tan^{-1} a = \pm \dfrac{1}{\sqrt{1 + a^2}}$.

15. $\sin \cot^{-1} a = \pm \dfrac{1}{\sqrt{1 + a^2}}$.   20. $\cos \cot^{-1} a = \pm \dfrac{a}{\sqrt{1 + a^2}}$.

16. $\sin \sec^{-1} a = \pm \dfrac{\sqrt{a^2 - 1}}{a}$.   21. $\cos \sec^{-1} a = \dfrac{1}{a}$.

17. $\sin \csc^{-1} a = \dfrac{1}{a}$.   22. $\cos \csc^{-1} a = \pm \dfrac{\sqrt{a^2 - 1}}{a}$.

For angles not greater than 90°, show that the following are true:

23. $\sin^{-1} \frac{24}{25} = \cos^{-1} \frac{7}{25}$.   24. $\tan^{-1} \frac{16}{63} = \sin^{-1} \frac{16}{65}$.

36. Trigonometric equations.—A trigonometric equation is an equation in which the unknown is involved in a trigonometric function.

The solution of a trigonometric equation is a value of the angle which satisfies the equation.

In general, both algebra and trigonometry are involved in solving a trigonometric equation. Algebra must be used when the trigonometric functions are involved algebraically in a trigonometric equation, for then the equation must first be solved for some trigonometric function.

Thus, $\sin^2 \theta - \frac{3}{2} \sin \theta + \frac{1}{2} = 0$ is a quadratic equation in $\sin \theta$; and, algebraically, is solved for $\sin \theta$ exactly as $x^2 - \frac{3}{2}x + \frac{1}{2} = 0$ is solved for x, either by the formula for solving a quadratic equation or by factoring. The solutions for $\sin \theta$ are

$$\sin \theta = \tfrac{1}{2}, \text{ and } \sin \theta = 1.$$

The trigonometry part of the solution is to find θ from these equations. They are solved by knowing the values of θ when $\sin \theta = \frac{1}{2}$ and $\sin \theta = 1$. They give

$$\theta = \sin^{-1} \tfrac{1}{2} = 30°, \text{ and } \theta = \sin^{-1} 1 = 90°.$$

Example 1.—Solve $\sin \theta = \frac{1}{2}\sqrt{2}$ for $\theta < 90°$.

Here all that is necessary is to know the angle less than 90° whose sine is $\frac{1}{2}\sqrt{2}$. From the table on page 24 this is found to be 45°,

$$\therefore \text{ if } \sin \theta = \tfrac{1}{2}\sqrt{2}, \theta = 45°.$$

Example 2.—Solve $\tan \theta = 0.43654$ for $\theta < 90°$.

This value of θ cannot be found by referring to page 24, as it requires a more extensive table of natural functions. By referring to **Table IV**, θ is found to be 23° 35′.

$$\therefore \text{ if } \tan \theta = 0.43654, \theta = 23° 35'.$$

Example 3.—Solve $\cos \theta = 0.77467$ for $\theta < 90°$.

From **Table IV**, θ is found to be 39° 13′ 30″.

$$\therefore \text{ if } \cos \theta = 0.77467, \theta = 39° 13' 30''.$$

In using **Table IV** for finding this value of θ, interpolation is required. If the method is not familiar, the explanation will be found on page 30 of the **Tables.**

Example 4.—Solve the equation $\cos^2 \alpha + 2 \cos \alpha - 3 = 0$ for values of α not greater than 90°.

Solution.—Factoring the equation,

$$(\cos \alpha + 3)(\cos \alpha - 1) = 0.$$

Equating each factor to 0 and solving for $\cos \alpha$,

$$\cos \alpha = 1 \text{ and } -3.$$

$$\therefore \alpha = \cos^{-1} 1 \text{ and } \alpha = \cos^{-1} (-3).$$

Since there is no angle with a cosine equal to -3, the only solution admissible is $\alpha = \cos^{-1} 1 = 0°$.

This can be checked by substituting $0°$ for α in the original equation.

Example 5.—Solve $7 \tan^2 \theta - 4 \sec^2 \theta + 3 = 0$ for values of θ not greater than $90°$.

Solution.—First transform so that but a single function is involved. This can be done in many ways, but very readily by changing $\sec^2 \theta$ to $1 + \tan^2 \theta$, which gives

$$7 \tan^2 \theta - 4(1 + \tan^2 \theta) + 3 = 0.$$

Simplifying, $\quad\quad\quad 3 \tan^2 \theta - 1 = 0.$

Solving for $\tan \theta$, $\quad\quad\quad \tan \theta = \pm\frac{1}{3}\sqrt{3}.$

Or $\quad\quad\quad \theta = \tan^{-1}\frac{1}{3}\sqrt{3}$, and $\theta = \tan^{-1}\left(-\frac{1}{3}\sqrt{3}\right).$

The first of these gives $\theta = 30°$, which is the only value of θ less than $90°$.

EXERCISES

Solve orally the following trigonometric equations for values of the angles not greater than $90°$:

1. $\sin \theta = 1.$
2. $\sin \theta = \frac{1}{2}\sqrt{2}.$
3. $\sin \theta = \frac{1}{2}.$
4. $\cos \theta = 1.$
5. $\cos \theta = \frac{\sqrt{3}}{2}.$

6. $\tan \theta = 1.$
7. $\csc \theta = 2.$
8. $\tan \theta = \sqrt{3}.$
9. $\cot \theta = \dfrac{1}{\sqrt{3}}.$
10. $\sec \theta = \sqrt{2}.$

11. $\sec \theta = 1.$
12. $\sin \theta = 0.$
13. $\csc \theta = \sqrt{2}.$
14. $\csc \theta = 1.$
15. $\csc \theta = \dfrac{2}{\sqrt{3}}.$

Solve orally the following anti-trigonometric equations for values of the angles not greater than $90°$:

16. $\theta = \cos^{-1}\frac{1}{2}\sqrt{2}.$
17. $\theta = \sin^{-1} 0.$
18. $\theta = \tan^{-1}\sqrt{3}.$
19. $\theta = \sec^{-1}\sqrt{2}.$

20. $\alpha = \tan^{-1}\dfrac{1}{\sqrt{3}}.$
21. $\alpha = \tan^{-1} 0.$
22. $\alpha = \csc^{-1} 2.$
23. $\alpha = \sec^{-1} 2.$

24. $\beta = \csc^{-1} 1.$
25. $\beta = \cot^{-1} 0.$
26. $\gamma = \cot^{-1}\sqrt{3}.$
27. $\gamma = \csc^{-1}\sqrt{2}.$

Use **Table IV** in solving the following trigonometric equations for values of the angles not greater than $90°$:

28. $\sin \theta = 0.50628.$
29. $\cos \theta = 0.85249.$
30. $\tan \theta = 0.58124.$
31. $\cot \theta = 1.6372.$
32. $\sin \theta = 0.27148.$

33. $\cot \theta = 3.6245.$
34. $\sin \theta = 0.74896.$
35. $\cos \theta = 0.61520.$
36. $\cot \theta = 3.2790.$
37. $\cos \theta = 0.57200.$

38. $\cos \theta = \frac{2}{3}.$
39. $\theta = \cos^{-1}\frac{4}{5}.$
40. $\theta = \tan^{-1}\sqrt{2}.$
41. $\theta = \cot^{-1}\frac{1}{4}.$
42. $\theta = \cos^{-1}\frac{5}{13}.$

Solve the following trigonometric equations for values of the angles not greater than $90°$:

43. $\sin^2 \theta - \sin \theta = 0.$ *Ans.* $0°, 90°.$
44. $(\cos \theta - 1)(2 \cos \theta - 1) = 0.$ *Ans.* $0°, 60°.$
45. $\tan^4 \theta - 9 = 0.$ *Ans.* $60°.$

46. $\sec^2 \theta = 4 \tan^2 \theta.$ *Ans.* 30°.

47. $\sqrt{3}(\tan \theta + \cot \theta) = 4.$ *Ans.* 30°, 60°.

48. $3 \tan \theta = 2 \cos \theta.$ *Ans.* 30°.

49. $3 \tan^2 \theta - 2\sqrt{3} \tan \theta + 1 = 0.$ *Ans.* 30°.

50. $4 \sin^2 \theta - 2(\sqrt{2} + 1) \sin \theta + \sqrt{2} = 0.$ *Ans.* 30°, 45°.

51. $2 \cos^2 \theta - (2 + \sqrt{2}) \cos \theta + \sqrt{2} = 0.$ *Ans.* 0°, 45°.

52. $4 \cos^2 \theta - 2(1 + \sqrt{3}) \cos \theta + \sqrt{3} = 0.$ *Ans.* 30°, 60°.

53. $3 \tan^2 \theta - 4\sqrt{3} \tan \theta + 4 = 0.$ *Ans.* 49° 6.4′.

54. $2 \cos \theta - \cot \theta = 0.$ *Ans.* 30°, 90°.

55. $4 \sin^2 \theta - 5 \sin \theta + 1 = 0.$ *Ans.* 14° 28′ 39″, 90°.

56. $\tan \theta (\sec \theta - \sqrt{2}) = \sqrt{3} (\sec \theta - \sqrt{2}).$ *Ans.* 45°, 60°.

57. $4 \sin^2 \theta - 3\sqrt{6} \sin \theta + 3 = 0.$ *Ans.* 37° 45.7′.

58. $7 \cos^2 \theta - 29 \cos \theta + 4 = 0.$ *Ans.* 81° 47.2′.

59. $2 \cos^2 \theta - \sin^2 \theta = 0.$ *Ans.* 54° 44′ 8″.

60. $\tan \theta + 4 = 2(\sin \theta + \sec \theta).$ *Ans.* 60°.

61. $\sin^3 \theta - \cos^3 \theta = 0.$ *Ans.* 45°.

62. $4 \tan^2 \theta = 3 \sec^2 \theta.$ *Ans.* 60°.

63. $\tan^2 \theta - 4 \tan \theta + 1 = 0.$ *Ans.* 15°, 75°.

64. $\sec \theta - 1 = (\sqrt{2} - 1) \tan \theta.$ *Ans.* 0°, 45°.

CHAPTER IV

RIGHT TRIANGLES

37. General statement.—One of the direct applications of trigonometry is the solution of triangles both right and oblique. It is in this way that the surveyor determines heights and distances that cannot be measured directly; for instance, the height of a mountain or the distance from one point to another where a lake or a mountain prevents direct measurement. It is well to note, however, that the solution of triangles is not the phase of trigonometry that is of most importance to the student who is to pursue more advanced subjects in mathematics. He will more often find use for the relations existing between the different functions, and in transforming one form of an expression involving trigonometric functions into an equivalent one.

It is a recognized fact in all walks of life, and it is certainly ingrained in mathematical science, that every real advance goes hand in hand with the invention of sharper tools and simpler methods. Practical geometry was developed in Egypt to help redetermine boundaries of the land after an overflow of the Nile. At an early date astronomy gave the main incentive for the development of trigonometry.

In attacking the triangle, trigonometry, in many ways, is a more powerful tool than geometry, which makes little use of the angles, while trigonometry makes use of the angles, as well as of the sides, of a triangle.

38. Solution of a triangle.—Every triangle, whether right or oblique, has six parts, *viz.*, three sides and three angles. When certain ones of these are given, the others can be found.

The process of finding the parts not given is called the **solution** of the triangle. By means of trigonometry a triangle can be solved when the parts given are sufficient to make a definite geometrical construction of the triangle. By geometry, a triangle can be constructed when three parts are given, at least one of which is a side. The remaining parts can then be measured and so a solution of the triangle obtained.

47

There are two ways of solving a triangle:

(1) *The graphical solution.*

(2) *The solution by computation.*

39. The graphical solution.—This consists in drawing a triangle such that its angles are equal to the given angles, and its sides equal to or proportional to the given sides. Of course, it is necessary that the given parts be consistent and sufficient to determine a definite triangle. For instance, two angles must not be given such that their sum is greater than 180°; nor can a construction be made if three sides are given such that one of them is as great as or greater than the sum of the other two.

EXERCISES

1. Construct triangles by means of the straightedge and compasses, having given:

(*a*) Two sides and the included angle.

(*b*) Two angles and the included side.

(*c*) Three sides.

(*d*) Two sides and an angle opposite one of them. Discuss and give drawings for all the possibilities.

(*e*) Three angles. Is the construction definite?

2. Construct right triangles by means of the straightedge and compasses, having given:

(*a*) Two legs.

(*b*) An acute angle and the hypotenuse.

(*c*) An acute angle and one leg.

(*d*) The hypotenuse and a leg.

Use the protractor in measuring the angles and construct the following:

(*a*) A right triangle with an acute angle equal to 42° and adjacent side 3.75 in.

(*b*) An oblique triangle with an angle equal to 35° 16′ and the including sides 9 and 18 in., respectively.

(*c*) A triangle with two angles 41° and 63°, respectively, and the side opposite the first angle 7.5 in.

(*d*) A triangle with sides 7.3, 4.5, and 3.8 in., respectively.

(*e*) A triangle with sides 11.5 and 4.7 ft. and the angle opposite the second side 120°.

40. The solution of right triangles by computation.—In the two previous articles, what was said referred to the oblique triangle as well as to the right triangle; here reference is to the right triangle only.

Since in a right triangle the right angle is always a given part, it is necessary to have given only two other parts, at least one of which is a side.

In what follows a, b, and c represent the altitude, base, and hypotenuse respectively, and A, B, and C, the angles opposite the respective sides.

The solutions depend upon the following relations, the first two of which are from geometry and the last eight from the definitions of trigonometric functions:

(1) $c^2 = a^2 + b^2$.   (6) $\sin B = \dfrac{b}{c}$.

(2) $A + B = 90°$.   (7) $\tan A = \dfrac{a}{b}$.

(3) $\sin A = \dfrac{a}{c}$.   (8) $\cot B = \dfrac{a}{b}$.

(4) $\cos B = \dfrac{a}{c}$.   (9) $\cot A = \dfrac{b}{a}$.

(5) $\cos A = \dfrac{b}{c}$.   (10) $\tan B = \dfrac{b}{a}$.

Number (2) shows that no other part can be derived from the two acute angles alone. In each of the other formulas, three parts are involved. If any two of these parts are given, the third can be found. Thus, in (3) if a and A are given, $c = \dfrac{a}{\sin A}$; if c and A are given, $a = c \sin A$; and if a and c are given, $A = \sin^{-1} \dfrac{a}{c}$.

Exercise.—Solve each of the above formulas for each letter in terms of the others.

SOLUTION OF RIGHT TRIANGLE BY NATURAL FUNCTIONS

41. Steps in the solution.—In solving a triangle, it is of the greatest importance to follow some regular order. The following is suggested:

(1) *Construct the triangle carefully to scale, using compasses, protractor, and ruler.* The required parts can then be measured and a check obtained on the computed values.

(2) *State the given and the required parts, and write down the formulas which are needed in the solution, solving each for the part required.* In choosing these formulas, select for each part required a formula that shall contain two known parts and one required part. Thus, if A and a are the given parts and c

the required part, then $\sin A = \dfrac{a}{c}$ contains the given parts and the required part c. This solved for c gives $c = \dfrac{a}{\sin A}$. In general, avoid the use of $c^2 = a^2 + b^2$ unless a table of squares and square roots is at hand.

(3) *Compute by substituting the given values in the formulas and evaluating.*

(4) *Arrange the work neatly and systematically, as this conduces to accuracy and therefore speed.*

(5) *Always check.* This can be done by making a careful construction, and also by using other formulas than those used in the solution.

Example 1.—Given $a = 3.25$ and $A = 47° \; 25.6'$; find b, c, and B.

Solution.   *Construction*

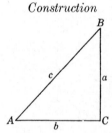

$$\text{Given}\begin{cases} a = 3.25. \\ A = 47° \; 25.6'. \end{cases}$$

$$\text{To find*}\begin{cases} b = 2.986. \\ c = 4.413. \\ B = 42° \; 34.4'. \end{cases}$$

Formulas

(1) $\quad \tan A = \dfrac{a}{b} \qquad\qquad \therefore \; b = \dfrac{a}{\tan A}.$

(2) $\quad \sin A = \dfrac{a}{c} \qquad\qquad \therefore \; c = \dfrac{a}{\sin A}.$

(3) $\quad A + B = 90° \qquad\qquad \therefore \; B = 90° - A.$

Computation

$$b = \frac{3.25}{1.0885} = 2.986.$$

$$c = \frac{3.25}{0.7364} = 4.413.$$

$$B = 90° - 47° \; 25.6' = 42° \; 34.4'.$$

Check

$$a^2 = c^2 - b^2 = (c + b)(c - b).$$
$$3.25^2 = (4.413 + 2.986)(4.413 - 2.986).$$
$$10.5625 = 10.5584.$$

* Results to be inserted when work is completed.

These agree to four significant figures.

The formula $\sin B = \dfrac{b}{c}$ could also be used in checking.

Example 2.—Given $a = 6.72$ and $b = 3.27$; find c, A, and B.
Solution.

Construction

$$\text{Given}\begin{cases} a = 6.72. \\ b = 3.27. \end{cases}$$

$$\text{To find}\begin{cases} c = 7.473. \\ A = 64° \ 3.1'. \\ B = 25° \ 56.9'. \end{cases}$$

Formulas

(1) $\tan A = \dfrac{a}{b}$ $\therefore A = \tan^{-1}\dfrac{a}{b}.$

(2) $\cot B = \dfrac{a}{b}$ $\therefore B = \cot^{-1}\dfrac{a}{b}.$

(3) $\sin A = \dfrac{a}{c}$ $\therefore c = \dfrac{a}{\sin A}.$

Computation

$$A = \tan^{-1}\frac{6.72}{3.27} = \tan^{-1} 2.0550 = 64° \ 3.1'-.$$

$$B = \cot^{-1}\frac{6.72}{3.27} = \cot^{-1} 2.0550 = 25° \ 56.9'+.$$

$$c = \frac{6.72}{0.89919} = 7.473+.$$

Check

$$a^2 = c^2 - b^2 = (c + b)(c - b).$$
$$6.72^2 = (7.473 + 3.27)(7.473 - 3.27).$$
$$45.158 = 10.743 \times 4.203 = 45.153.$$

It is to be noted that, in computing c, the angle A was used. Though A was not a given part, it was used to avoid the formula $c = \sqrt{a^2 + b^2}$.

EXERCISES

Solve the following right triangles using natural functions. Use the formulas $(c + a)(c - a) = b^2$ and $(c + b)(c - b) = a^2$ as a check.

Given	*Find*

1. $b = 32$, $B = 35°$; a, c, A. Check.
2. $a = 11$, $A = 43°$; b, c, B. Check.
3. $a = 77$, $A = 72° 30'$; b, c, B. Check.
4. $b = 130$, $B = 67° 15'$; a, c, A. Check.
5. $a = 27$, $c = 45$; b, A, B. Check.
6. $b = 100$, $A = 70°$; a, c, B. Check.
7. $c = 30$, $A = 51°$; a, b, B. Check.
8. $c = 130$, $B = 22° 28'$; a, b, A. Check.
9. $a = 40$, $B = 29°$; b, c, A. Check.
10. $a = 48$, $b = 26$; c, A, B. Check.
11. $b = 150$, $c = 200$; a, A, B. Check.
12. $b = 7.636$, $B = 73° 45.7'$; $A = 16° 14.3'$, $a = 2.224$, $c = 7.9534$.
13. $c = 0.532$, $B = 50° 21.9'$; $A = 39° 38.1'$, $a = 0.3394$, $b = 0.4097$.
14. $a = 192.56$, $b = 437.98$; $A = 23° 44'$, $B = 66° 16'$, $c = 478.44$.
15. $c = 65.8$, $A = 47° 59.8'$; $B = 42° 0.2'$, $a = 48.897$, $b = 44.032$.
16. $b = 1.30$, $B = 79° 27'$; $A = 10° 33'$, $a = 0.242$, $c = 1.322$.
17. $b = 5.21$, $c = 8.42$; $A = 51° 46.4'$, $B = 38° 13.6'$, $a = 6.615$.
18. $b = 52.02$, $c = 769.96$; $A = 86° 7.6'$, $B = 3° 52.4'$, $a = 768.22$.
19. $b = 89.49$, $A = 3° 47.6'$; $B = 86° 12.4'$, $a = 5.934$, $c = 89.685$.
20. $a = 0.1515$, $A = 40° 46.9'$; $B = 49° 13.1'$, $b = 0.1757$, $c = 0.232$.

21. The shadow of a flagpole 75 ft. high is 98 ft. What is the angle of elevation of the sun at that instant?   *Ans.* 37° 25.6'.

22. If side a is three times side b in a right triangle, find angle A.
Ans. $A = 71° 33.9'$.

23. What angle does a mountain slope make with the horizontal plane

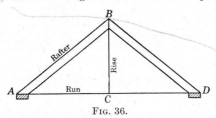

if it rises 450 ft. in 60 rods on the horizontal? *Note:* 1 rod = $16\frac{1}{2}$ ft.   *Ans.* 24° 26.6'.

24. What is the angle of inclination of a stairway with the floor if the steps have a tread of 10 in. and a rise of 8 in.?   *Ans.* 38° 39.6'.

Fig. 36.

25. What angle does a rafter make with the horizontal if it has a rise of 6 ft. in a run of 15 ft.?
Ans. 21° 48.1'.

26. Certain lots in a city are laid out by lines perpendicular to B street, and running through to A street as shown in Fig. 37. Required the width of the lots on A street if the angle between the streets is 35° 50'.
Ans. 123.35 ft.

27. Find the angle between the rafters and the horizontal in roofs of the following pitches: two-thirds, half, third, fourth.
Ans. 53° 7.75'; 45°; 33° 41.4'; 26° 33.9'.

Note.—By the pitch of a roof is meant the ratio of the rise of the rafters to twice the run, or, in a V-shaped roof, it is the ratio of the distance from the plate to the ridge, to the width of the building.

28. One of the equal sides of an isosceles triangle is 5.74 in. and one of the base angles is 23° 35'; find the altitude and the base.
Ans. 2.296 in.; 10.521 in.

29. The base of an isosceles triangle is 40 ft. and the vertex angle is 48° 30′; find the equal sides and the base angles.   *Ans.* 48.7 ft.; 65° 45′.

30. One side of a regular pentagon inscribed in a circle is 8 in.; find the radius of the circle.   *Ans.* 6.8 in.

31. One side of a regular octagon inscribed in a circle is 15 in.; find the radius of the circle.   *Ans.* 19.6 in.

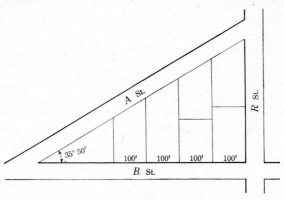

Fig. 37.

32. One side of a regular decagon inscribed in a circle is 8.56 in.; find the radius of the circle.   *Ans.* 13.85 in.

33. One side of a regular octagon circumscribed about a circle is 12.8 in.; find the radius of the circle.   *Ans.* 15.45 in.

34. The radius of a circle is 24 in.; find the side of a regular inscribed pentagon. Of a regular circumscribed pentagon. *Ans.* 28.2 in.; 34.9 in.

Find the areas of the following isosceles triangles:

35. Altitude 28 ft. and base angles each 55° 27′.   *Ans.* 539.85 sq. ft.

36. Base 35.6 ft. and base angles each 64° 51′.   *Ans.* 674.85 sq. ft.

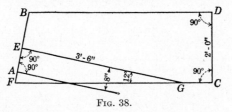

Fig. 38.

37. Equal sides each 10.8 in. and vertex angle 48° 17′.   *Ans.* 43.53 sq. in.

38. The radius of a circle is 11 ft. What angle will a chord 14 ft. long subtend at the center?   *Ans.* 79° 2.5′.

39. The chord of a circle is 12 ft. long and the angle which it subtends at the center is 41.6°. Find the radius of the circle.   *Ans.* 16.9 ft.

40. Five holes are drawn on a piece of steel with their centers equally spaced on the circumference of a circle 10 in. in diameter. Find the distance in a straight line between the centers of two consecutive holes.

Ans. 5.9 in.

41. Thirty holes are drawn with their centers equally spaced on the circumference of a circle 22 in. in diameter. Find the distance between the centers of two consecutive holes.   *Ans.* 2.3 in.

42. Using Fig. 38, with the dimensions as given, find *AB*.

Ans. 23.61 in.

SOLUTION OF RIGHT TRIANGLE BY LOGARITHMS

42. Remark on logarithms.—By the use of logarithms, the processes of multiplication, division, raising to powers, and extracting roots may be shortened. In the solution of triangles, logarithms are very advantageous in saving time and labor, and thus conduce to accuracy. The student should bear in mind, however, that logarithms are not necessary for this work. The computer must decide for himself whether or not it will be of advantage to use logarithms in any given problem.

Formulas which have been so arranged that they involve only operations of multiplication, division, raising to powers, and extracting roots are said to be adapted to computation by logarithms.

43. Solution of right triangles by logarithmic functions.—The solution of a right triangle is the same by logarithms as by natural functions, except that logarithms are used to avoid the long multiplications and divisions. The tables of logarithmic functions are used instead of the tables of natural functions.

Example 1.—Given $a = 33.75$ and $c = 45.72$; find A, B, and b.

Solution.   *Construction*

$$\text{Given}\begin{cases} a = 33.75 \\ c = 45.72. \end{cases}$$

$$\text{To find}*\begin{cases} A = 47° 34.6'. \\ B = 42° 25.4'. \\ b = 30.843. \end{cases}$$

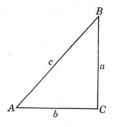

Formulas

(1) $\sin A = \dfrac{a}{c}.$

(2) $\cos B = \dfrac{a}{c}.$

(3) $\cos A = \dfrac{b}{c},$ or $b = c \cos A.$

* Results to be inserted when work is completed.

Logarithmic formulas

(1) $\qquad \log \sin A = \log a - \log c.$
(2) $\qquad \log \cos B = \log a - \log c.$
(3) $\qquad \log b = \log c + \log \cos A.$

Computation	*Check*

Computation

$\log a = 1.52827$
$\log c = 1.66011$

$\log \sin A = 9.86816 - 10$
$A = 47° 34.6'$

$\log \cos B = 9.86816 - 10$
$B = 42° 25.4'$

$\log c = 1.66011$
$\log \cos A = 9.82905 - 10$

$\log b = 1.48916$
$b = 30.843$

Check

$a^2 = c^2 - b^2 = (c + b)(c - b)$
$\quad = 76.563 \times 14.877$

$\log (c + b) = 1.88402$
$\log (c - b) = 1.17251$

$\log a^2 = 3.05653$
$\log a = 1.52827$

$a = 33.75$

Example 2.—Given $b = 8.724$ and $A = 29°$ 52.3′; find B, c and a.

Solution.　　　　　　　　　　　　　　　*Construction*

Given $\begin{cases} b = 8.724. \\ A = 29° 52.3'. \end{cases}$

To find $\begin{cases} B = 60° 7.7'. \\ c = 10.061. \\ a = 5.011. \end{cases}$

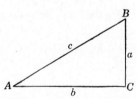

Formulas

(1) $\qquad A + B = 90°,$ or $B = 90° - A.$

(2) $\qquad \tan A = \dfrac{a}{b},$ or $a = $ b $\tan A.$

(3) $\qquad \cos A = \dfrac{b}{c},$ or $c = \dfrac{b}{\cos A}.$

Logarithmic formulas

(1) $\qquad \log a = \log b + \log \tan A.$
(2) $\qquad \log c = \log b - \log \cos A.$

Computation	*Check*

$B = 90° - 29° 52.3' = 60° 7.7'$ $b^2 = c^2 - a^2 = (c + a)(c - a)$

$\log b = 0.94072$ $= 15.072 \times 5.050$

$\log \tan A = 9.75919 - 10$ $\log (c + a) = 1.17817$

$\log a = 0.69991$ $\log (c - a) = 0.70329$

$a = 5.0109$ $\log b^2 = 1.88146$

$\log b = 0.94072$ $\log b = 0.94073$

$\log \cos A = 9.93809 - 10$ $b = 8.7242$

$\log c = 1.00263$

$c = 10.061$

Note.—It is best to make a full *skeleton solution* before proceeding to the use of the **Tables.** The skeleton solution can be seen in this example by erasing the numerical quantities.

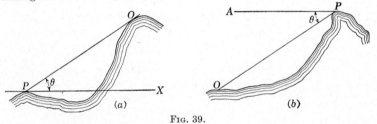

Fɪɢ. 39.

In using the **Tables,** plan so as to save time as much as possible. For instance, if both log sine and log cosine of some angle are required, look up both of them while the tables are open at that page.

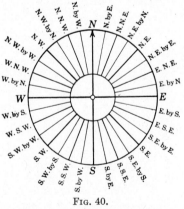

Fɪɢ. 40.

44. Definitions.—The **angle of elevation** is the angle between the line of sight and the horizontal plane through the eye when the object observed is above that horizontal plane. When the object observed is below this horizontal plane, the angle is called the **angle of depression.**

Thus, in Fig. 39a, an object O is seen from the point P. The angle θ between the line PO and the horizontal PX is the angle of elevation. In Fig. 39b an object O is seen from the point of observation P. The angle θ between the line PO and the horizontal AP is called the angle of depression.

Directions on the surface of the earth are often given by directions as located on the **mariner's compass.** As seen from Fig. 40, these directions are located with reference to the four cardinal points, north, south, east, and west. The directions are often spoken of as **bearings.** Present practice, however, gives the bearing of a line in degrees. The bearing of a line is defined to be the acute angle the line makes with the north-and-south line.

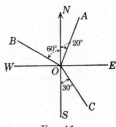

Fig. 41.

Thus, in Fig. 41, if O is the point of observation, the bearing of OA is north, 20° east, written N. 20° E. The bearing of OB is N. 60° W., and that of OC is S. 30° E.

EXERCISES

Solve the following right triangles for the parts not given. The first two parts printed are the given parts. Use logarithms.

1. $a = 31.756$, $A = 54°\ 43.5'$. Check results.

2. $b = 13.98$, $B = 21°\ 54'$. Check results.

3. $b = 1676.34$, $c = 5432.8$. Check results.

4. $a = 4.5612$, $B = 43°\ 3.7'$. Check results.

5. $b = 54.78$, $A = 35°\ 43.2'$. Check results.

6. $a = 25.13$, $c = 43.412$. Check results.

7. $c = 23.746$, $A = 32°\ 54.21'$. Check results.

8. $a = 134.90$, $b = 101.43$. Check results.

9. $a = 14.23$, $b = 9.499$. Check results.

10. $c = 143.89$, $B = 39°\ 54.8'$. Check results.

11. $a = 18.091$, $b = 1378.2$. Check results.

12. $a = 896$, $B = 2°\ 6'\ 10''$. Check results.

13. $a = 653$, $c = 680$, $b = 189.7$, $A = 73°\ 48'$, $B = 16°\ 12'$.

14. $b = 675.31$, $B = 78°\ 34.6'$, $a = 136.46$, $c = 688.97$, $A = 11°\ 25.4'$.

15. $b = 1100$, $c = 1650$, $a = 1229.9$, $A = 48°\ 11.4'$, $B = 41°\ 48.6'$.

16. $c = 11.003$, $A = 45°\ 32'\ 19''$, $a = 7.8530$, $b = 7.7067$, $B = 44°\ 27.7'$.

17. $a = 0.001348$, $b = 0.0009896$, $c = 0.0016722$, $A = 53°\ 43'$, $B = 36°\ 17'$.

18. A ladder 30 ft. long rests against a building standing on level ground, and makes an angle of 65° 35' with the ground. Find the distance it reaches up the building. *Ans.* 27.3 ft.

Monday

19. A tower stands on level ground. At a point 161.7 ft. distant and 5.5 ft. above the ground the angle of elevation of the top of the tower is 62° 48'. Find the height of the tower to the nearest foot. *Ans.* 320 ft.

20. From the top of a tower 375 ft. high, the angle of depression of a man on the horizontal plane through the foot of the tower is 37° 24.6'. Find the distance the man is from the foo: of the tower.   *Ans.* 490.3 ft.

21. What is the angle of inclination of a roadbed having a grade of 14 per cent? One with a grade of 26 per cent? (A road with a rise of 14 ft. in 100 ft. on the horizontal has a grade of 14 per cent).

Ans. 7° 58.2'; 14° 34.4'.

22. Locate the centers of the holes B and C (Fig. 42) by finding the distance each is to the right and above the center O. The radius of the circle is 4.5 in. Compute correct to four decimals.

Ans. (3.6406, 2.6450); (1.3906, 4.2798).

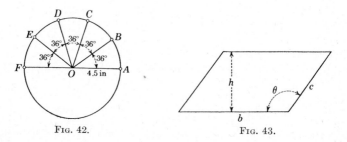

FIG. 42.   FIG. 43.

23. In the parallelogram of Fig. 43, $b = 33.7$ in., $c = 14.8$ in., and $\theta = 126°\ 15'$. Find the altitude h of the parallelogram.   *Ans.* 11.94 in.

24. A ladder 32 ft. long is resting against a wall at an angle of 21.7°. If the foot of the ladder is drawn away 4 ft., how far down the wall will the top of the ladder fall?   *Ans.* 1.9 ft.

25. A man surveying a mine, measures a length $AB = 1240$ ft. due east with a dip of 6° 15'; then a length $BC = 3425$ ft. due south with a dip of 10° 45'. How much deeper is C than A?   *Ans.* 773.84 ft.

26. Find the number of square yards of cloth in a conical tent with a circular base, and vertical angle 78°, the center pole being 12 ft. high.

Ans. 52.4 sq. yd.

Find the areas of the following isosceles triangles:

27. Altitude is 27 ft. and base angles each 55.6°. *Ans.* 499.2 sq. ft.

28. Base is 3 ft. and vertical angle 38° 24'.   *Ans.* 6.46 sq. ft.

29. Each leg is 15 ft. and base angles each 63° 18.6'. *Ans.* 90.29 sq. ft.

30. Find the area of a regular pentagon one of whose sides is 10 in.

Ans. 172.05 sq. in.

31. Find the area of a regular octagon one of whose sides is 15 in.

Ans. 1086.4 sq. in.

32. Find the difference in the areas of a regular hexagon and a regular octagon, each of perimeter 80 ft.   *Ans.* 20.96. sq. ft.

33. Prove that the area of a right triangle is given by each of the following, where S is the area:

$$S = \tfrac{1}{2}bc \sin A.$$
$$S = \tfrac{1}{2}ac \cos A.$$
$$S = \tfrac{1}{2}c^2 \sin A \cos A.$$

34. If R is the radius of a circle, show that the area of a regular circumscribed polygon of n sides is given by the formula:

$$A = nR^2 \tan \frac{180°}{n}.$$

35. Show that the area of a regular inscribed polygon of n sides is given by the formula:

$$A = nR^2 \sin \frac{180°}{n} \cos \frac{180°}{n} = \frac{1}{2}nR^2 \sin \frac{360°}{n}.$$

36. The radius of a circle is 30 in. Find the perimeter of a regular inscribed pentagon.   *Ans.* 176.34 in.

37. Find the area of a regular octagon inscribed in a circle whose radius is 8 in.   *Ans.* 181.02 sq. in.

38. What diameter of stock must be chosen so that a hexagonal end 3 in. across the flats may be milled upon it?   *Ans.* 3.46 in.

Answer the question for an octagon. The meaning of "across the flats" is shown in Fig. 44.   *Ans.* 3.25 in.

39. From a point 460 ft. above the level of a lake the angle of depression of a point on the near shore is 21° 56', and of a point directly beyond on the opposite shore is 4° 31'. Find the width of the lake.   *Ans.* 4680.7 ft.

Fig. 44.

40. Find the angles at the base made by the sides of a tower with the horizontal, if the tower is 47 ft. 6 in. high, has a square base 6 ft. on a side, and a top 8 in. square.   *Ans.* 86° 47.2'.

41. Suppose the earth a sphere with a radius of 3960 miles; find the length of the arctic circle which is at latitude 66° 32'.   *Ans.* 9908.3 miles.

42. Find the length of 1° of longitude in the latitude of Chicago, 41° 50', if the earth is a sphere with a radius of 3960 miles.   *Ans.* 51.497 miles.

43. A circle 12 in. in diameter is suspended from a point and held in a horizontal position by 12 strings each 8 in. long and equally spaced around the circumference. Find the angle between two consecutive strings.   *Ans.* 22° 23.2'.

44. A girder to carry a bridge is in the form of a circular arc. The length of the span is 120 ft. and the height of the arch is 30 ft. Find the angle at the center of the circle such that its sides intercept the arc of the girder; and find the radius of the circle.   *Ans.* 106° 15.7'; 75 ft.

45. A tree stands upon the same plane as a house whose height is 65 ft. The angle of elevation and depression of the top and base of the tree from the top of the house are 45° and 62°, respectively. Find the height of the tree.   *Ans.* 99.6 ft.

46. From a point 20 ft. above the surface of the water, the angle of elevation of a tree standing at the edge of the water is 41° 15', while the angle of depression of its image in the water is 58° 45′.   Find the height of the tree, and its horizontal distance from the point of observation.

Ans. 51.88 ft.; 65.50 ft.

47. The legs supporting a tank tower are 50 ft. long and 18 ft. apart at the base, forming a square.   The angle which the legs make with the horizontal line between the feet diagonally opposite is 83° 30′.   How far apart are the tops of the legs?   *Ans.* 10 ft.

48. The angle of elevation of a balloon from a point due south of it is 50°, and from another point 1 mile due west of the former the angle of elevation is 40°.   Find the height of the balloon.   *Ans.* 1.18 miles.

49. At a point P on a level plain the angle of elevation of an airplane that is southwest of P is 38° 35′.   At a point Q, 2 miles due south of P, the airplane appears in the northwest.   What is the height of the airplane?

Ans. 1.13 miles.

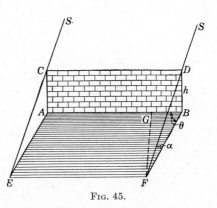

FIG. 45.

50. From a point on a level plain the angle of elevation of the top of a hill is 23° 46′; and a tower 45 ft. high standing on the top of the hill subtends an angle of 5° 16′.   Find the height of the hill above the plain.   *Ans.* 172.7 ft.

51. A flagstaff stands upon the top of a building 150 ft. high.   At a horizontal distance of 225 ft. from the base of the building the flagstaff subtends an angle of 6° 30′.   Find the height of the flagstaff.

Ans. 40.07 ft.

52. Two observers are stationed 1 mile apart on a straight east-and-west level road.   An airplane flying north passes between them, and, as it is over the road, the angles of elevation are observed to be 72° 30′ and 65° 15′. Find the height of the airplane.   *Ans.* 1.29 miles.

53. A ship is sailing due east at 16 miles per hour.   A lighthouse is observed due south at 8:30 A.M.   At 9:45 A.M. the bearing of the same lighthouse is S. 38° 30′ W.   Find the distance the ship is from the lighthouse at the time of the first observation.   *Ans.* 25.14 miles.

54. Find the width of the shadow of the wall shown in Fig. 45.   If the height of the wall is h ft., the angle of elevation of the sun α, and the angle between the vertical plane through the sun and the plane of the wall θ, show that width of shadow $= h \cot \alpha \sin \theta$.

55. A wall extending east and west is 8 ft. high. The sun has an inclination of 49° 30′ and is 47° 15′ 30″ west of south. Find the width of the shadow of the wall. *Ans.* 4.637 ft.

56. A tripod is made of three sticks, each 5 ft. long, by tying together the ends of the sticks, the other ends resting on the ground 3 ft. apart. Find the height of the tripod. *Ans.* 4.690 ft.

57. At a certain point the angle of elevation of a mountain peak is 40° 30′. At a distance of 3 miles farther away in the same horizontal plane, its angle of elevation is 27° 40′. Find the distance of the top of the mountain above the horizontal plane, and the horizontal distance from the first point of observation to the point directly below the peak. *Ans.* 4.77 miles.

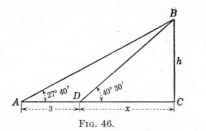

Fig. 46.

Suggestion.—Find two simultaneous equations involving the unknowns h and x representing the distances as shown in Fig. 46. These are $\tan 40° 30′ = \dfrac{h}{x}$ and $\tan 27° 40′ = \dfrac{h}{3 + x}$. Solve these algebraically for h and x.

58. At a certain point A the angle of elevation of a mountain peak is α; at a point B that is a miles farther away in the same horizontal plane its angle of elevation is β. If h represents the distance the peak is above the plane and x the horizontal distance the peak is from A, derive the formulas:

$$h = \frac{a \tan \alpha \tan \beta}{\tan \alpha - \tan \beta}; \; x = \frac{a \tan \beta}{\tan \alpha - \tan \beta}$$

Note.—In using these formulas, it is convenient to use natural functions. In Exercise 5, page 150, is given a solution of the same problem, obtaining formulas adapted to logarithms.

59. Find the height of a tree if the angle of elevation of its top changes from 35° to 61° 30′ on walking toward it 200 ft. in a horizontal line through its base. *Ans.* 225.93 ft.

60. A man walking on a level plain toward a tower observes that at a certain point the angle of elevation of the top of the tower is 30°, and, on walking 305 ft. directly toward the tower, the angle of elevation of the top is 52°. Find the height of the tower if the point of observation each time is 5 ft. above the ground. *Ans.* 325.8 ft.

61. At a certain point the angle of elevation of the top of a mountain is 36° 15′. At a second point 700 ft. farther away in the same horizontal plane the angle of elevation is 28° 30′. Find the height of the mountain above the horizontal plane. *Ans.* 1464.6 ft.

CHAPTER V

FUNCTIONS OF LARGE ANGLES

45. It is proved in **Art. 16** that, for any angle, each of the trigonometric functions has just one value. On the other hand, it ·was shown later that a particular value of a function may go with more than one angle. For instance, $\sin^{-1} \frac{1}{2}$ is 30° and 150° and, in fact, may be any one of the other angles whose terminal sides lie in the same positions as the terminal side of 30° or 150°. This would suggest that possibly any function of a large angle may be equal to a function of an angle that is not greater than 90°. Further, it would seem that some such relation must exist for the tables have only the functions of angles of 90° or less tabulated. We shall now proceed to show that a function of a large angle can be expressed as a function of an angle less than 90°.

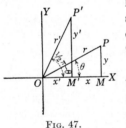

Fig. 47.

46. Functions of $\frac{1}{2}\pi - \theta$ in terms of functions of θ.—It has been shown in previous articles that a function of an acute angle is equal to the *cofunction* of the *complement* of that angle. This will now be proved in a different manner.

Let θ be any acute angle drawn as in Fig. 47. Construct $\frac{1}{2}\pi - \theta$, take $OP' = OP$, and let x, y, and r be the abscissa, ordinate, and distance, respectively, of P; and x', y', and r' those for P'. It is evident that right triangles OMP and $O'M'P'$ are equal.

Then, since $y' = x$, $x' = y$, and $r' = r$,

$$\sin \left(\tfrac{1}{2}\pi - \theta\right) = \frac{y'}{r'} = \frac{x}{r} = \cos \theta.$$

$$\cos \left(\tfrac{1}{2}\pi - \theta\right) = \frac{x'}{r'} = \frac{y}{r} = \sin \theta.$$

$$\tan \left(\tfrac{1}{2}\pi - \theta\right) = \frac{y'}{x'} = \frac{x}{y} = \cot \theta.$$

$$\cot \left(\tfrac{1}{2}\pi - \theta\right) = \frac{x'}{y'} = \frac{y}{x} = \tan \theta.$$

62

$$\sec\left(\tfrac{1}{2}\pi - \theta\right) = \frac{r'}{x'} = \frac{r}{y} = \csc\theta.$$

$$\csc\left(\tfrac{1}{2}\pi - \theta\right) = \frac{r'}{y'} = \frac{r}{x} = \sec\theta.$$

Notice that in each line the function at the end is the cofunction of the one at the beginning.

47. Functions of $\tfrac{1}{2}\pi + \theta$ in terms of functions of θ.—In Fig. 48, let θ be any acute angle. Construct $\tfrac{1}{2}\pi + \theta$, take $OP' = OP$, and represent the other parts as shown.

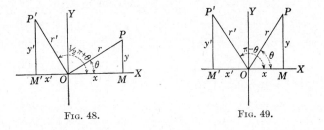

FIG. 48.   FIG. 49.

Then, since $y' = x$, $x' = -y$, and $r' = r$,

$$\sin\left(\tfrac{1}{2}\pi + \theta\right) = \frac{y'}{r'} = \frac{x}{r} = \cos\theta.$$

$$\cos\left(\tfrac{1}{2}\pi + \theta\right) = \frac{x'}{r'} = \frac{-y}{r} = -\frac{y}{r} = -\sin\theta.$$

$$\tan\left(\tfrac{1}{2}\pi + \theta\right) = \frac{y'}{x'} = \frac{x}{-y} = -\frac{x}{y} = -\cot\theta.$$

$$\cot\left(\tfrac{1}{2}\pi + \theta\right) = \frac{x'}{y'} = \frac{-y}{x} = -\frac{y}{x} = -\tan\theta.$$

$$\sec\left(\tfrac{1}{2}\pi + \theta\right) = \frac{r'}{x'} = \frac{r}{-y} = -\frac{r}{y} = -\csc\theta.$$

$$\csc\left(\tfrac{1}{2}\pi + \theta\right) = \frac{r'}{y'} = \frac{r}{x} = \sec\theta.$$

Notice that here, also, in each line the function at the end is the cofunction of the one at the beginning.

Examples.—sin $130° = \sin(90° + 40°) = \cos 40°$.
                 cot $110° = \cot(90° + 20°) = -\tan 20°$.

48. Functions of $\pi - \theta$ in terms of functions of θ.—In Fig. 49, let θ be an acute angle. Construct $\pi - \theta$, take $OP' = OP$, and represent the other parts as shown.

Then, since $x' = -x$, $y' = y$, and $r' = r$,

$$\sin (\pi - \theta) = \frac{y'}{r'} = \frac{y}{r} = \sin \theta.$$

$$\cos (\pi - \theta) = \frac{x'}{r'} = \frac{-x}{r} = -\frac{x}{r} = -\cos \theta.$$

$$\tan (\pi - \theta) = \frac{y'}{x'} = \frac{y}{-x} = -\frac{y}{x} = -\tan \theta.$$

$$\cot (\pi - \theta) = \frac{x'}{y'} = \frac{-x}{y} = -\frac{x}{y} = -\cot \theta.$$

$$\sec (\pi - \theta) = \frac{r'}{x'} = \frac{r}{-x} = -\frac{r}{x} = -\sec \theta.$$

$$\csc (\pi - \theta) = \frac{r'}{y'} = \frac{r}{y} = \csc \theta.$$

Notice that in each line the function at the end is the same function as the one at the beginning.

Examples.—$\cos 160° = \cos (180° - 20°) = -\cos 20°$.
$\csc 140° = \csc (180° - 40°) = \csc 40°$.

49. Functions of $\pi + \theta$ in terms of functions of θ.—In Fig. 50, let θ be an acute angle. Construct $\pi + \theta$, take $OP' = OP$, and represent the other parts as shown.

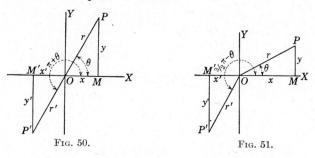

Fig. 50.   Fig. 51.

Then, since $x' = -x$, $y' = -y$, and $r' = r$,

$$\sin (\pi + \theta) = \frac{y'}{r'} = \frac{-y}{r} = -\frac{y}{r} = -\sin \theta.$$

$$\cos (\pi + \theta) = \frac{x'}{r'} = \frac{-x}{r} = -\frac{x}{r} = -\cos \theta.$$

$$\tan (\pi + \theta) = \frac{y'}{x'} = \frac{-y}{-x} = \frac{y}{x} = \tan \theta.$$

$$\cot (\pi + \theta) = \frac{x'}{y'} = \frac{-x}{-y} = \frac{x}{y} = \cot \theta.$$

$$\sec (\pi + \theta) = \frac{r'}{x'} = \frac{r}{-x} = -\frac{r}{x} = -\sec \theta.$$

$$\csc (\pi + \theta) = \frac{r'}{y'} = \frac{r}{-y} = -\frac{r}{y} = -\csc \theta.$$

Notice that here, also, in each line the function at the end is the same function as the one at the beginning.

Examples.—tan 230° = tan (180° + 50°) = tan 50°.
cos 205° = cos (180° + 25°) = −cos 25°.

50. Functions of $\frac{3}{2}\pi - \theta$ in terms of functions of θ.—In Fig. 51, let θ be an acute angle. Construct $\frac{3}{2}\pi - \theta$, take $OP' = OP$, and represent the other parts as shown.

Then, since $y' = -x$, $x' = -y$, and $r' = r$,

$$\sin \left(\tfrac{3}{2}\pi - \theta\right) = \frac{y'}{r'} = \frac{-x}{r} = -\frac{x}{r} = -\cos \theta.$$

$$\cos \left(\tfrac{3}{2}\pi - \theta\right) = \frac{x'}{r'} = \frac{-y}{r} = -\frac{y}{r} = -\sin \theta.$$

$$\tan \left(\tfrac{3}{2}\pi - \theta\right) = \frac{y'}{x'} = \frac{x}{y} = \cot \theta.$$

$$\cot \left(\tfrac{3}{2}\pi - \theta\right) = \frac{x'}{y'} = \frac{y}{x} = \tan \theta.$$

$$\sec \left(\tfrac{3}{2}\pi - \theta\right) = \frac{r'}{x'} = \frac{r}{-y} = -\frac{r}{y} = -\csc \theta.$$

$$\csc \left(\tfrac{3}{2}\pi - \theta\right) = \frac{r'}{y'} = \frac{r}{-x} = -\frac{r}{x} = -\sec \theta.$$

Notice that here again in each line the function at the end is the cofunction of the one at the beginning.

Examples.—sin 250° = sin (270° − 20°) = −cos 20°.
tan 210° = tan (270° − 60°) = cot 60°.

51. Functions of $\frac{3}{2}\pi + \theta$ in terms of functions of θ.—In Fig. 52, let θ be an acute angle. Construct $\frac{3}{2}\pi + \theta$, take $OP' = OP$, and represent the other parts as shown.

Then, since $y' = -x$, $x' = y$, and $r' = r$,

$$\sin \left(\tfrac{3}{2}\pi + \theta\right) = \frac{y'}{r'} = \frac{-x}{r} = -\frac{x}{r} = -\cos \theta.$$

$$\cos \left(\tfrac{3}{2}\pi + \theta\right) = \frac{x'}{r'} = \frac{y}{r} = \sin \theta.$$

$$\tan \left(\tfrac{3}{2}\pi + \theta\right) = \frac{y'}{x'} = \frac{-x}{y} = -\frac{x}{y} = -\cot \theta.$$

$$\cot\left(\tfrac{3}{2}\pi + \theta\right) = \frac{x'}{y'} = \frac{y}{-x} = -\frac{y}{x} = -\tan\theta.$$

$$\sec\left(\tfrac{3}{2}\pi + \theta\right) = \frac{r'}{x'} = \frac{r}{y} = \csc\theta.$$

$$\csc\left(\tfrac{3}{2}\pi + \theta\right) = \frac{r'}{y'} = \frac{r}{-x} = -\frac{r}{x} = -\sec\theta.$$

Notice that here, also, in each line the function at the end is the cofunction of the one at the beginning.

Examples.—cot 310° = cot (270° + 40°) = −tan 40°.
           sec 340° = sec (270° + 70°) = csc 70°.

52. Functions of −θ or 2π − θ in terms of functions of θ.—
In Fig. 53, let θ be an acute angle. Construct $2\pi - \theta$, $OP' = OP$, and represent the other parts as shown.

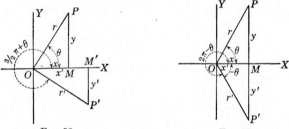

FIG. 52.   FIG. 53.

Then, since $x' = x$, $y' = -y$, and $r' = r$,

$$\sin(-\theta) = \frac{y'}{r'} = \frac{-y}{r} = -\frac{y}{r} = -\sin\theta.$$

$$\cos(-\theta) = \frac{x'}{r'} = \frac{x}{r} = \cos\theta.$$

$$\tan(-\theta) = \frac{y'}{x'} = \frac{-y}{x} = -\frac{y}{x} = -\tan\theta.$$

$$\cot(-\theta) = \frac{x'}{y'} = \frac{x}{-y} = -\frac{x}{y} = -\cot\theta.$$

$$\sec(-\theta) = \frac{r'}{x'} = \frac{r}{x} = \sec\theta.$$

$$\csc(-\theta) = \frac{r'}{y'} = \frac{r}{-y} = -\frac{r}{y} = -\csc\theta.$$

These formulas can readily be remembered by noting that the functions of the negative angle are the same as those of the positive angle, but of opposite sign, except the cosine and the secant, which are of the same sign.

53. Functions of an angle greater than 2π.—Any angle α greater than 2π has the same trigonometric functions as α minus an integral multiple of 2π, because α and $\alpha - 2n\pi$ have the same initial and terminal sides. That is, the functions of α equal the same functions of $\alpha - 2n\pi$, where n is an integer.

That is, a function of an angle that is larger than $360°$ can be found by dividing the angle by $360°$ and finding the required function of the remainder.

54. Summary of the reduction formulas.—The formulas of the previous articles are here collected so as to be convenient for reference. It will be well to memorize the last group, the one expressing the functions of negative angles as functions of positive angles.

$\sin\left(\tfrac{1}{2}\pi - \theta\right) = \cos\theta.$ $\qquad$ $\sin\left(\tfrac{1}{2}\pi + \theta\right) = \cos\theta.$

$\cos\left(\tfrac{1}{2}\pi - \theta\right) = \sin\theta.$ $\qquad$ $\cos\left(\tfrac{1}{2}\pi + \theta\right) = -\sin\theta.$

$\tan\left(\tfrac{1}{2}\pi - \theta\right) = \cot\theta.$ $\qquad$ $\tan\left(\tfrac{1}{2}\pi + \theta\right) = -\cot\theta.$

$\cot\left(\tfrac{1}{2}\pi - \theta\right) = \tan\theta.$ $\qquad$ $\cot\left(\tfrac{1}{2}\pi + \theta\right) = -\tan\theta.$

$\sec\left(\tfrac{1}{2}\pi - \theta\right) = \csc\theta.$ $\qquad$ $\sec\left(\tfrac{1}{2}\pi + \theta\right) = -\csc\theta.$

$\csc\left(\tfrac{1}{2}\pi - \theta\right) = \sec\theta.$ $\qquad$ $\csc\left(\tfrac{1}{2}\pi + \theta\right) = \sec\theta.$

$\sin\left(\pi - \theta\right) = \sin\theta.$ $\qquad$ $\sin\left(\pi + \theta\right) = -\sin\theta.$

$\cos\left(\pi - \theta\right) = -\cos\theta.$ $\qquad$ $\cos\left(\pi + \theta\right) = -\cos\theta.$

$\tan\left(\pi - \theta\right) = -\tan\theta.$ $\qquad$ $\tan\left(\pi + \theta\right) = \tan\theta.$

$\cot\left(\pi - \theta\right) = -\cot\theta.$ $\qquad$ $\cot\left(\pi + \theta\right) = \cot\theta.$

$\sec\left(\pi - \theta\right) = -\sec\theta.$ $\qquad$ $\sec\left(\pi + \theta\right) = -\sec\theta.$

$\csc\left(\pi - \theta\right) = \csc\theta.$ $\qquad$ $\csc\left(\pi + \theta\right) = -\csc\theta.$

$\sin\left(\tfrac{3}{2}\pi - \theta\right) = -\cos\theta.$ $\qquad$ $\sin\left(\tfrac{3}{2}\pi + \theta\right) = -\cos\theta.$

$\cos\left(\tfrac{3}{2}\pi - \theta\right) = -\sin\theta.$ $\qquad$ $\cos\left(\tfrac{3}{2}\pi + \theta\right) = \sin\theta.$

$\tan\left(\tfrac{3}{2}\pi - \theta\right) = \cot\theta.$ $\qquad$ $\tan\left(\tfrac{3}{2}\pi + \theta\right) = -\cot\theta.$

$\cot\left(\tfrac{3}{2}\pi - \theta\right) = \tan\theta.$ $\qquad$ $\cot\left(\tfrac{3}{2}\pi + \theta\right) = -\tan\theta.$

$\sec\left(\tfrac{3}{2}\pi - \theta\right) = -\csc\theta.$ $\qquad$ $\sec\left(\tfrac{3}{2}\pi + \theta\right) = \csc\theta.$

$\csc\left(\tfrac{3}{2}\pi - \theta\right) = -\sec\theta.$ $\qquad$ $\csc\left(\tfrac{3}{2}\pi + \theta\right) = -\sec\theta.$

$\sin\left(2\pi - \theta\right) = -\sin\theta.$ $\qquad$ $\sin\left(-\theta\right) = -\sin\theta.$

$\cos\left(2\pi - \theta\right) = \cos\theta.$ $\qquad$ $\cos\left(-\theta\right) = \cos\theta.$

$\tan\left(2\pi - \theta\right) = -\tan\theta.$ $\qquad$ $\tan\left(-\theta\right) = -\tan\theta.$

$\cot\left(2\pi - \theta\right) = -\cot\theta.$ $\qquad$ $\cot\left(-\theta\right) = -\cot\theta.$

$\sec\left(2\pi - \theta\right) = \sec\theta.$ $\qquad$ $\sec\left(-\theta\right) = \sec\theta.$

$\csc\left(2\pi - \theta\right) = -\csc\theta.$ $\qquad$ $\csc\left(-\theta\right) = -\csc\theta.$

learn

While the proofs of these formulas have all been based upon the assumption that θ is an acute angle, they are true for all values of θ, and can be carried through for any value of θ in exactly the same manner as for θ an acute angle.

Tables of trigonometric functions, in general, do not contain angles greater than 90°. Since the principal application of the reduction formulas is made in determining the numerical values of functions of angles greater than 90°, it will be found convenient to have a rule for the application of the formulas for θ an acute angle. The rule gives a final summary of the preceding articles.

RULE.—*Express the given angle in the form* $n \cdot 90° \pm \theta$, *where* θ *is acute. If* n *is even, take the same function of* θ *as of the given angle; if* n *is odd, take the cofunction of* θ. *In either case the final sign is determined by the function of the given angle and the quadrant in which that angle lies.*

If the given angle is negative, first express its function as the function of the given angle with its sign changed, and then proceed as before.

Example 1.—Find cos 825°.

Solution.—By the rule and **Table V,**

$$\cos 825° = \cos (9 \times 90° + 15°) = -\sin 15° = -0.25882.$$

Since $9 \times 90°$ is an odd number times 90°, we take the sine of 15°. It is negative because 825° lies in the second quadrant in which cosine is negative.

Another solution of this is as follows:

$$\cos 825° = \cos (2 \times 360° + 105°) = \cos 105°$$
$$= \cos (90° + 15°) = -\sin 15°.$$

Example 2.—Find cot $(-1115°)$.

Solution.—First express as a positive angle and then apply the rule.

$$\cot (-1115°) = -\cot 1115° = -\cot (12 \times 90° + 35°)$$
$$= -\cot 35° = -1.4281.$$

Example 3.—Find the value of $\dfrac{2 \sec 3\pi - 3 \sin \frac{9}{2}\pi + 2 \cos \frac{7}{2}\pi}{3 \csc \frac{15}{2}\pi + 7 \cos \frac{5}{2}\pi - \sec 7\pi}$.

Solution.—First evaluate each of the functions.

$$\sec 3\pi = \sec (6 \times \tfrac{1}{2}\pi + 0) = -\sec 0 = -1.$$
$$\sin \tfrac{9}{2}\pi = \sin (9 \times \tfrac{1}{2}\pi + 0) = \cos 0 = 1.$$
$$\cos \tfrac{7}{2}\pi = \cos (7 \times \tfrac{1}{2}\pi + 0) = \sin 0 = 0.$$
$$\csc \tfrac{15}{2}\pi = \csc (15 \times \tfrac{1}{2}\pi + 0) = -\sec 0 = -1.$$
$$\cos \tfrac{5}{2}\pi = \cos (5 \times \tfrac{1}{2}\pi + 0) = \sin 0 = 0.$$
$$\sec 7\pi = \sec (14 \times \tfrac{1}{2}\pi + 0) = -\sec 0 = -1.$$

Substituting these values,

$$\frac{2 \sec 3\pi - 3 \sin \frac{9}{2}\pi + 2 \cos \frac{7}{2}\pi}{3 \csc 1\frac{5}{2}\pi + 7 \cos \frac{5}{2}\pi - \sec 7\pi} = \frac{2(-1) - 3 \cdot 1 + 2 \cdot 0}{3(-1) + 7 \cdot 0 - (-1)}$$

$$= \frac{-5}{-2} = \frac{5}{2}.$$

Example 4.—Evaluate $\sin \theta \big]_{\frac{3}{2}\pi}^{6}$.

Solution.—The notation given is a form frequently used, and means that: (1) the upper number 6 is to be substituted for θ; (2) the lower number $\frac{3}{2}\pi$ is to be substituted for θ; and (3) the result of (2) is to be subtracted from that of (1).

Then $\qquad \sin \theta \big]_{\frac{3}{2}\pi}^{6} = \sin 6 - \sin \frac{3}{2}\pi.$

Since 6 is a number of radians and

$$6 \text{ radians} = 6(57° \ 17' \ 44.8'') = 343° \ 46' \ 29'',$$
$$\sin 6 = \sin 343° \ 46' \ 29'' = -\cos 73° \ 46' \ 29'' = -0.27941.$$
$$\therefore \sin \theta \big]_{\frac{3}{2}\pi}^{6} = -0.27941 - (-1) = 0.72059.$$

EXERCISES

In Exercises 1 to 47 do the work orally. Express each of the following as a function of θ:

1. $\sin (720° + \theta)$.
2. $\sin (720° - \theta)$.
3. $\sin (630° + \theta)$.
4. $\cot (630° - \theta)$.
5. $\sec (1080° + \theta)$.
6. $\cos (990° + \theta)$.
7. $\tan (720° - \theta)$.
8. $\sin (\theta - 540°)$.
9. $\cos (\theta - 1080°)$.
10. $\tan (\theta - 810°)$.
11. $\csc (1890° + \theta)$.
12. $\sec (2880° - \theta)$.

Express the following functions as functions of acute angles. Give two answers, one where the angle is less than 45° and one where it is greater.

13. $\sin 150°$.
14. $\cos 100°$.
15. $\tan 210°$.
16. $\cot 265°$.
17. $\cos 320°$.
18. $\cos (-45°)$.
19. $\tan 290°$.
20. $\cot 185°$.
21. $\sec 275°$.
22. $\sin (-85°)$.
23. $\sin 127° \ 30'$.
24. $\cos 281° \ 30'$.
25. $\cot 235° \ 15'$.
26. $\tan 347° \ 20'$.
27. $\tan (-68° \ 30')$.

Express the following functions as functions of angles less than 45°.

28. $\sec 165°$.
29. $\cot 430°$.
30. $\tan 305°$.
31. $\cos 195°$.
32. $\sin 145°$.
33. $\cos 2000°$.
34. $\sec 600°$.
35. $\cot 1050°$.
36. $\csc 840°$.
37. $\sin 700°$.
38. $\sec (-300)$.
39. $\cot (-425)$.
40. $\tan (-600)$.
41. $\sin (-450)$.
42. $\cos (-325)$.

What is the value of each of the following:

43. $3 \sin (90° + \theta) + 4 \cos (180° - \theta)$.
44. $3 \sin (360° - \theta) - 3 \cos (270° + \theta)$.

45. $2 \tan (180° - \theta) - 2 \cot (90° + \theta)$.

46. $5 \sin (270° + \theta) - 3 \sin (270° - \theta)$.

47. $4 \cos (180° - \theta) + 5 \sin (270° + \theta)$.

Show that the following are true equalities:

48. $\tan (225° - \theta) = \tan (45° - \theta)$.

49. $\sin (135° + \theta) = \cos (45° + \theta)$.

50. $\cot (135° + \theta) = - \cot (45° - \theta)$.

51. $\tan (45 \pm \theta) = \cot (45 \mp \theta)$.

By the use of the table of natural functions, find the sine, cosine, tangent, and cotangent of the following angles:

52. 156°.	**56.** 835° 40′.	**60.** −481°.
53. 215°.	**57.** 460° 18′.	**61.** −1301°.
54. 268°.	**58.** 934° 52′.	**62.** −152° 13′.
55. 297°.	**59.** 1045° 25′.	**63.** −209° 24′.

64. Find the sine, cosine, tangent, and cotangent of 135°, 150°, 240°, 330°, 315°, 120°, 210° by expressing them in terms of functions of 30°, 45°, or 60°.   Compare the results with the table of values given on page 24.

65. Simplify $\dfrac{\sin (\frac{3}{2}\pi - \theta) \cos (\frac{1}{2}\pi + \theta)}{\tan (\frac{1}{2}\pi + \theta)} - \dfrac{\sin (\frac{3}{2}\pi - \theta)}{\sec (\pi + \theta)}$.   *Ans.* -1.

Verify Exercises 66 to 71.

66. $\dfrac{\tan \pi - \tan \theta}{1 + \tan \pi \tan \theta} = \tan (\pi - \theta)$.

67. $\cos \frac{3}{2}\pi \cos \theta - \sin \frac{3}{2}\pi \sin \theta = \cos (\frac{3}{2}\pi + \theta)$.

68. $\sin \frac{3}{2}\pi \cos \theta - \cos \frac{3}{2}\pi \sin \theta = \sin (\frac{3}{2}\pi - \theta)$.

69. $\sin (\frac{1}{2}\pi + \alpha) \cos (\pi - \alpha) + \cos (\frac{1}{2}\pi + \alpha) \sin (\pi - \alpha) = -1$.

70. $\dfrac{\sin (-\theta) + \cos (-\theta)}{\tan (-\theta) - \cot (-\theta)} = \dfrac{\sin (90° + \theta) + \cos (270° - \theta)}{\cot (180° + \theta) + \tan (360° - \theta)}$.

71. $\dfrac{3(\sin \frac{3}{2}\pi - \tan 2\pi + \cos 3\pi)}{4 \csc \frac{3}{2}\pi \cdot \sec 5\pi} = -\dfrac{3}{2}$.

72. Evaluate $12(\frac{1}{2}\theta - \frac{1}{4} \sin 2\theta) \Big]_0^\pi$.   *Ans.* 6π.

73. Evaluate $(\tan x + \cos x) \Big]_0^\pi$.   *Ans.* -2.

74. Evaluate $(\frac{1}{3}x - \frac{2}{3} \sin 2x) \Big]_{\frac{1}{4}\pi}^{2\pi}$.   *Ans.* 2.323.

75. Evaluate $\frac{1}{2}a^2(\frac{3}{2}\theta + 2\sin\theta + \frac{1}{4}\sin 2\theta) \Big]_0^{\frac{3}{2}\pi}$.   *Ans.* $2.534a^2$.

76. Evaluate $\pi a^3(\theta - 4\sin\theta + \frac{3}{4}\sin 2\theta + \frac{1}{3}\sin^3\theta) \Big]_0^\pi$.   *Ans.* $a^3\pi^2$.

77. Evaluate $-\cos x \Big]_2^\pi + \cos x \Big]_\pi^4$.   *Ans.* 0.9302.

78. Evaluate $-\sin x \Big]_1^{\frac{3}{4}\pi} + \sin x \Big]_{\frac{3}{4}\pi}^3$.   *Ans.* -0.4313.

79. If $\sin \theta = -\frac{16}{65}$, with θ in the fourth quadrant, show that vers $(\theta - \pi)$ $= \frac{128}{65}$.

80. If $\cot 250° = \dfrac{1}{b}$, show that $\tan 160° = -\dfrac{1}{b}$, and $\sec 430° = \sqrt{1 + b^2}$.

81. If covers $115° = 1 - \dfrac{1}{c}$ find $\dfrac{\text{vers } 205° \cos 335°}{\cot 245°}$.   *Ans.* $\dfrac{\sqrt{c^2 - 1}}{c^3 - c^2}$.

82. If tan $200° = c$, find $\dfrac{\sin 110° - \cos 250°}{\csc 160° + \sec 340°}$. *Ans.* $\dfrac{c}{c^2 + 1}$.

83. If csc $160° = c$, find $\dfrac{\sin 250° + \tan 290°}{\cot 200° + \cos 340°}$. *Ans.* -1.

Draw the figures and derive the formulas in each of the following:

84. Functions of $90° + \theta$ in terms of functions of θ when θ is in the third quadrant.

85. Functions of $270° - \theta$ in terms of functions of θ when θ is in the second quadrant.

86. Functions of $180° + \theta$ in terms of functions of θ when θ is in the fourth quadrant.

55. Solution of trigonometric equations.—All the angles less than $360°$ that have the same absolute value for each of the trigonometric functions are called **corresponding angles.** In general, there are four such angles for each trigonometric function. For instance, if sin θ is $\frac{1}{2}$ in absolute value, that is, if sin $\theta = \pm\frac{1}{2}$, then $\theta = 30, 150, 210,$ and $330°$. These four angles are called the corresponding angles when the absolute value of sin θ is $\frac{1}{2}$.

In general, the corresponding angles lie one in each quadrant, and have their terminal sides placed equally above and below the x-axis. The exception is when the angles lie between the quadrants, and then there are but two corresponding angles. Thus, if sin $\theta = \pm 1$, the corresponding angles are 90 and $270°$.

It follows that, if ϕ is the angle lying in the first quadrant, then the other corresponding angles are $180° \pm \phi$ and $360° - \phi$.

If the value of a trigonometric function is given, the angle can be found by the following:

RULE.—*First find the acute angle ϕ by the table of natural functions, using the absolute value of the given function. The remaining, or corresponding, angles which have the same trigonometric function in absolute value are $180° \pm \phi$ and $360° - \phi$. From these four angles the angles can be chosen in the proper quadrants to satisfy the given function.*

That is, if the function is positive, the angle is taken in those quadrants in which that function is positive.

Example 1.—Given sin $\theta = -\frac{1}{2}$; find $\theta < 360°$.

Solution.—First find $\phi = \sin^{-1} \frac{1}{2} = 30°$.

By the rule, the remaining angles which have their sine equal to $\frac{1}{2}$ in absolute value are $180° - 30° = 150°$,

$$180° + 30° = 210°,$$
and
$$360° - 30° = 330°.$$

Since the sine is negative, θ must be in the third and fourth quadrants.

$$\therefore \theta = 210 \text{ and } 330°.$$

Example 2.—Given $\cos \theta = -\frac{1}{2}\sqrt{2}$; find $\theta < 360°$.
Solution.—Find $\phi = \cos^{-1} \frac{1}{2}\sqrt{2} = 45°$.
The corresponding angles are 135, 225, and 315°.
But the cosine is negative in the second and third quadrants,

$$\therefore \theta = 135 \text{ and } 225°.$$

Example 3.—Given $2 \sin \theta + \cos \theta = 2$; solve for $\theta < 360°$.
Solution.—First express all the functions in terms of one function as in **Art. 33.** Then, since $\cos \theta = \sqrt{1 - \sin^2 \theta}$, we have

$$2 \sin \theta + \sqrt{1 - \sin^2 \theta} = 2.$$

Transposing and squaring, $4 \sin^2 \theta - 8 \sin \theta + 4 = 1 - \sin^2 \theta$.
Transposing, $5 \sin^2 \theta - 8 \sin \theta + 3 = 0$, which is a quadratic equation in $\sin \theta$.
Solving for $\sin \theta$ by the formula,

$$\sin \theta = \frac{8 \pm \sqrt{64 - 60}}{10} = 1 \text{ or } \frac{3}{5}.$$

Then $\theta = \sin^{-1} 1 = 90°$, and $\theta = \sin^{-1} \frac{3}{5} = 36° \ 52.2'$ or $143° \ 7.8'$.
By substituting these values in the original equation, it will be found that only 90° and 36° 52.2′ satisfy that equation.

$$\therefore \theta = 90° \text{ and } 36° \ 52.2'.$$

Example 4.—Given $\tan \theta \sec \theta = -\sqrt{2}$; solve for $\theta < 2\pi$
Solution.—Substituting $\sec \theta = \sqrt{1 + \tan^2 \theta}$,

$$\tan \theta \sqrt{1 + \tan^2 \theta} = -\sqrt{2}.$$

Squaring, $\tan^2 \theta (1 + \tan^2 \theta) = 2$.

$$\tan^4 \theta + \tan^2 \theta - 2 = 0, \text{a quadratic equation in } \tan^2 \theta.$$

Solving, $\tan^2 \theta = 1$ or -2
$$\tan \theta = \pm 1 \text{ or } \pm\sqrt{-2}.$$
$$\therefore \theta = \tan^{-1} (\pm 1) = \tfrac{1}{4}\pi, \tfrac{3}{4}\pi, \tfrac{5}{4}\pi, \tfrac{7}{4}\pi.$$

Since $\sqrt{-2}$ is imaginary, no such angle as $\tan^{-1} (\pm\sqrt{-2})$ exists.

From the original equation the product of $\tan \theta$ and $\sec \theta$ is negative. Therefore, these functions must be opposite in sign, and the angle θ must be in the third or fourth quadrant. It is necessary, then, to reject $\frac{1}{4}\pi$ and $\frac{3}{4}\pi$.

$$\therefore \theta = \tfrac{5}{4}\pi \text{ and } \tfrac{7}{4}\pi.$$

Example 5.—Given $\tan \theta + \cot \theta = 2$; solve for $\theta < 2\pi$.
Solution.—Expressing in terms of $\cot \theta$,

$$\frac{1}{\cot \theta} + \cot \theta = 2.$$

Solving for $\cot \theta$, $\cot \theta = 1$.
$$\therefore \theta = \cot^{-1} 1 = \tfrac{1}{4}\pi \text{ or } \tfrac{5}{4}\pi.$$

Example 6.—Given $\tan 2\theta = \sqrt{3}$, solve for $\theta < 360°$.
Solution.—$\tan 2\theta = \sqrt{3}$.

Then
$$2\theta = 60°, 240°, 420°, 600°.$$
$$\therefore \theta = 30°, 120°, 210°, 300°.$$

Notice that, in order to find all values of $\theta < 360°$, we take all values of $2\theta < 720°$.

EXERCISES

Give orally the values of the following angles less than 360°:

1. $\sin \theta = \frac{1}{2}\sqrt{2}$. **6.** $\cos \theta = -\dfrac{1}{\sqrt{2}}$. **11.** $\theta = \cos^{-1}(-\frac{1}{2}\sqrt{3})$.

2. $\cos \theta = \frac{1}{2}\sqrt{2}$. **7.** $\cos \theta = 0$. **12.** $\theta = \cot^{-1}(\frac{1}{3}\sqrt{3})$.

3. $\cos \theta = -\frac{1}{2}$. **8.** $\tan \theta = -1$. **13.** $\theta = \sin^{-1}\left(-\dfrac{1}{\sqrt{2}}\right)$.

4. $\sin \theta = -1$. **9.** $\sin \theta = \frac{1}{2}\sqrt{3}$. **14.** $\theta = \sin^{-1}\left(-\dfrac{3}{2}\dfrac{1}{\sqrt{3}}\right)$.

5. $\sin \theta = -\frac{1}{2}$. **10.** $\sin \theta = -\frac{1}{2}\sqrt{3}$. **15.** $\theta = \cos^{-1}(-\frac{1}{2}\sqrt{2})$.

Give orally the general measures of the following angles:

16. $\sin \theta = -1$. **18.** $\cos \theta = -\dfrac{1}{\sqrt{2}}$. **20.** $\theta = \tan^{-1}\dfrac{\sqrt{3}}{3}$.

17. $\cos \theta = 1$. **19.** $\theta = \tan^{-1}\sqrt{3}$. **21.** $\theta = \sin^{-1}(-\frac{1}{2}\sqrt{3})$.

Solve the following for values of $\theta < 360°$:

22. $\tan \theta = -0.69321$. *Ans.* 145° 16′ 11″, 325° 16′ 11″.

23. $\cos \theta = -0.27689$. *Ans.* 106° 4′ 28″, 253° 55′ 32″.

24. $\cos \theta = \pm 0.89613$.
  Ans. 26° 20′ 46″, 153° 39′ 14″, 206° 20′ 46″, 333° 39′ 14″.

25. $\sin \theta = \pm 0.80001$.
  Ans. 53° 7′ 53″, 126° 52′ 7″, 233° 7′ 53″, 306° 52′ 7″.

26. $\cot \theta = 2.1801$. *Ans.* 24° 38′ 26″, 204° 38′ 26″.

27. $\tan \theta = 1.2345$. *Ans.* 50° 59′ 26″, 230° 59′ 26″.

28. $\cos \theta = \pm 0.73218$.
  Ans. 42° 55′ 51″, 137° 4′ 9″, 222° 55′ 51″, 317° 4′ 9″.

29. $\sin \theta = \pm 0.29868$.

Ans. $17° 22' 42''$, $162° 37' 18''$, $197° 22' 42''$, $342° 37' 18''$.

30. $\cot \theta = 0.81638$.   Ans. $50° 46' 21''$, $230° 46' 21''$.

31. $\sin \frac{1}{2}\theta = \frac{1}{2}$.   Ans. $60°$, $300°$.

32. $\cos 2\theta = \frac{1}{2}\sqrt{2}$.   Ans. $22° 30'$, $157° 30'$, $202° 30'$, $337° 30'$.

33. $\tan 3\theta = 1$.   Ans. $15°$, $75°$, $135°$, $195°$, $255°$, $315°$.

34. $\sec 2\theta = \pm 2$.   Ans. $30°$, $60°$, $120°$, $150°$, $210°$, $240°$, $300°$, $330°$.

35. $\sin 2\theta = 0.65923$.   Ans. $20° 37' 14''$, $69° 22' 46''$.
$200° 37' 14''$, $249° 22' 46''$.

36. $\cos \frac{1}{2}\theta = \pm 0.57916$.   Ans. $109° 13'$, $250° 47'$.

37. $\tan \frac{1}{2}\theta = 0.51804$.   Ans. $54° 46' 20''$.

38. $\sin \theta = -\cos \theta$.   Ans. $135°$, $315°$.

39. $\tan \theta = \cot \theta$.   Ans. $45°$, $135°$, $225°$, $315°$.

40. $2 \sin^2 \theta - 3 \sin \theta = 2$.   Ans. $210°$, $330°$.

41. $4 \cos^2 \theta + 2\sqrt{2} \cos \theta = 2 \cos \theta + \sqrt{2}$.

Ans. $60°$, $135°$, $225°$, $300°$.

42. $2 \sin^2 \theta + 3 \sin \theta + 1 = 0$.   Ans. $210°$, $270°$, $330°$.

43. $2 \cos^2 \theta + \sqrt{3} \cos \theta = 3(\sqrt{3} + 2 \cos \theta)$.   Ans. $150°$, $210°$.

44. $\csc^2 \theta = 1 + \tan^2 \theta$.   Ans. $45°$, $135°$, $225°$, $315°$.

45. $\sqrt{3} \cos \theta + \sin \theta = 2$.   Ans. $30°$.

46. $2 \cos^2 \theta + 11 \cos \theta = 6$.   Ans. $60°$, $300°$.

47. $2 \cos^2 \theta + \sin \theta = 1$.   Ans. $90°$, $210°$, $330°$.

48. $\cos 2\theta(1 - 2 \sin \theta) = 0$.   Ans. $30°$, $45°$, $135°$, $150°$, $225°$, $315°$.

49. $\cos \theta(3 - 4 \sin^2 2\theta) = 0$.

Ans. $30°$, $60°$, $90°$, $120°$, $150°$, $210°$, $240°$, $270°$, $300°$, $330°$.

50. $\sqrt{3} \tan \theta + 1 = \sqrt{3} + \cot \theta$.   Ans. $45°$, $150°$, $225°$, $330°$.

51. Eliminate θ from the equations $\sin^3 \theta = x$, and $\cos^3 \theta = y$.

Ans. $x^{\frac{2}{3}} + y^{\frac{2}{3}} = 1$.

Suggestion.—Find $\sin^2 \theta$ and $\cos^2 \theta$ and add.

52. Eliminate θ from the equations

$$a \cos \theta + b \sin \theta = c$$
$$d \cos \theta + e \sin \theta = f.$$

Ans. $(bf - ce)^2 + (cd - af)^2 = (bd - ae)^2$.

Suggestion.—Solve for $\sin \theta$ and $\cos \theta$.

$\sin \theta = \dfrac{cd - af}{bd - ae}$, $\cos \theta = \dfrac{bf - ce}{bd - ae}$; substitute these values in $\sin^2 \theta + \cos^2 \theta = 1$.

53. Given $r \cos \theta = x$, and $r \sin \theta = y$; solve for r and θ.

Ans. $r = \sqrt{x^2 + y^2}$; $\theta = \tan^{-1} \dfrac{y}{x}$.

54. Given $r \sin \theta \cos \varphi = x$, $r \cos \theta \cos \varphi = y$, $r \sin \varphi = z$; solve for r, θ, and φ.

Ans. $r = \sqrt{x^2 + y^2 + z^2}$; $\varphi = \sin^{-1} \dfrac{z}{\sqrt{x^2 + y^2 + z^2}}$; $\theta = \tan^{-1} \dfrac{x}{y}$.

55. Find the value of: $\dfrac{\sin (-60°)}{\cos 150°} + \dfrac{\cos (-60°)}{\sin 150°} + \dfrac{\cot (-60°)}{\tan 150°}$.

Ans. 3.

56. Prove that $\dfrac{\tan 230°}{\tan 130°} \cdot \dfrac{\cot 130°}{\cot 230°} \cdot \dfrac{\sec 310°}{\csc 410°} = \tan 50°.$

57. If $\sin 130° = a$, show that $\dfrac{\sec 230° \sin 320°}{\cot 220°} = \dfrac{\sqrt{1 - a^2}}{a}.$

58. If $\cos (\tfrac{3}{2}\pi + \theta) = \tfrac{12}{13}$, show that $\cot (\pi - \theta) = -\tfrac{5}{12}$ and $\csc (\pi + \theta) = -\tfrac{13}{12}.$

In the following problems, find all values of θ less than 360°.   Check each angle.

59. $\sin 3\theta = -\dfrac{\sqrt{3}}{2}.$

60. $\cos 3\theta = -\tfrac{1}{2}.$

61. $\cot 3\theta = -1.$

62. $\sec 4\theta = 2.$

CHAPTER VI

GRAPHICAL REPRESENTATION OF TRIGONOMETRIC FUNCTIONS

56. Line representation of the trigonometric functions.— Construct a circle of radius OH, with its center at the origin of coordinates (Fig. 54). Since, in finding the trigonometric functions of an angle with its vertex at the origin of coordinates and its initial side on the positive part of the axis of abscissas, any

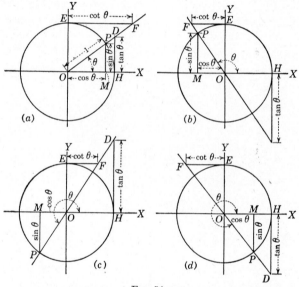

(a)   (b)

(c)   (d)

FIG. 54.

point may be chosen in the terminal side of the angle, we may take the point where the terminal side cuts the circumference of the circle. Draw angle θ = angle XOP in each of the four quadrants, and draw $MP \perp OX$ in each case. Now choose OH as the unit of measure, that is, $OH = 1$. Then in each of the four quadrants,

$$\sin \theta = \frac{MP}{OP} = \frac{MP}{OH} = \frac{MP}{1} = MP.$$

$$\cos \theta = \frac{OM}{OP} = \frac{OM}{OH} = \frac{OM}{1} = OM.$$

Stated in words these are as follows:

The sine of an angle θ is represented by the ordinate of the point where the terminal side cuts the circumference of the unit circle.

The cosine of an angle θ is represented by the abscissa of the point where the terminal side cuts the unit circle.

It should be noted that the ordinate gives the value of the sine both in magnitude and in sign. That is, when the point is above the x-axis, the sine is positive, and when below it is negative; likewise, for the cosine with reference to the y-axis. In this way one can visualize the sine and the cosine.

Draw tangents to the circle at H and E (Fig. 54), to meet the terminal side OP extended or produced back through the origin as the position of the angle requires. In each of the four figures, triangles OMP, OHD, and OEF are similar. Assume that HD is positive when measured upward, and negative when measured downward; also that EF is positive when measured to the right, and negative when measured to the left.

From the similar triangles, $\dfrac{MP}{OM} = \dfrac{HD}{OH}$ and $\dfrac{OM}{MP} = \dfrac{EF}{OE}$.

Then in each of the four quadrants,

$$\tan \theta = \frac{MP}{OM} = \frac{HD}{OH} = \frac{HD}{1} = HD.$$
$$\cot \theta = \frac{OM}{MP} = \frac{EF}{OE} = \frac{EF}{1} = EF.$$

Or, in words, these are:

The tangent of an angle θ is represented by the ordinate of the point where the terminal side of θ is cut by a tangent line drawn to the unit circle where the circle cuts the positive part of the axis of abscissas.

The cotangent of an angle θ is represented by the abscissa of the point where the terminal side of θ is cut by a tangent line drawn to the unit circle where the circle cuts the positive part of the axis of ordinates.

Let it be assumed that OD and OF are positive when measured on the terminal side OP of the angle, and that they are negative when measured on OP produced back through the origin. Then in each of the four quadrants,

$$\sec \theta = \frac{OP}{OM} = \frac{OD}{OH} = \frac{OD}{1} = OD.$$

$$\csc \theta = \frac{OP}{MP} = \frac{OF}{OE} = \frac{OF}{1} = OF.$$

Or, in words, these are:

The secant of an angle θ is represented by the segment of the terminal side of θ from the origin to the point where the line representing the tangent of θ cuts the terminal side.

The cosecant of an angle θ is represented by the segment of the terminal side of θ from the origin to the point where the line representing the cotangent of θ cuts the terminal side.

It is not to be understood that the functions are lines; but that, where the radius is taken as the unit of measure, and the lines are expressed in terms of this unit, the numbers which then represent the lines are the functions. Thus, if MP (Fig. 54) is 4 in. and the radius is 7 in., MP in terms of OH is $\frac{4}{7}$, which is then the sine of θ.

Historically, the line definitions of the trigonometric functions were given before the ratio definitions. This graphical way of representing the functions assists in clarifying many questions arising in connection with the functions. For instance, it makes apparent the origin of the terms tangent and secant of an angle.

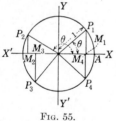

This manner of defining the functions gave rise to the term **circular functions** by which they are often called.

FIG. 55.

EXERCISES

Draw the following angles and represent their trigonometric functions as lines:

1. 30°.   3. 245°.   5. 90°.
2. 160°.   4. 330°.   6. 180°.

57. Changes in the value of the sine and cosine as the angle increases from 0 to 360°.—Draw a circle with unit radius (Fig. 55) and construct an angle θ in each of the four quadrants. Since in a unit circle the sine of an angle θ is represented by the ordinate of the point where the terminal side of the angle intersects the circle, the variation in the ordinate will represent the variation in the sin θ. At 0° the ordinate is 0. As the angle increases from 0 to 90°, the ordinate increases from 0 to 1. As θ increases from 90 to 180°, the ordinate decreases from 1 to 0. From 180 to 270°, the ordinate becomes negative and decreases from

0 to −1. From 270 to 360°, the ordinate increases from −1 to 0. Therefore as the angle varies from 0 to 360°, the sine varies from 0 at 0° to 1 at 90°, to 0 at 180°, to −1 at 270°, and back to 0 at 360°.

The cosine, being represented by the abscissa of the point where the terminal side of the angle intersects the unit circle, will then decrease from 1 to 0 as the angle increases from 0 to 90°. From 90 to 180°, the cosine is negative and decreases from 0 to −1. From 180 to 360°, the cosine increases from −1 through 0 at 270° to 1 at 360°.

EXERCISES

Discuss orally the changes in the following functions as θ varies from 0 to 360°:

1. $\sin 2\theta$.
2. $\sin 3\theta$.
3. $\sin 4\theta$.
4. $\sin \frac{1}{2}\theta$.
5. $2 \sin \theta$.
6. $\cos \theta$.

7. $\cos 3\theta$.
8. $\cos \frac{1}{2}\theta$.
9. $\cos (-\theta)$.
10. $\tan \theta$.
11. $\tan 2\theta$.
12. $2 \tan \theta$.

13. $\cot 2\theta$.
14. $\sec \theta$.
15. $\sin (\theta + 30°)$.
16. $\cos (\theta + 45°)$.
17. $\sin (\theta - 45°)$.
18. $\sin (\theta + \alpha)$.

19. Trace the changes in $\sin^2 \alpha$ as α varies from 0 to 2π.

20. Trace the changes in $\sin \alpha + \cos \alpha$. What is the maximum value? The minimum value? Find the values of α for these values of $\sin \alpha + \cos \alpha$. For what values of α is $\sin \alpha + \cos \alpha = 0$?

TRIGONOMETRIC CURVES

58. Graph of $y = \sin \theta$.—The changes which take place in $\sin \theta$, as indicated in the preceding article, are best shown by a

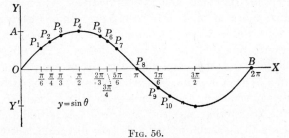

Fig. 56.

graph. Referring again to Fig. 55 (**Art. 57**), let OA be the unit of measure. Then the complete circumference is the measure of 360°, that is, 360° may be represented by a line 2π units in length. Lay off $OB = 6.2832$ on OX (Fig. 56). OB is then the radian measure of 2π, or $OB = 2\pi$. Then lay off the proportional parts as indicated in the figure, using multiples of $\frac{1}{6}\pi$ and $\frac{1}{4}\pi$ only. (Other angles could be used as well as, or in addition to these, making the curve more nearly accurate; but for our purpose the easy proportional parts of 2π are used.) Lay off OA on the y-axis. This will represent the unit for plotting the sines of the angles.

Select various values of θ from 0 to 2π, determine the corresponding values of y, and plot the points of which these values are the coordinates.

Values of θ:	0	$\frac{1}{6}\pi$	$\frac{1}{4}\pi$	$\frac{1}{3}\pi$	$\frac{1}{2}\pi$	$\frac{2}{3}\pi$	$\frac{3}{4}\pi$	$\frac{5}{6}\pi$	π	$\frac{7}{6}\pi$	$\frac{5}{4}\pi$	etc.
Values of y:	0	$\frac{1}{2}$	$\frac{1}{2}\sqrt{2}$	$\frac{1}{2}\sqrt{3}$	1	$\frac{1}{2}\sqrt{3}$	$\frac{1}{2}\sqrt{2}$	$\frac{1}{2}$	0	$-\frac{1}{2}$	$-\frac{1}{2}\sqrt{2}$	etc.
Points:	O	P_1	P_2	P_3	P_4	P_5	P_6	P_7	P_8	P_9	P_{10}	etc.

Draw a curve through these points. *The curve is the graph of* $y = \sin \theta$. It shows the change in $\sin \theta$ as the angle changes from 0 to 2π.

It is evident that the curve will repeat its form if θ were given values from 2π to 4π, from 4π to 6π, etc., or from 0 to -2π, etc. The curve is then periodic.

Here the angle and the function are both plotted to the same unit or scale, that is, the unit on the y-axis is the same length as that to represent 1 radian on the x-axis. The curve so plotted may be called the **proper sine curve**. Often, however, for convenience when plotting on coordinate paper, the angles are plotted according to the divisions on the paper. For example, 1 space = 6° or 10°, or some other convenient angle, depending on the size of the plot.

59. Periodic functions and periodic curves.—In nature, there are many motions that are recurrent. Sound waves, light waves, and water waves are familiar examples. Motions in machines are repeated in a periodic manner. The vibration of a pendulum is a simple case, as is also the piston-rod motion in an engine. Other familiar illustrations are the vibration of a piano string, breathing movements, heart beats, and the motion of tides. An alternating electric current has periodic changes. It increases to a maximum value in one direction, decreases to zero, and on down to a minimum, that is, to a maximum value in the opposite direction, rises again, and repeats these changes. It is thus an *alternating* current passing from a maximum in one direction to a maximum in the other direction, say, 60 times a second.

Before physical quantities that change in a periodic fashion can be dealt with mathematically, it is necessary to find a mathematical statement for such a periodic change.

Definitions.—A curve that repeats in form as illustrated by the sine curve is called a **periodic curve**. The function that gives rise to a periodic curve is called a **periodic function**. The least repeating part of a periodic curve is called a **cycle** of the curve. The change in the value of the variable necessary for a cycle is called the **period** of the function. The greatest absolute value of the ordinates of a periodic function is called the **amplitude** of the function.

Example 1.—Find the period of sin $n\theta$, and plot $y = \sin 2\theta$.

Since, in finding the value of sin $n\theta$, the angle θ is multiplied by n before finding the sine, the period is $\dfrac{2\pi}{n}$.

The curve for $y = \sin 2\theta$ is shown in Fig. 57. The period of the function is π radians, and there are two cycles of the curve in 2π radians.

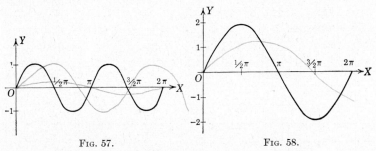

Fig. 57.   Fig. 58.

The number n in sin $n\theta$ is called the **periodicity factor**.

Example 2.—Find the amplitude of $b \sin \theta$, and plot $y = 2 \sin \theta$.

Since, in finding the value of $b \sin \theta$, sin θ is found and then multiplied by b, the amplitude of the function is b, for the greatest value of sin θ is 1.

The curve for $y = 2 \sin \theta$ is shown in Fig. 58. The amplitude is 2.

The number b in $b \sin \theta$ is sometimes called the **amplitude factor**.

By a proper choice of a periodicity factor and an amplitude factor, a function of any amplitude and any period desired can be found.

While the sine function is perhaps the most frequently used of the periodic functions, the cosine function can be used quite as readily. By a proper choice and combination of sines and cosines a function can be built up that will represent exactly or approxi-

mately any periodic phenomenon.   Just how this may be done can
hardly be explained here.

60. Mechanical construction of graph of sin θ.—On one of
the heavy horizontal lines of a sheet of coordinate paper, choose
an origin and lay off angles every 15° from 0 to 360°, using each
small space to represent 15°, as in Fig. 59.   With any convenient
point on this horizontal axis as a center, describe a circle with a
radius equal to 30 spaces.   Choose the initial side of all the angles
on the axis of the angles.

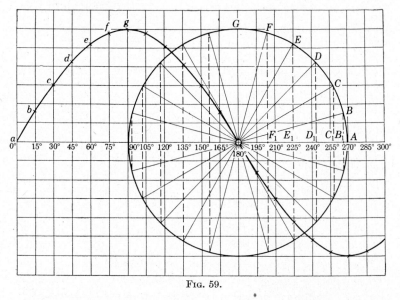

FIG. 59.

By means of the protractor lay off the central angles every 15°
from 0 to 360°, such as ∠AOB, ∠AOC, etc.   Let the radius of
the circle be the unit of measure.   Then the sines of the angles
are the ordinates of the points A, B, C, etc.   Through B draw a
horizontal line to intersect the vertical line through 15° as plotted
on the horizontal axis.   The point b, thus determined, has as
coordinates (15°, sin 15°).   In the same way locate c (30°, sin 30°);
d (45°, sin 45°); e (60°, sin 60°); etc.   Through these points
draw a curve.

With the sine curve thus constructed, one can determine the
value of the sine of an angle approximately by measurement.
For example, find the sin 51°.   By measurement, the ordinate for
sin 51° is 23.3 spaces.   Since the unit is 30 spaces,

(handwritten at top)
ampl.
$y = R \sin(\omega t + \alpha)$. ← angle from which it starts (0°)
$y = 12 \sin 2\pi t$

$$\sin 51° = \frac{23.3}{30} = 0.7766.$$

From the table of natural functions $\sin 51° = 0.77715$. A comparison of the results with **Table IV** for a number of angles will give an idea of the accuracy of the graph.

Exercise.—Measure the ordinates for the angles given in the following table, compute the sines, and tabulate the results. Find the sines of the same angles from the **Tables** and tabulate. Compare the results.

θ	Sine from curve	Sine from table	Difference
18°			
57°			
78°			
99°			
123°			
138°			
171°			

(handwritten left margin) Fri Jan. 11

EXERCISES

1. Plot $y = \sin \theta$, first, using as a unit on the x-axis a length twice as great as that on the y-axis; second, using as a unit on the x-axis a length one-half as great as that on the y-axis. Plot both curves on the same set of axes.

2. Plot $y = \cos \theta$. Give its period and amplitude.

3. Plot $y = \tan \theta$ and $y = \cot \theta$ on the same set of axes.

4. Plot $y = \sec \theta$ and $y = \csc \theta$ on the same set of axes.

5. Plot $y = \sin x + \cos x$.

Suggestion.—Plot $y_1 = \sin x$ and $y_2 = \cos x$ on the same set of axes. Then find the points on the curve $y = \sin x + \cos x$ from the relation $y = y_1 + y_2$, by adding the ordinates for various values of x.

6. Plot $y = \sin^2 x$ and $y = \cos^2 x$ on the same set of axes. Note that the curves never extend below the x-axis.

7. Plot $y = \frac{1}{2} \sin x$, $y = \sin x$, $y = 2 \sin x$, and $y = \frac{3}{2} \sin x$ on the same set of axes. Give the period and the amplitude of each.

8. Plot $y = \sin \frac{1}{2}x$, $y = \sin x$, $y = \sin 2x$, and $y = \sin \frac{3}{2}x$ on the same set of axes. Give the period and the amplitude of each.

61. Projection of a point having uniform circular motion.

Example 1.—A point P (Fig. 60) moves around a vertical circle of radius 3 in. in a counterclockwise direction. It starts with the point at A and moves with an angular velocity of 1 revolution in 10 sec. Plot a curve showing the distance the projection of P on the vertical diameter is from O at any time t, and find its equation.

Plotting.—Let OP be any position of the radius drawn to the moving point. OP starts from the position OA and at the end of 1 sec. is in position OP_1, having turned through an angle of $36° = 0.6283$ radian. At the end of 2 sec. it has turned to OP_2, through an angle of $72° = 1.2566$ radians, and so on to positions $OP_3, OP_4, \cdots, OP_{10}$.

The points $N_1, N_2, \cdots$ are the projections of $P_1, P_2, \cdots$, respectively, on the vertical diameter.

Produce the horizontal diameter OA through A, and lay off the seconds on this to some scale, taking the origin at A.

For each second plot a point whose ordinate is the corresponding distance of N from O. These points determine a curve of

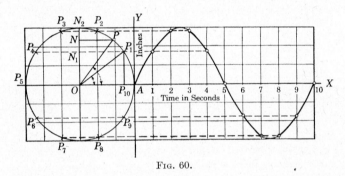

Fig. 60.

which any ordinate y is the distance from the center O of the projection of P upon the vertical diameter at the time t represented by the abscissa of the point.

It is evident that for the second and each successive revolution, the curve repeats, that is, it is a periodic curve.

Since the radius OP turns through 0.6283 radian per second,

angle $AOP = 0.6283t$ radian,

and $ON = OP \cdot \sin 0.6283t$,

or $y = 3 \sin 0.6283t$ is the equation of the curve.

In general, then, it is readily seen that, if a straight line of length r starts in a horizontal position when time $t = 0$, and revolves in a vertical plane around one end at a uniform angular velocity ω per unit of time, the projection y of the moving end upon a vertical straight line has a motion represented by the equation

$$y = r \sin \omega t.$$

Similarly, the projection of the moving point upon the horizontal is given by the ordinates of the curve whose equation is

$$y = r \cos \omega t.$$

If the time is counted from some other instant than that from which the above is counted, then the motion is represented by

$$y = r \sin (\omega t + \alpha),$$

where α is the angle that OP makes with the line OA at the instant from which t is counted. As an illustration of this consider the following:

Example 2.—A crank OP (Fig. 61) of length 2 ft. starts from a position making an angle $\alpha = 40° = \frac{2}{9}\pi$ radians with the horizontal line OA when $t = 0$. It rotates in the positive direction at the rate of 2 revolutions per second. Plot the curve

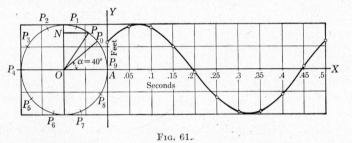

Fig. 61.

showing the projection of P upon a vertical diameter, and write the equation.

Plotting.—The axes are chosen as before, and points are found for each 0.05 sec. The curve is as shown in Fig. 61.

The equation is $y = 2 \sin (4\pi t + \frac{2}{9}\pi)$.

Definitions.—The number of cycles of a periodic curve in a unit of time is called the **frequency**.

It is evident that

$$f = \frac{1}{T},$$

where f is the frequency and T is the period.

In $y = r \sin (\omega t + \alpha)$, $f = \frac{\omega}{2\pi}$ and $T = \frac{2\pi}{\omega}$.

The angle α is called the **angle of lag**.

62. Summary.—In summary it may be noted again that the equation

$$y = a \sin (nx + \alpha)$$

gives a periodic curve. In this equation there are three arbitrary constants, a, n, and α. A change in any one of these constants will change the curve.

(1) If a is changed, the *amplitude* of the curve is changed.

(2) If n is changed, the *period* of the curve is changed.

(3) If α is changed, the curve is moved without change in shape from left to right or *vice versa*.

63. Simple harmonic motion.—If a point moves at a uniform rate around a circle and the point be projected on a straight line in the plane of the circle, the oscillating motion, that is, the back-and-forth motion, of the projected point is called **simple harmonic motion.** The name is abbreviated s.h.m. In **Art. 61,** the point N of Fig. 61 is the projection of the point P. As P moves around the circle the point N moves back-and-forth along the vertical diameter and performs a simple harmonic motion. It is readily seen that the point N moves more slowly near the ends of the diameter and more rapidly near the center. It thus changes its velocity or is accelerated.

It can be shown that many motions that one wishes to deal with are simple harmonic. Such is the motion of a swinging weight suspended by a string, a pendulum, a vibrating tuning fork, the particles of water in a wave, a coiled wire spring supporting a weight when the weight is pulled downward and released. Also many motions which are not simple harmonic may be treated as resulting from several such motions. Such motions occur in alternating electric currents, in sound waves, and in light waves.

EXERCISES

1. A crank 12 in. long starts from a horizontal position and rotates in the positive direction in a vertical plane at the rate of 2π radians per second. The projection of the moving end of the crank upon a vertical line oscillates with a simple harmonic motion. Construct a curve that represents this motion, and write its equation.   *Ans.* $y = 12 \sin 2\pi t$.

2. A crank 6 in. long starts from a position making an angle of 55° with the horizontal, and rotates in a vertical plane in the positive direction at the rate of 1 revolution in 5 sec. Construct a curve showing the projection of the moving end of the crank on a vertical line. Write the equation of the curve and give the period and the frequency.

Ans. $y = 6 \sin (t \cdot 72° + 55)$; 5; $\frac{1}{5}$.

3. Plot the curves that represent the following motions:

$$(a)\quad y = 10 \sin (4t + 0.6);$$
$$(b)\quad y = 4 \sin (\tfrac{1}{8}\pi t + \tfrac{1}{12}\pi).$$

Give the period and frequency of each.   *Ans.* (a) 1.571, 0.637; (b) 16, $\frac{1}{16}$.

4. Plot $y = r \sin \pi t$ and $y = r \sin (\pi t + \frac{1}{4}\pi)$ on the same set of axes. Notice that the highest points on each are separated by the constant angle $\frac{1}{4}\pi$. Such curves are said to be out of phase. The difference in phase is stated in time or as an angle. In the latter case it is called the phase angle.

5. Plot $y = r \sin \frac{1}{4}\pi t$, $y = r \sin (\frac{1}{4}\pi t - \frac{1}{4}\pi)$, and $y = r \cos \frac{1}{4}\pi t$ all on the same set of axes. What is the difference in phase between these?

6. What is the difference in phase between the curves of $y = \sin x$ and $y = \cos x$? Between $y = \cos x$ and $y = \sin (x + \frac{1}{2}\pi)$.

PRINCIPAL VALUES OF INVERSE FUNCTIONS

64. Inverse functions.—We have seen that $\sin^{-1} t$ means the angle whose sine is t. In **Art. 57,** it was shown that the sine function varied from -1 to $+1$. Then the equation $\theta = \sin^{-1} t$ has real solutions when and only when t is not less than -1 or greater than $+1$. In the same way it can be shown that $\theta = \cos^{-1} t$ has a solution when and only when t is not less than -1, or greater than $+1$.

Since $\tan \theta$ and $\cot \theta$ can have any value from $-\infty$ to $+\infty$, the equations $\theta = \tan^{-1} t$ and $\theta = \cot^{-1} t$ have solutions for all values of t.

The two expressions $\sin \theta = t$ and $\theta = \sin^{-1} t$ both express the same thing, namely, that θ is an angle whose sine is equal to t. In the first expression t is a function of θ and in the second θ is a function of t.

In $\sin \theta = t$, there is but one value of t for every value of θ. $\sin \theta$ is then said to be a **single valued function** of θ.

In $\theta = \sin^{-1} t$ for every value of t, there are an indefinite number of values of θ, as was seen in **Art. 53.** $\sin^{-1} t$ is then said to be a **multiple valued function** of t.

65. Graph of y = $\sin^{-1}$ x, or y = arc sin x.—Stating $y = \sin^{-1} x$ in the form $\sin y = x$, it is readily seen by comparison with $y = \sin x$, that $\sin y = x$ is obtained from $y = \sin x$ by interchanging x and y. Then the graph of $y = \sin^{-1} x$ is obtained by plotting the sine curve on the y-axis instead of the x-axis as in **Art. 58.** The curve is shown in Fig. 62.

In many mathematical operations where $\sin^{-1} x$ enters, it is often desirable and, indeed, necessary to consider a portion of the curve (Fig. 62) for which there will be but one value of y for every value of x.

A glance at the figure will show that for the portion AOC of the curve the function is single-valued. That is, for every value of x between and including -1 and $+1$, y takes values between and including $-\frac{1}{2}\pi$ and $\frac{1}{2}\pi$.

Definition.—The values of $\sin^{-1} x$ between and including $-\frac{1}{2}\pi$ and $\frac{1}{2}\pi$ for each value of x are called the **principal values** of $\sin^{-1} x$.

To represent the principal value of the function, the s is often written a capital, thus, $\text{Sin}^{-1} x$. The other functions are denoted in a similar manner.

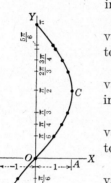

Fig. 62

The notation $\text{Sin}^{-1} x$ denotes the principal values of $\sin^{-1} x$. The values are from $-\frac{1}{2}\pi$ to $\frac{1}{2}\pi$.

The notation $\text{Cos}^{-1} x$ denotes the principal values of $\cos^{-1} x$. The values are from 0 to π inclusive.

The notation $\text{Tan}^{-1} x$ denotes the principal values of $\tan^{-1} x$. The values are from $-\frac{1}{2}\pi$ to $\frac{1}{2}\pi$.

The notation Cot^{-1} denotes the principal values of $\cot^{-1} x$. The values are from 0 to π.

Example.—Evaluate $(\frac{1}{5}x\sqrt{15^2 - 9x^2} + 15 \sin^{-1} \frac{1}{5}x)\Big]_2^5$.

Solution.—The notation is explained in the solution to Example 4, page 69.

Substituting $x = 5$,

$$\tfrac{1}{5} \cdot 5\sqrt{225 - 9 \cdot 5^2} + 15 \sin^{-1} 1 =$$
$$\tfrac{15}{2}\pi = 23.5620.$$

Substituting $x = 2$,

$$\tfrac{1}{5} \cdot 2\sqrt{225 - 9 \cdot 2^2} + 15 \sin^{-1} \tfrac{2}{5}$$
$$= 5.4991 + 6.1728 = 11.6719.$$
$$23.5620 - 11.6719 = 11.890. \qquad \textit{Ans.}$$

EXERCISES

Give the results of the following orally:

1. $\text{Cos}^{-1} (-1)$.
2. $\text{Sin}^{-1} (-1)$.
3. $\text{Sin}^{-1} \frac{1}{2}$.
4. $\text{Cos}^{-1} \frac{1}{2}\sqrt{3}$.
5. $\text{Cos}^{-1} (-\frac{1}{2}\sqrt{3})$.

6. $\text{Sin}^{-1} (-\frac{1}{2})$.
7. Arc cot $\frac{1}{3}\sqrt{3}$.
8. Arc tan $\sqrt{3}$.
9. Arc cos $(-\frac{1}{2}\sqrt{2})$.
10. Arc sin $\frac{1}{2}\sqrt{3}$.

11. tan $\text{Cot}^{-1} \sqrt{3}$.
12. cos $\text{Sin}^{-1} (-\frac{1}{2})$.
13. sin $\text{Cos}^{-1} \frac{1}{2}$.
14. sin $\text{Cos}^{-1} (-\frac{1}{2})$.
15. cos $\text{Sin}^{-1} \frac{1}{2}$.

In the following find the numerical values of the given expressions, using the principal values of the angles. In many applications of anti-functions, as in the calculus, they enter into the expressions for areas, volumes, etc., and the angles must be expressed in radians.

16. $\frac{3}{5}[\sin^{-1} 1 - \tan^{-1}(-1)]$.   *Ans.* $\dfrac{9\pi}{20}$.

17. $16[\sin^{-1}(-0.2) - \sin^{-1}(-0.4)]$.   *Ans.* 3.363.

18. $\tan^{-1}\frac{1}{2} + \tan^{-1}(-1)$.   *Ans.* −0.3217.

19. $\sin^{-1}\left(-\dfrac{1}{2}\right) + \cos^{-1}\dfrac{\sqrt{3}}{2}$.   *Ans.* 0.

20. $\cos^{-1} 0 - \tan^{-1}(-\sqrt{3})$.   *Ans.* $\dfrac{5\pi}{6}$.

21. $\cos^{-1}\left(-\dfrac{\sqrt{3}}{2}\right) + \sin^{-1}(-1)$.   *Ans.* $\dfrac{\pi}{3}$.

22. $\cot^{-1}(-\sqrt{3}) + \sin^{-1}\left(-\dfrac{\sqrt{2}}{2}\right)$.   *Ans.* 1.833.

23. $\sin^{-1}\left(-\dfrac{\sqrt{3}}{2}\right) - \cos^{-1}(-1.)$ *Ans.* $-\dfrac{4\pi}{3}$.

24. $8[\cos^{-1}(0.2) - \cos^{-1}(0.4)]$.   *Ans.* 1.681.

25. $\tan^{-1}\left(-\dfrac{1}{\sqrt{3}}\right) - \tan^{-1}(-\sqrt{3})$ *Ans.* $\dfrac{\pi}{6}$.

26. Plot $y = \cos^{-1} x$ and show that for values of y from 0 to π inclusive the values of x range from $+1$ to -1, inclusive.

27. Evaluate $\sin^{-1}\dfrac{x}{2}\Big]_{-2}^{2}$ *Ans.* π.

28. Evaluate $\dfrac{1}{2}\left(x\sqrt{9-x^2} + 9\sin^{-1}\dfrac{x}{3}\right)\Big]_{0}^{3}$ *Ans.* $\dfrac{9\pi}{4}$.

29. Evaluate $4\pi b\left[\dfrac{1}{2}\left(x\sqrt{a^2-x^2} + a^2\ \sin^{-1}\dfrac{x}{a}\right)\right]_{-a}^{a}$ *Ans.* $2\pi^2 a^2 b$.

30. Evaluate $10\left(x\sqrt{a^2-x^2} + a^2\ \sin^{-1}\dfrac{x}{a}\right)\Big]_{0}^{a}$.   *Ans.* $5a^2\pi$.

31. $\frac{1}{2}\left[(x^2+1)\tan^{-1}x - x\right]_{-1}^{1}$.   *Ans.* 0.5707.

32. $(x-1)\operatorname{vers}^{-1}x + \sqrt{2x - x^2}\,\Big]_{0}^{1}$.   *Ans.* 1.

CHAPTER VII

PRACTICAL APPLICATIONS AND RELATED PROBLEMS

66. Accuracy.—It is of very great importance that one should bear in mind as far as possible the limitations as regards accuracy. The degree of accuracy that can be depended upon in a computation is limited by the accuracy of the tables of trigonometric functions and logarithms used, and by the data involved in the computation.

The greater the number of decimal places in the table, the more accurately, in general, can the angles be determined from the natural or logarithmic functions; but, in a given table, the accuracy is greater the more rapidly the function is changing. Since the cosine of the angle changes slowly when the angle is near 0°, small angles should not be determined from the cosine. For a like reason, the sines should not be used when the angle is near 90°. The tangent and the cotangent change more rapidly throughout the quadrant and so can be used for any angle.

Most of the data used in problems are obtained from measurements made with instruments devised to determine those data more or less accurately. The inability to be precise in the data depends not only upon the instruments used, but upon the person making the measurements and upon the thing measured.

A man in practical work uses instruments which are of such accuracy as to secure results suitable for his purpose. The data given in problems for practice are supposed to be of such accuracy as the instruments that are used in such measurements would warrant.

In the solution of a problem it is useless to carry out the computations with a greater degree of accuracy than that of the data. That is, if the data are accurate only to, say, four significant figures, there is no necessity to compute accurately to more figures than this. If the measuring instrument can be read only to minutes of angle, in the computation there is no object in carrying the work to seconds of angle.

In general, the following is the agreement between the measurement of distances and the related angles:

90

(1) Distances to two significant figures, angles to the nearest 0.5°.

(2) Distances to three significant figures, angles to the nearest 5′.

(3) Distances to four significant figures, angles to the nearest 1′.

(4) Distances to five significant figures, angles to the nearest 0.1′.

In drill problems, the angles are often expressed as if accurate to seconds when the distances are expressed in five figures. This gives variety in interpolating, but one should not be misled by the implied accuracy. The United States Coast and Geodetic Survey sets the following standards for its finest surveys: A line 1 mile long may turn to the one side or the other not more than $\frac{1}{8}$ in. The average closing error in leveling work must be less than 1 in. in 100 miles. The first gives a variation in the angle of 0.4″ to each side, or a total of 0.8″. In making such accurate computations, a 10-place table is used.

67. Tests of accuracy.—The practical man endeavors in one way or another to check both his measurements and his computations. In our work here we are interested in checks on the computation.

(1) Often a graphical construction to scale will give results that will check the numerical work. If the construction is made free-hand, only the gross mistakes in computation will be discovered; but if the construction is made carefully with accurate instruments, results may be obtained as accurate as the data will warrant. This, then, may be considered a graphical solution of the problem.

(2) Mistakes in the computations may be found by making another computation using a different set of data; or by recomputing, using the same data but using a different set of formulas. Many ways will present themselves to the thoughtful student.

EXERCISES

1. In determining an angle by means of a table of natural functions that is correct to five places, if the angle is near 1° can seconds be determined from the cosine of the angle? Can tenths of minutes? Can minutes?

2. Answer the same questions as in Exercise 1 if the sine is used instead of the cosine. If the tangent is used. If the cotangent.

3. Answer similar questions if the angle is near 89°, 80°, 10°, 20°, 70°, 45°.

4. From the results obtained in the first three exercises, state conclusions as to what sized angles can be determined most accurately from sine, cosine, tangent, and cotangent of the angle.

5. Compare the logarithms of 92.8766 and 92.876; 99.8375, 99.837, and 99.838; 121.575, 121.57, and 121.6.

6. Can a number be determined correct to six figures by using a five-place logarithm table? When? When is it not possible to determine five figures of a number by means of a five-place table of logarithms?

APPLICATION OF RIGHT TRIANGLES TO VECTORS

68. Orthogonal projection.—If from a point P (Fig. 63a), a perpendicular PQ be drawn to any straight line RS, then the

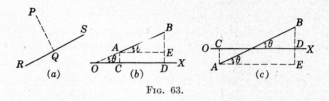

$$(a) \qquad (b) \qquad (c)$$

Fig. 63.

foot of the perpendicular Q is said to be the **orthogonal projection**, or simply the **projection**, of P upon RS.

The **projection of a line segment** upon a given straight line is the portion of the given line lying between the projections of the ends of the segment.

In Fig. 63b and c, CD is the projection of AB on OX. In each case $AE = CD$ and $AE = AB \cos \theta$.

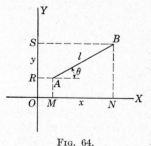

Fig. 64.

The projections usually made are upon a horizontal line OX and a vertical line OY, as in Fig. 64. Hence, if l is the length of the segment of line projected, x the projection on OX, y the projection on OY, and θ the angle of inclination, that is, the angle that the line segment makes with the x-axis, then

[9] $x = l \cos \theta,$

and

[10] $y = l \sin \theta.$

This may be stated in the following:

THEOREM.—*The projection of any line segment upon a horizontal line equals the length of the segment multiplied by the cosine of the angle of inclination; the projection upon a vertical line equals the length of the segment multiplied by the sine of the angle of inclination.*

69. Vectors.—In physics and engineering, line segments are often used to represent quantities that have direction as well as magnitude. Velocities, accelerations, and forces are such quantities.

For instance, a force of 100 lb. acting in a northeasterly direction may be represented by a line, say, 10 in. long, drawn in a northeasterly direction. The line is drawn so as to represent the force to some scale; here it is 10 lb. to the inch. An arrow head is put on one end of the line to show its direction.

In Fig. 65, $OP = v$ is a line representing a directed quantity. Such a line is called a **vector**. O is the **beginning** of the vector and P is the **terminal**. $OQ = x$ is the **projection of the vector**

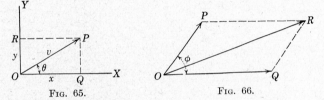

FIG. 65.   FIG. 66.

on the horizontal OX, $OR = y$ is the **projection on the vertical** OY, and θ is the **inclination** of the vector. The vectors x and y are called **components** of the vector v. As before,

$$x = v \cos \theta,$$

and

$$y = v \sin \theta.$$

Suppose the vectors OQ and OP (Fig. 66), represent the magnitude and direction of two forces acting at the point O, and having any angle ϕ between their lines of action. If the parallelogram $OQRP$ is completed, then the diagonal OR represents in magnitude and direction a force that will produce the same effect as the two given forces.

The vector OR is called the **resultant** of the vectors OQ and OP. The process of finding the resultant of two or more given forces is called **composition of forces**.

Conversely, the vectors OQ and OP are **components** of OR.

Since QR is equal and parallel to OP, it follows that the two components and their resultant form a closed triangle OQR. The relations between forces and their resultant may then be found by solving a triangle which is, in general, an oblique triangle.

Example 1.—Suppose that a weight W is resting on a rough horizontal table as shown in Fig. 67. Suppose that a force of 40 lb. is acting on the weight in the direction OP, making an angle of 20° with the horizontal; then the horizontal pull on the weight is $OQ = 40 \cos 20° = 37.588$ lb., and the vertical lift on the weight is $OR = 40 \sin 20° = 13.68$ lb.

Example 2.—A car is moving up an incline, making an angle of 35° with the horizontal, at the rate of 26 ft. per second. What is its horizontal velocity?

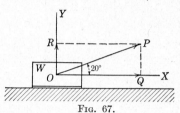

Horizontal velocity = 26 cos 35° = 21.3 ft. per second.

Vertical velocity = 26 sin 35° = 14.9 ft. per second.

Fig. 67.

EXERCISES

1. Find the projection of a line segment 31.2 ft. long upon a straight line making an angle of 34° 16.4′ with the segment.   *Ans.* 25.78.

2. The line segment AB, 32.67 in. long makes an angle of 45° 23′ with the line OX. Find the projection on OX. Find the projection on OY perpendicular to OX and in the same plane as OX and AB.

Ans. 22.95; 23.26.

3. A steamer is moving S. 21° W. at the rate of 28 miles per hour. How fast is it moving in a westerly direction? In a southerly direction?

Ans. 10.03 miles per hour; 26.14 miles per hour.

4. The direction a force of 1800 lb. is acting, makes an angle of 26° 35′ with the horizontal. Find the horizontal and vertical components of the force.   *Ans.* 1610 lb.; 805.5 lb.

5. A ship is sailing at 20.5 miles per hour in a direction N. 24° 35′ E. Find the northerly and easterly components of its speed.

Ans. 18.64 miles per hour; 8.528 miles per hour.

6. A force of 300 lb. is acting on a body lying on a horizontal plane, in a direction which makes an angle of 20° with the horizontal. What is the force tending to lift the body from the plane?   *Ans.* 102.6 lb.

7. A body weighing 58 lb. rests on a horizontal table and is acted upon by a force of 55 lb., acting at an angle of 27° 45′ with the surface of the table. What is the pressure on the table?   *Ans.* 32.39 lb.

8. A body weighing 71 lb. rests on a horizontal table and is acted upon by a force of 125 lb. acting at an angle of (−31° 30′) with the surface of the table. What is the pressure on the table?   *Ans.* 136.3 lb.

9. The horizontal and vertical components of a force are respectively 234.5 and 654.3 lb. What is the magnitude of the force, and what angle does its line of action make with the horizontal?

Ans. 695.1 lb.; 70° 16.95′.

10. The horizontal and vertical components of a force are respectively 145.7 and −175.3 lb.   What is the magnitude of the force, and what angle does its line of action make with the horizontal?

Ans. 227.95 lb.; −50° 16.1′.

11. A river runs directly south at 5 miles per hour.   A man starts at the west bank and rows directly across at the rate of 4.5 miles per hour.   In what direction does his boat move?   *Ans.* 41° 59.2′ with bank.

12. A ferryboat at a point on one bank of a river ¾ mile wide wishes to reach a point directly across the river.   If the river flows 3.75 miles per hour and the ferryboat can steam 8.1 miles per hour, in what direction should the boat be pointed?   *Ans.* 27° 34.7′ upstream.

13. Two men are lifting a stone by means of ropes in the same vertical plane.   One man pulls 143 lb. in a direction 40° from the vertical and the other 130 lb. in a direction 45° from the other side of the vertical.   Determine the weight of the stone.   *Ans.* 201.47 lb.

14. Two forces of 245 and 195 lb. act in the same vertical plane upon a heavy body, the first at an angle of 42 with° the horizontal and the second at an angle of 60°.   Find the total force tending to move the body horizontally; to lift it vertically.   *Ans.* 279.6 or 84.77 lb.; 332.8 lb.

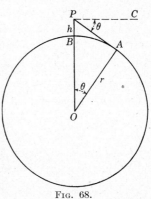

FIG. 68.

USEFUL AND MORE DIFFICULT PROBLEMS

70. Distance and dip of the horizon. In Fig. 68, let O be the center of the earth, r the radius of the earth, and h the height of a point P above its surface; to find the distance from the point P to the horizon at A.

By geometry, $\overline{PA}^2 = \overline{PO}^2 - \overline{OA}^2 = (r + h)^2 - r^2 = 2rh + h^2$.

$$\therefore PA = \sqrt{2rh + h^2}.$$

For points above the surface that are reached by man, h^2 is very small compared with $2rh$,

$$\therefore PA = \sqrt{2rh}, \text{ approximately.}$$

In the above, PA, r, and h are in the same units.   A very simple formula can be derived, however, if h be taken in feet, r and PA in miles, and $r = 3960$ miles.   Then

$$PA = \sqrt{2 \times 3960 \times \frac{h}{5280}} = \sqrt{\frac{3}{2}h} \text{ miles.}$$

The following approximate rules may then be stated:

The distance of the horizon in miles is approximately equal to the square root of ⅔ times the height of the point of observation in feet.

The height of the point of observation in feet is $\frac{2}{3}$ *times the square of the distance of the horizon in miles.*

Definition.—The angle $APC = \theta$ in Fig. 68 is called the **dip of the horizon.**

Evidently, $\tan \theta = \dfrac{PA}{r}$.

71. Areas of sector and segment.—Formulas for solving for the areas of the sector and segment of a circle are derived here so that they may be used for reference.

From geometry, the area of the sector of a circle as XOA (Fig. 69) equals the arc XnA times one-half the radius OX.

By **Art. 8,** arc $XnA = OX \times \theta$, where θ is expressed in radians.

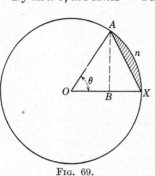

Hence, using r for the radius and S for the area of sector,

$$S = \tfrac{1}{2}r^2\theta.$$

Evidently, the area of the segment $XAn = S -$ area of triangle XOA. But area of triangle $XOA = \tfrac{1}{2}OX \cdot BA = \tfrac{1}{2}OX \cdot OA \sin \theta = \tfrac{1}{2}r^2 \sin \theta$. Hence, using G for area of segment,

$$G = \tfrac{1}{2}r^2\theta - \tfrac{1}{2}r^2 \sin \theta.$$

Fig. 69.　　[11]　$\therefore G = \tfrac{1}{2}r^2(\theta - \sin \theta).$

As an exercise, the student may later show that this formula holds when θ is an obtuse angle. Also when $\pi < \theta < 2\pi$.

This is the simplest accurate formula for finding the area of a segment of a circle. It is of frequent use in many practical problems. Various approximate formulas for finding the area of a segment are given for the use of practical men not having a knowledge of trigonometry. Two of the best known of these are the following:

(1) $$A = \tfrac{2}{3}hw + \frac{h^3}{2w},$$

(2) $$A = \tfrac{4}{3}h^2\sqrt{\frac{2r}{h} - 0.608},$$

where r is the radius, h the height of the segment, and w the length of the chord.

Example 1.—Fine the area of the segment of a circle of radius 16 in., and having a central angle of 78° 30′.

Solution.—By **Table V,** 78° 30′ = 1.3701 radians.

$$\sin 78° \; 30' = 0.9799.$$

Substituting these values in [**11**],

$$G = \tfrac{1}{2} \times 16^2(1.3701 - 0.9799) = 49.94$$
$$\therefore \text{ area of segment} = 49.94 \text{ sq. in.}$$

72. Widening of pavements on curves.—The tendency of a motorist to "cut the corners" is due to his unconscious desire to give the path of his car around a turn the longest possible radius. Many highway engineers recognize this tendency by widening the pavement on the inside of the curve, as shown in Fig. 70. The practice adds much to the attractive appearance of the highway. If the pavement is the same width around the curve as on the tangents, the curved section appears narrower than the normal width; whereas, if the curved section is widened gradually to the midpoint G of the turn, the pavement appears to have a uniform width all the way around.

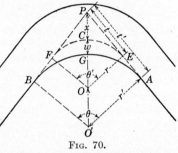

FIG. 70.

In order that the part added may fit the curve properly, it is necessary to have the curve of the inner edge a true arc of a circle, tangent to the edge of the straightaway sections, and therefore it must start before the point E of the curve is reached. The part added may be easily staked out on the ground with transit and tape, by means of data derived from the radius r, the central angle θ of the curve, and the width w. In practice, the width w is taken from 2 to 8 ft. according to the value of r. The area added can be readily computed when values for r, w, and θ are given.

Referring to the figure, derive the following formulas:

$$x = r \sec \tfrac{1}{2}\theta - r = \frac{r}{\cos \tfrac{1}{2}\theta} - r \; .$$

$$x + w = r' \sec \tfrac{1}{2}\theta - r' = \frac{r'}{\cos \tfrac{1}{2}\theta} - r'.$$

$$\therefore r' = \frac{x + w}{\sec \tfrac{1}{2}\theta - 1} = \frac{(x + w) \cos \tfrac{1}{2}\theta}{1 - \cos \tfrac{1}{2}\theta}$$

$$t = r \tan \tfrac{1}{2}\theta.$$

$$t' = r' \tan \tfrac{1}{2}\theta.$$

Area added $= BFCEAG = BPAO' - FPEC - BGAO'$.

$$BPAO' = r't'.$$

$$FPEC = FPEO - FCEO = rt - \frac{\theta}{360}\pi r^2.$$

$$BGAO' = \frac{\theta}{360}\pi r'^2.$$

$\therefore$ area added $= r't' - \left(rt - \frac{\theta}{360}\pi r^2\right) - \frac{\theta}{360}\pi r'^2$

$$= r't' - rt - \frac{\theta}{360}\pi(r' + r)(r' - r).$$

EXERCISES

1. A cliff 2500 ft. high is on the seashore. How far away is the horizon?
Ans. 61.24 miles.

2. Find the greatest distance at which the lamp of a lighthouse can be seen from the deck of a ship. The lamp is 75 ft. above the surface of the water and the deck of the ship 40 ft. *Ans.* 18.4 miles.

3. Find the radius of one's horizon if located 1000 ft. above the earth. How large when located 2.5 miles above the earth?
Ans. 38.73 miles; 140.7 miles.

4. How high above the earth must one be to see a point on the surface 35 miles away? *Ans.* 816.7 ft.

5. Two lighthouses, one 100 ft. high and the other 75 ft. are just barely visible from each other over the water. Find how far apart they are.
Ans. 22.86 miles.

6. In **Art. 72**, find the area if $r = 300$ ft., $w = 4$ ft., and $\theta = 100°$.
Ans. 1395 sq. ft.

7. A thin rope is fastened by its ends to two points 25 ft. apart and in a horizontal plane. It has a heavy weight hanging at its midpoint causing it to sag 5 ft., and making the rope from center to ends extend in practically straight lines. Find the angle between one-half of the rope and a horizontal, and find the total length of the rope between the points of support.
Ans. 21° 48.1′; 26.93 ft.

8. The radius of a circle is 72.52 ft. In this circle a chord subtends an angle of 40° 32.4′ at the center. Find the difference between the length of the chord and the length of its arc. *Ans.* 1.066 ft.

9. Compute the volume for each foot in the depth of a horizontal cylindrical oil tank of length 40 ft. and diameter 4 ft.
Ans. 98.27 cu. ft.; 251.33 cu. ft.; 404.39 cu. ft.; 502.66 cu. ft.

10. A cylindrical tank in a horizontal position is filled with water to within 10 in. of the top. Find the volume of the water if the tank is 10 ft. long and 5 ft. in diameter. *Ans.* 174.84 cu. ft.

11. Find the angle between the diagonal of a cube and one of the diagonals of a face of the cube. *Ans.* 35° 15.8′.

12. If R and r are the radii of two pulleys, D the distance between the centers, and L the length of the belt, show that, when the belt is not crossed

(Fig. 71), the length is given by the following formula where the angle is taken in radians:

$$L = 2\sqrt{D^2 - (R - r)^2} + \pi(R + r) + 2(R - r)\sin^{-1}\frac{R - r}{D}.$$

13. Using the same notation as in Exercise 12, show that, when the belt is crossed (Fig. 72), the length is given by the following formula:

$$L = 2\sqrt{D^2 - (R + r)^2} + (R + r)\left(\pi + 2\sin^{-1}\frac{R + r}{D}\right).$$

Note.—These formulas would seldom be used in practice. An approximate formula would be more convenient, or the length would be measured with a tape line.

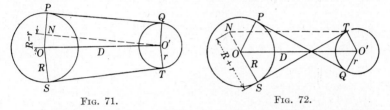

FIG. 71.   FIG. 72.

A rule often given for finding the length of an uncrossed belt is: Add twice the distance between the centers of the shafts to half the sum of the circumferences of the two pulleys.

14. Using the formula of Exercise 12, and given $R = 16$ in., $r = 8$ in., and $D = 12$ ft., find the length of the belt. Find the length by the approximate rule. *Ans.* 30.32 ft.; 30.28 ft.

15. Use the same values as in Exercise 14, and find by the formula of Exercise 13 the length of the belt when crossed. *Ans.* 30.62 ft.

16. An open belt connects two pulleys of diameters 6 and 2 ft., respectively. If the distance between their centers is 12 ft., find the length of the belt. *ns.* 36.9 ft.

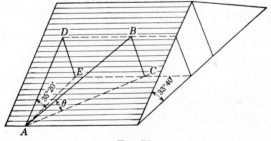

FIG. 73.

17. Two pulleys of diameters 8 and 3 ft., respectively, are connected by a crossed belt. If the centers of pulleys are 14 ft. apart, find the length of the belt. *Ans.* 47.47 ft.

18. The slope of the roof in Fig. 73 is 33° 40′. Find the angle θ which is the inclination to the horizontal of the line AB, drawn in the roof and making an angle of 35° 20′ with the line of greatest slope.

Solution.—$\sin \theta = \dfrac{CB}{AB}.$

$$\cos 35° 20' = \frac{AD}{AB}, \text{ or } AB = \frac{AD}{\cos 35° 20'}.$$

$$\sin 33° 40' = \frac{ED}{AD}, \text{ or } ED = CB = AD \sin 33° 40'.$$

Then $\qquad \sin \theta = AD \sin 33° 40' \div \dfrac{AD}{\cos 35° 20'}$

$$= \sin 33° 40' \times \cos 35° 20'$$
$$= 0.55436 \times 0.81580 = 0.45225.$$
$$\therefore \theta = \sin^{-1} 0.45225 = 26° 53.3'.$$

19. A hill slopes at an angle of 32° with the horizontal. A path leads up it, making an angle of 47° 30' with the line of steepest slope; find the inclination of the path with the horizontal.   *Ans.* 20° 58' 40''.

20. Two roofs have their ridges at right angles, and each is inclined to the horizontal at an angle of 30°. Find the inclination of their line of intersection to the horizontal.

Ans. 22° 12' 28''.

21. A mountain side has a slope of 30°. A road ascending the mountain is to be built and is to have a grade of 7 per cent. Find the angle it will make with the line of greatest slope.   *Ans.* 81° 57.2'.

22. Two set squares whose sides are 3, 4, and 5 in. are placed as in Fig. 74, so that their 4-in. sides and right angles coincide, and the angle between the 3-in. sides is 46° 35'. Find the angle θ between the longest sides. *Ans.* 27° 26.9'.

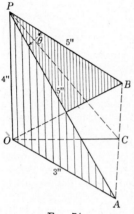

Fig. 74.

23. Show that placing the carpenter's square as shown in Fig. 75b will determine the miter for making a regular pentagonal frame as shown in *a*. What is the angle θ of the miter?   *Ans.* $\theta = 54°$.

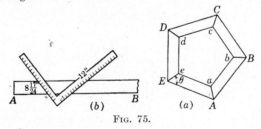

Fig. 75.

24. If 12 in. is taken on one leg of a carpenter's square, how many inches must be taken on the other leg to cut miters for making regular polygons of the following numbers of sides: 3, 4, 6, 8, and 10? Express results to the sixteenth of an inch.   *Ans.* $20\frac{13}{16}$; 12; $6\frac{15}{16}$; 5; $3\frac{7}{8}$.

25. In the frame of a tower shown in Fig. 76, determine the distances from A and B, C and D, etc., to make the holes in the braces so that they may be

bolted at points a, b, c, etc. These distances should be accurate to tenths of
an inch. Can these distances be determined by means of geometry?
    Ans. $Aa = 10$ ft. 5.3 in., etc.; yes.

26. A street-railway track is to turn a
corner on the arc of a circle. If the track is
at a distance a from the curbstone and the
turn is through an angle θ, show that the
radius $r = OR = ON$ (Fig. 77) of the curve
to pass at a distance b from the corner is
given by the formula

$$r = \frac{a - b \cos \tfrac{1}{2}\theta}{1 - \cos \tfrac{1}{2}\theta}.$$

27. When the 8-in. crank of a horizontal
engine is vertical, the piston is 1.5 in. past
the midstroke. What is the length of the
connecting rod and what angle does the connecting rod make with the guides at this
instant?   *Ans.* 22.08 in.; 21° 14.6′.

28. In Fig. 78, LGA is an arc of a circle
with center at O, LV and AV are tangents at
the extremities of the arc, GF is tangent to
the arc at its center point G, and θ is the

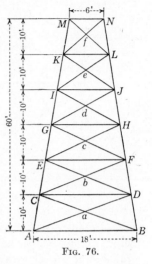

Fɪɢ. 76.

angle at the center of the circle and intercepting the arc. Derive the following formulas useful in railway surveying:

$t = r \tan \tfrac{1}{2}\theta$.	$c = 2r \sin \tfrac{1}{2}\theta$.	$m = r \text{ vers } \tfrac{1}{2}\theta$.
$e = r (\sec \tfrac{1}{2}\theta - 1)$.	$e = t \tan \tfrac{1}{4}\theta$.	$c = 2m \cot \tfrac{1}{4}\theta$.
$c = 2t \cos \tfrac{1}{2}\theta$.	$GA = \tfrac{1}{2}c \sec \tfrac{1}{4}\theta$.	

29. A salesman for a wire-screen company wishes formulas for laying out
a screen in the form of the frustum of a right circular cone of large diameter

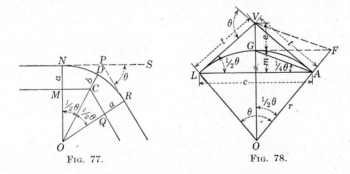

Fɪɢ. 77.   Fɪɢ. 78.

D, small diameter d, and slant height s. He also wishes the dimensions
l and w of the rectangular piece from which the screen is to be cut. The
layout is in the form of a section of a ring bounded by two concentric circles
of radii R and r, and having a central angle θ. Determine formulas for R,

r, and θ in terms of D, d, and s; and formulas for l and w in terms of R, r, and θ.

$$Ans. \quad R = \frac{sD}{D-d}; \, r = \frac{sd}{D-d}; \, \theta = \frac{D-d}{s}180°;$$
$$l = 2R \sin \tfrac{1}{2}\theta; \, w = R - r \cos \tfrac{1}{2}\theta.$$

REFLECTION AND REFRACTION OF LIGHT

73. Reflection of a ray of light.—The path of a ray of light in a homogeneous medium as air is a straight line. But when a ray of light strikes a polished surface it is **reflected** according to the well-known law which states that *the angle of incidence is equal to the angle of reflection.*

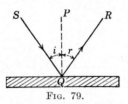

Fig. 79.

Thus, in Fig. 79, the incident ray SQ strikes the polished surface at Q and is reflected in the direction QR. The line QP is perpendicular to the surface at Q. The angle $SQP = i$ is the **angle of incidence,** and the angle $PQR = r$ is the **angle of reflection.** The law states that these two angles are equal.

74. Refraction of a ray of light.—When a ray of light passes from one transparent medium to another which is more or less dense, its direction is changed, that is, the ray of light is **refracted.**

Thus, in Fig. 80, a ray of light SQ, passing through air, meets the surface of a piece of glass at Q and is refracted toward the normal, or perpendicular, QP'. It continues in the direction QT until it meets the other surface of the glass at T, where it is again refracted, but this time away from the normal; and passes into the air in the direction TR. If the two surfaces of the glass are parallel, it has been found by experiment that the direction of TR is the same as that of SQ.

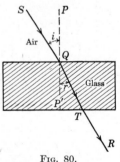

Fig. 80.

The lines QP and QP' are perpendicular to the surface at Q. The angle $SQP = i$ is the **angle of incidence,** and the angle $P'QT = r$ is the **angle of refraction.**

It has been found by experiment that for a given kind of glass the ratio

$$\frac{\sin i}{\sin r} = \mu$$

is constant whatever the angle of incidence may be. This means that, for a certain kind of glass, if the angle of incidence is changed, then the angle of refraction also changes in such a manner that the ratio of the sines is constant. This ratio for **a ray of light** passing from air to crown glass is very nearly $\frac{3}{2}$, and for water it is $\frac{4}{3}$.

The value of the ratio $\dfrac{\sin i}{\sin r} = \mu$ is called the **index of refraction** of the glass with respect to air.

It follows that the index of refraction of air with respect to glass is the reciprocal of that of glass with respect to air. That is, if the index of refraction of glass with respect to air is μ, then the index of refraction of air with respect to glass is $\dfrac{1}{\mu}$. The same may be stated for any other two transparent substances.

EXERCISES

1. Prove that if a mirror that is reflecting a ray of light is turned through an angle α, the reflected ray is turned through an angle 2α.

2. The eye is 20 in. in front of a mirror and an object appears to be 25 in. back of the mirror, while the line of sight makes an angle of 32° 30′ with the mirror. Find the distance and direction of the object from the eye.

Ans. 70.8 in. in a direction making an angle of 4° 3′ with plane of mirror.

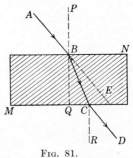

Fɪɢ. 81.

3. A ray of light passes from air into carbon disulphide. Find the angle of refraction if the angle of incidence is 33° 10′ and the index of refraction is 1.758. *Ans.* 18° 7.9′.

4. When $\mu = 1.167$ and the angle of incidence is 19° 30′, find the angle of refraction.

Ans. 16° 37.3′.

5. A ray of light travels the path $ABCD$ (Fig. 81) in passing through the plate glass MN 0.625 in. thick. What is the displacement CE if the ray strikes the glass at an angle $ABP = 42°\ 10′$ the index of refraction being $\frac{3}{2}$? *Ans.* 0.1887 in.

6. If the eye is at a point under water, what is the greatest angle from the zenith that a star can appear to be? *Ans.* 48° 35.4′.

7. A source of light is under water. What is the greatest angle a ray can make with the normal and pass into the air? For any greater angle the ray is totally reflected. *Ans.* 48° 35.4′.

8. A straight rod is partially immersed in water. The image in the water appears inclined at an angle of 45° with the surface. Find the inclination of the rod to the surface of the water if the index of refraction is $\frac{4}{3}$.

Ans. 70° 31.6′.

SIDES OPPOSITE VERY SMALL ANGLES

75. Relation between sin θ, θ, and tan θ, for small angles.— Draw angle $BOE = \theta$ (Fig. 82). With O as a center and $OB = 1$ as radius, describe the arc BD. Draw $DA \perp$ to OB and BE

tangent to the arc at B.   Then $\sin\theta = AD$, $\theta = $ arc DB, and $\tan\theta = BE$.   Comparing areas of triangles and sector;

$$\triangle OBD < \text{sector } OBD < \triangle OBE.$$

But $\triangle OBD = \frac{1}{2}OB \times AD$, sector $OBD = \frac{1}{2}\overline{OB^2} \cdot \theta$, where θ is in radians (see **Art. 8**) and $\triangle OBE = \frac{1}{2}OB \cdot BE$.

Then $\qquad\qquad \frac{1}{2}OB \cdot AD < \frac{1}{2}\overline{OB^2} \cdot \theta < \frac{1}{2}OB \cdot BE.$

Dividing by $\frac{1}{2}$ and substituting $OB = 1$, $AD = \sin\theta$, and $BE = \tan\theta$,

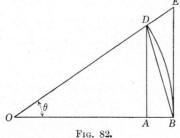

FIG. 82.

$$\sin\theta < \theta < \tan\theta.$$

Dividing by $\sin\theta$ and remembering that $\tan\theta = \dfrac{\sin\theta}{\cos\theta}$,

$$1 < \frac{\theta}{\sin\theta} < \sec\theta$$

Now as θ approaches 0 as a limit $\sec\theta$ approaches 1 as a limit, written $\displaystyle\lim_{\theta\to 0}\sec\theta = 1$.

Then, since $\dfrac{\theta}{\sin\theta}$ is always less than a quantity which approaches 1 as a limit, and at the same time is greater than 1, we have

[12] $$\lim_{\theta\to 0}\frac{\theta}{\sin\theta} = 1.$$

Again, dividing $\sin\theta < \theta < \tan\theta$ by $\tan\theta$ and simplifying,

$\cos\theta < \dfrac{\theta}{\tan\theta} < 1$.   But $\displaystyle\lim_{\theta\to 0}\cos\theta = 1$; therefore, $\displaystyle\lim_{\theta\to 0}\frac{\theta}{\tan\theta} = 1$.

By computing the following table, the student will find [12] verified.

Angle in degrees	$\sin\theta$	θ in radians	$\tan\theta$	$\dfrac{\theta}{\sin\theta}$
20°				
10°				
5°				
4°				
3°				
2°				
1°				
$\frac{1}{2}$°				

These results show that, for small angles, sin θ and tan θ may be replaced by θ in radians and the results will be approximately correct.

For example, $\quad$ sin 5° 9.4′ = 0.0899,

$$5° 9.4' = 0.0900 \text{ radian,}$$

and $\qquad$ tan 5° 9.4′ = 0.0902.

For a smaller angle the agreement will be still closer.

76. Side opposite small angle given.—When a very small angle and the side opposite are given in a right triangle, another side can be found by means of the sine or tangent of the small angle considered as a number of radians. The short side, considered as an arc, divided by the number of radians in the small angle will give a long side.

Example 1.—A tower is 125 ft. high. The angle of elevation of the top of the tower, from a point in the same horizontal plane as the base, is 1°. Find the distance from the point of observation to the tower.

Solution.—Let x = distance to the tower in feet.

Then $\qquad$ $\tan 1° = \dfrac{125}{x}$, or $x = \dfrac{125}{\tan 1°}$.

But $\qquad$ 1° = 0.01745 radian = tan 1°, approximately.

$$\therefore x = \frac{125}{0.01745} = 7163 \text{ ft.}$$

Example 2.—A railway track has a 2 per cent grade for a certain distance. Find the inclination of the track to the horizontal.

Solution.—The per cent of a grade is the ratio of the number of feet rise to the number of feet on the horizontal. Then, for a 2 per cent grade the tangent of the angle of inclination is 0.02, which is approximately the angle in radians.

By **Table V**, 0.02 radian = 1° 8.7′.

77. Lengths of long sides given.—In a right triangle having two sides, including an acute angle, given, the angle can be found by the formula

$$\tan \tfrac{1}{2}A = \sqrt{\frac{c-b}{c+b}},$$

where A is the angle included by the hypotenuse c and the side b.

This formula is derived as follows:

In Fig. 83, ABC is a right triangle.

Draw AE bisecting angle A, and draw DB perpendicular to AE.

Then $\frac{1}{2}A = \angle DAE = \angle CBD$.

Also $AD = AB = c$, and $CD = c - b$.

In triangle CBD, $\tan CBD = \tan \frac{1}{2}A = \dfrac{CD}{CB} = \dfrac{c - b}{a}$.

But $\qquad a = \sqrt{c^2 - b^2} = \sqrt{(c + b)(c - b)}$.

$$\therefore \tan \tfrac{1}{2}A = \sqrt{\frac{c - b}{c + b}}.$$

When angle A is small, $2 \tan \frac{1}{2}A$ gives approximately the value of A in radians, which can be used as already explained.

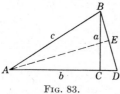

Fig. 83.

Example.—At what distance may a mountain 1 mile high be seen at sea, if the earth's radius is 3960 miles?

Solution.—Let s = distance in miles, and let the angle at the center of the earth between the radius to the mountain and the radius to the point at sea be θ.

By the formula, $\tan \frac{1}{2}\theta = \sqrt{\dfrac{3961 - 3960}{3961 + 3960}} = \sqrt{\dfrac{1}{7921}}$.

Then θ in radians $= 2\sqrt{\dfrac{1}{7921}}$.

By the formula $s = r\theta$ of **Art. 8**,

$$s = 2\sqrt{\frac{1}{7921}} \times 3960 = 89 \text{ miles.}$$

This example can also be computed by the rule given in **Art. 70**, which gives $s = \sqrt{\frac{3}{2}h}$, where h is the height of the mountain in feet.

$$\therefore \sqrt{\tfrac{3}{2}} \times 5280 = 89 \text{ miles.}$$

EXERCISES

1. A certain plane is inclined to the horizontal at an angle of $1° 10'$. Find the per cent of grade of a railway track constructed on this plane.

Ans. 2.04 per cent.

2. A railway track rises 100 ft. to the mile. Find the angle of inclination of the track.

Ans. $1° 5.1'$.

3. If the diameter of the earth as seen from the moon makes an angle of 1° 54', find the distance from the moon to the earth, taking the earth's radius as 3960 miles. *Ans.* 239,000 miles.

4. If the distance from the earth to the sun is 93,000,000 miles and the diameter of the sun makes an angle of 32' at the earth, find the diameter of the sun in miles. *Ans.* 870,000 miles.

5. Telescopes at the ends of a base line 350 ft. long, on the deck of a ship, are turned upon a distant fort. The lines of sight of the telescopes are found to make angles of 89° 10' and 89° 40' with the base line. Find the distance from the ship to the fort. *Ans.* 3.26 miles.

6. The diameter of the moon subtends an angle of 31' 5'' at the earth. The moon is approximately 240,000 miles from the earth. Find the diameter of the moon in miles. *Ans.* 2170 miles.

7. At what distance may a mountain 2.5 miles high be seen at sea, taking the earth's radius at 3960 miles. *Ans.* 140.7 miles.

CHAPTER VIII

FUNCTIONS INVOLVING MORE THAN ONE ANGLE

78. In the previous chapters, we have worked with, and established the relations between, the functions of a single angle. But, in solving oblique triangles and in many of the applications of trigonometry to other subjects, formulas are used which are derived from the functions of the sums or differences of angles. These functions are expressed in terms of the functions of the individual angles and are as follows for the sine and cosine:

[13] $\sin(\alpha + \beta) = \sin \alpha \cos \beta + \cos \alpha \sin \beta.$

[14] $\cos(\alpha + \beta) = \cos \alpha \cos \beta - \sin \alpha \sin \beta.$

[15] $\sin(\alpha - \beta) = \sin \alpha \cos \beta - \cos \alpha \sin \beta.$

[16] $\cos(\alpha - \beta) = \cos \alpha \cos \beta + \sin \alpha \sin \beta.$

Formulas [13] and [14] are often called **addition formulas**, and [15] and [16] **subtraction formulas.**

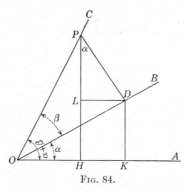

FIG. 84.

79. Derivation of the formulas for the sine and cosine of the sum of two angles.—Let $\angle AOB = \alpha$ and $\angle BOC = \beta$ (Fig. 84), each of which is acute and so chosen that $\alpha + \beta = \angle AOC$ is less than 90°. In order that the functions of α, β, and $\alpha + \beta$ may be involved in the same formula, we may form right triangles which have α, β, and $\alpha + \beta$ as acute angles.

Choose any point P in the terminal side OC. Draw $PH \perp OA$ $PD \perp OB$, $DK \perp OA$, and $DL \perp PH$. $\triangle KOD$ is similar to $\triangle LPD$, since their sides are perpendicular each to each. Then $\angle LPD = \alpha.$

By definition, $\sin(\alpha + \beta) = \dfrac{HP}{OP} = \dfrac{KD + LP}{OP} = \dfrac{KD}{OP} + \dfrac{LP}{OP}.$

Now multiply numerator and denominator of $\dfrac{KD}{OP}$ by OD, the common side of the two triangles of which KD and OP are sides respectively. Also, multiply $\dfrac{LP}{OP}$ in the same way by PD, the common side of triangles DOP and LPD. Then

$$\sin (\alpha + \beta) = \frac{KD}{OD} \cdot \frac{OD}{OP} + \frac{LP}{PD} \cdot \frac{PD}{OP}.$$

But $\dfrac{KD}{OD} = \sin \alpha,\ \dfrac{OD}{OP} = \cos \beta,\ \dfrac{LP}{PD} = \cos \alpha,$ and $\dfrac{PD}{OP} = \sin \beta.$

[13] $\therefore \sin (\alpha + \beta) = \sin \alpha \cos \beta + \cos \alpha \sin \beta.$

By definition,

$$\cos (\alpha + \beta) = \frac{OH}{OP} = \frac{OK - HK}{OP} = \frac{OK}{OP} - \frac{LD}{OP} = \frac{OK}{OD} \cdot \frac{OD}{OP} - \frac{LD}{PD} \cdot \frac{PD}{OP}.$$

But $\dfrac{OK}{OD} = \cos \alpha,\ \dfrac{OD}{OP} = \cos \beta,\ \dfrac{LD}{PD} = \sin \alpha,$ and $\dfrac{PD}{OP} = \sin \beta.$

[14] $\therefore \cos (\alpha + \beta) = \cos \alpha \cos \beta - \sin \alpha \sin \beta.$

80. Derivation of the formulas for the sine and cosine of the difference of two angles.—Let $\angle AOB = \alpha$ and $\angle COB = \beta$ be the two acute angles (Fig. 85). Then angle $AOC = \alpha - \beta$. For reasons similar to those given in the preceding article, choose any point P in the terminal side OC of $(\alpha - \beta)$. Draw $PH \perp OA, PR \perp OB, RD \perp OA,$ and $PE \perp DR.$ $\triangle DOR$ is similar to $\triangle PER$ and $\angle ERP = \alpha.$

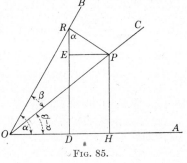

Fig. 85.

By definition,

$$\sin (\alpha - \beta) = \frac{HP}{OP} = \frac{DR - ER}{OP} = \frac{DR}{OP} - \frac{ER}{OP} = \frac{DR}{OR} \cdot \frac{OR}{OP} - \frac{ER}{RP} \cdot \frac{RP}{OP}.$$

But $\dfrac{DR}{OR} = \sin \alpha,\ \dfrac{OR}{OP} = \cos \beta,\ \dfrac{ER}{RP} = \cos \alpha,$ and $\dfrac{RP}{OP} = \sin \beta.$

[15] $\therefore \sin (\alpha - \beta) = \sin \alpha \cos \beta - \cos \alpha \sin \beta.$

By definition,

$$\cos (\alpha - \beta) = \frac{OH}{OP} = \frac{OD + EP}{OP} = \frac{OD}{OP} + \frac{EP}{OP} = \frac{OD}{OR} \cdot \frac{OR}{OP} + \frac{EP}{RP} \cdot \frac{RP}{OP}.$$

[16] $\therefore \cos (\alpha - \beta) = \cos \alpha \cos \beta + \sin \alpha \sin \beta.$

In the proof of [15] and [16], it was assumed that $\alpha > \beta$. Now suppose $\beta > \alpha$. Then $\alpha - \beta = -(\beta - \alpha)$.

By **Art. 52** $\sin (\alpha - \beta) = \sin [-(\beta - \alpha)] = -\sin (\beta - \alpha)$.

By [15] $-\sin (\beta - \alpha) = -(\sin \beta \cos \alpha - \cos \beta \sin \alpha)$.

$$= \sin \alpha \cos \beta - \cos \alpha \sin \beta,$$

which is the same result as was obtained before.

81. Proof of the addition formulas for other values of the angles.—In Art. **79** formulas [13] and [14] were proved when α, β, and $\alpha + \beta$ are each less than 90°. They are, however, true for all values of the angles.

(1) *Suppose that α and β are acute and such that $\alpha = 90° - \phi$ and $\beta = 90° - \gamma$, where ϕ and γ are each less than 45°.* On this assumption, $(\alpha + \beta) > 90°$, $(\phi + \gamma) < 90°$, $\sin \alpha = \cos \phi$, $\cos \alpha = \sin \phi$, $\sin \beta = \cos \gamma$, and $\cos \beta = \sin \gamma$.

$$\therefore \sin (\alpha + \beta) = \sin [(90° - \phi) + (90° - \gamma)]$$
$$= \sin [180° - (\phi + \gamma)]$$
$$= \sin (\phi + \gamma) = \sin \phi \cos \gamma + \cos \phi \sin \gamma.$$

Substituting for the functions of ϕ and γ their values in terms of the functions of α and β,

$$\sin (\alpha + \beta) = \cos \alpha \sin \beta + \sin \alpha \cos \beta$$
$$= \sin \alpha \cos \beta + \cos \alpha \sin \beta.$$

That is, the formula for $\sin (\alpha + \beta)$ is true when $(\alpha + \beta)$ is an angle in the second quadrant and α and β as stated.

In the same way we may show that the formula for $\cos (\alpha + \beta)$ is true for values of the angles as given above.

(2) *Suppose that α is in the second quadrant and β in the third, such that $\alpha = 90° + \phi$ and $\beta = 180° + \gamma$.* On this assumption, $\sin \alpha = \sin (90° + \phi) = \cos \phi$; $\cos \alpha = \cos (90° + \phi) = -\sin \phi$; $\sin \beta = \sin (180° + \gamma) = -\sin \gamma$; $\cos \beta = \cos (180° + \gamma) = -\cos \gamma$; $\sin (\alpha + \beta) = \sin [(90° + \phi) + (180° + \gamma)] = \sin [270° + (\phi + \gamma)]$
$$= -\cos (\phi + \gamma) = -\cos \phi \cos \gamma + \sin \phi \sin \gamma.$$

Substituting for the functions of ϕ and γ their values in terms of the functions of α and β,

$$\sin (\alpha + \beta) = -(\sin \alpha)(-\cos \beta) + (-\cos \alpha)(-\sin \beta)$$
$$= \sin \alpha \cos \beta + \cos \alpha \sin \beta.$$

In the same manner it may be shown that the addition formulas are true for any angles. It will now be assumed that the addition formulas for sine and cosine are true for all values of the angles.

82. Proof of the subtraction formulas for all values of the angles.—Since the addition formulas are true for all values of α and β, they are true when $-\beta$ is put for β. Then

$$\sin(\alpha - \beta) = \sin[\alpha + (-\beta)]$$
$$= \sin\alpha\cos(-\beta) + \cos\alpha\sin(-\beta),$$

and

$$\cos(\alpha - \beta) = \cos[\alpha + (-\beta)]$$
$$= \cos\alpha\cos(-\beta) - \sin\alpha\sin(-\beta).$$

But $\sin(-\beta) = -\sin\beta$, and $\cos(-\beta) = \cos\beta$.

$$\therefore \sin(\alpha - \beta) = \sin\alpha\cos\beta - \cos\alpha\sin\beta,$$

and

$$\cos(\alpha - \beta) = \cos\alpha\cos\beta + \sin\alpha\sin\beta.$$

That is, the subtraction formulas are true in general.

Example 1.—Given $\sin\alpha = \frac{3}{5}$ and $\cos\beta = \frac{5}{13}$; find $\sin(\alpha + \beta)$ and $\cos(\alpha + \beta)$ if α and β are acute.

Solution.—The formulas to be used are

$$\sin(\alpha + \beta) = \sin\alpha\cos\beta + \cos\alpha\sin\beta,$$

and

$$\cos(\alpha + \beta) = \cos\alpha\cos\beta - \sin\alpha\sin\beta.$$

To substitute in these formulas it is necessary first to find $\cos\alpha$ and $\sin\beta$.

$$\cos\alpha = \sqrt{1 - \sin^2\alpha} = \sqrt{1 - (\tfrac{3}{5})^2} = \tfrac{4}{5}.$$
$$\sin\beta = \sqrt{1 - \cos^2\beta} = \sqrt{1 - (\tfrac{5}{13})^2} = \tfrac{12}{13}.$$

Substituting in the formulas,

$$\sin(\alpha + \beta) = \tfrac{3}{5}\cdot\tfrac{5}{13} + \tfrac{4}{5}\cdot\tfrac{12}{13} = \tfrac{3}{13} + \tfrac{48}{65} = \tfrac{63}{65}.$$
$$\cos(\alpha + \beta) = \tfrac{4}{5}\cdot\tfrac{5}{13} - \tfrac{3}{5}\cdot\tfrac{12}{13} = \tfrac{4}{13} - \tfrac{36}{65} = -\tfrac{16}{65}.$$

Example 2.—Prove that $\sin^{-1}\frac{3}{5} + \sin^{-1}\frac{4}{5} = \frac{1}{2}\pi$, using only the principal values of the anti-functions.

Proof.— Let $\alpha = \sin^{-1}\frac{3}{5}$ and $\beta = \sin^{-1}\frac{4}{5}$.

$$\therefore \sin\alpha = \tfrac{3}{5} \text{ and } \sin\beta = \tfrac{4}{5}.$$

Then

$$\sin(\alpha + \beta) = \sin\alpha\cos\beta + \cos\alpha\sin\beta$$
$$= \tfrac{3}{5}\cdot\tfrac{3}{5} + \tfrac{4}{5}\cdot\tfrac{4}{5} = 1.$$

But

$$\sin^{-1}1 = \tfrac{1}{2}\pi.$$

$$\therefore \sin^{-1}\tfrac{3}{5} + \sin^{-1}\tfrac{4}{5} = \tfrac{1}{2}\pi.$$

EXERCISES

Answer Exercises 1 to 10 orally. Apply the addition and subtraction formulas in the following expansions:

1. Expand $\sin(15° + 30°)$.
2. Expand $\cos(45° + 15°)$.
3. Expand $\sin(75° - 60°)$.
4. Expand $\cos(23° - 10°)$.
5. Expand $\sin(240° - 30°)$.
6. Expand $\cos(30° - 120°)$.
7. Does $\sin 60° = \sin(40° + 20°)$?

8. Does $2 \sin 25° = \sin (25° + 25°)$?

9. Does $\sin (40° + 30°) = \sin 40° + \sin 30°$?

10. Does $\cos (360° + 120°) = \cos 120°$?

11. Given $\sin \alpha = \frac{12}{13}$ and $\sin \beta = \frac{7}{25}$, α and β acute; find $\sin (\alpha + \beta)$, $\cos (\alpha + \beta)$, $\sin (\alpha - \beta)$, and $\cos (\alpha - \beta)$.   *Ans.* $\frac{323}{325}$; $\frac{36}{325}$; $\frac{252}{325}$; $\frac{204}{325}$.

12. Given $\sin \alpha = \frac{\sqrt{2}}{2}$, and $\tan \beta = \sqrt{3}$, α and β acute; find $\sin (\alpha + \beta)$ and $\cos (\alpha + \beta)$.   *Ans.* 0.9659; -0.2588.

13. Given $\sin \alpha = \frac{1}{2}$, and $\tan \beta = \frac{1}{3}$, α and β acute; find $\sin (\alpha + \beta)$, $\cos (\alpha + \beta)$, $\sin (\alpha - \beta)$, and $\cos (\alpha - \beta)$.

Ans. 0.74820; 0.66347; 0.20048; 0.97970.

14. Given $\sin \alpha = -\frac{3}{5}$, $\cos \beta = -\frac{12}{13}$, α in the fourth quadrant and β in the third. Find $\sin (\alpha + \beta)$, $\cos (\alpha + \beta)$, $\cos (\alpha - \beta)$, and $\sin (\alpha - \beta)$.   *Ans.* $\sin (\alpha + \beta) = \frac{16}{65}$; $\cos (\alpha + \beta) = -\frac{63}{65}$.

15. Given $\cos \alpha = -\frac{4}{5}$, α in the second quadrant, and $\cot \beta = \frac{12}{5}$, β in the third quadrant. Find $\sin (\alpha + \beta)$, $\cos (\alpha + \beta)$, $\sin (\alpha - \beta)$, and $\cos (\alpha - \beta)$.   *Ans.* $\sin (\alpha + \beta) = -\frac{16}{65}$; $\cos (\alpha + \beta) = \frac{63}{65}$.

16. Find $\sin 90°$ by using $90° = 60° + 30°$.

17. Find $\sin 90°$ by using $90° = 150° - 60°$.

18. Find $\cos 180°$ by using $180° = 135° + 45°$.

19. Find $\sin 75°$ by using $75° = 120° - 45°$.

Ans. $\frac{1}{4}(\sqrt{2} + \sqrt{6}) = 0.9659$.

20. Find $\sin 150°$ by using (*a*) $150° = 120° + 30°$, (*b*) $150° = 210° - 60°$, (*c*) $150° = 75° + 75°$.

21. Find $\sin 120$ by using (*a*) $120° = 60° + 60°$, (*b*) $120° = 90° + 30°$, (*c*) $120° = 210° - 90°$.

Find the values of the following expressions, using only the principal values of the angles:

22. $\sin (\sin^{-1} \frac{16}{65} + \cos^{-1} \frac{12}{13})$.   *Ans.* $\frac{3}{5}$.

23. $\cos \left(\sin^{-1} \frac{1}{\sqrt{5}} + \tan^{-1} \frac{1}{3} \right)$.   *Ans.* $\frac{1}{\sqrt{2}}$.

24. $\sin \left(\tan^{-1} \frac{1}{2} + \tan^{-1} \frac{1}{3} \right)$.   *Ans.* $\frac{1}{\sqrt{2}}$.

25. $\cos (\tan^{-1} \frac{1}{2} - \cos^{-1} \frac{1}{5})$.   *Ans.* 0.617.

26. $\sin [\tan^{-1} (-\frac{1}{2}) + \sin^{-1} \frac{1}{2}]$.   *Ans.* 0.05993.

27. $\sin (\sin^{-1} a + \sin^{-1} b)$.   *Ans.* $a\sqrt{1 - b^2} + b\sqrt{1 - a^2}$.

28. $\cos (\sin^{-1} a + \sin^{-1} b)$.   *Ans.* $\sqrt{1 - a^2}\sqrt{1 - b^2} - ab$.

29. $\sin (\cos^{-1} a - \sin^{-1} b)$.   *Ans.* $\sqrt{1 - a^2}\sqrt{1 - b^2} - ab$.

30. $\cos (\sin^{-1} a - \cos^{-1} b)$.   *Ans.* $b\sqrt{1 - a^2} + a\sqrt{1 - b^2}$.

Prove the following by expanding by the addition and subtraction formulas:

31. $\sin (90° + \theta) = \cos \theta$.   **34.** $\cos (180° + \theta) = -\cos \theta$.

32. $\sin (180° - \theta) = \sin \theta$.   **35.** $\cos (270° - \theta) = -\sin \theta$.

33. $\sin (270° - \theta) = -\cos \theta$.   **36.** $\cos (360° - \theta) = \cos \theta$.

37. If $\cos \alpha = \frac{2}{\sqrt{5}}$, and $\tan \beta = \frac{1}{3}$, α and β are acute angles, prove that $\alpha + \beta = 45°$.

In the following use only principal values of the angles:

38. Prove $\sin^{-1} \frac{5}{13} + \sin^{-1} \frac{12}{13} = \frac{\pi}{2}$.

39. Prove $\sin^{-1} \frac{1}{4} + \cos^{-1} \frac{1}{4} = \frac{\pi}{2}$. *See* *Ex. #2 p-111*

40. Prove $\sin^{-1} x + \cos^{-1} x = \frac{\pi}{2}$.

41. Prove $\sin^{-1} a \pm \sin^{-1} b = \sin^{-1} (a\sqrt{1 - b^2} \pm b\sqrt{1 - a^2})$.

42. Prove $\cos^{-1} a \pm \cos^{-1} b = \cos^{-1} [ab \mp \sqrt{(1 - a^2)(1 - b^2)}]$.

43. Prove that in any right triangle $\cos (A - B) = \frac{2ab}{c^2}$.

Find a value of θ in the following exercises:

44. $\cos (50° + \alpha) \cos (50° - \alpha) + \sin (50° + \alpha) \sin (50° - \alpha) = \cos \theta$.
$$Ans. \ \theta = 2\alpha.$$

45. $\cos 30° \cos (105° - \alpha) - \sin 30° \sin (105° - \alpha) = \cos \theta$.
$$Ans. \ \theta = 135° - \alpha.$$

46. $\sin (60° + \tfrac{1}{2}\beta) \cos (60° - \tfrac{1}{2}\beta) + \cos (60° + \tfrac{1}{2}\beta) \sin (60° - \tfrac{1}{2}\beta) = \sin \theta$.
$$Ans. \ \theta = 120°.$$

47. $\cos (45° - x) \cos (45° + x) + \sin (45° - x) \sin (45° + x) = \cos \theta$.
$$Ans. \ \theta = -2x.$$

48. Prove that $\cos (\alpha - \beta)$ gives the same result whether $\alpha > \beta$ or $\alpha < \beta$
Prove that formulas [13] and [14] are true in the following cases:

49. α in the fourth quadrant and β in the first.

50. α in the third quadrant and β in the third.

51. α in the first quadrant and β in the third.

Expand and derive the formulas expressed in the following:

52. $\sin (\alpha + \beta + \gamma) = \sin \alpha \cos \beta \cos \gamma + \cos \alpha \sin \beta \cos \gamma$
$$+ \cos \alpha \cos \beta \sin \gamma - \sin \alpha \sin \beta \sin \gamma.$$

Suggestion.—$\sin (\alpha + \beta + \gamma) = \sin [(\alpha + \beta) + \gamma]$.
$$= \sin (\alpha + \beta) \cos \gamma + \cos (\alpha + \beta) \sin \gamma.$$

53. $\cos (\alpha + \beta + \gamma) = \cos \alpha \cos \beta \cos \gamma - \sin \alpha \sin \beta \cos \gamma$
$$- \sin \alpha \cos \beta \sin \gamma - \cos \alpha \sin \beta \sin \gamma.$$

83. Formulas for the tangents of the sum and the difference of two angles.—By [7], [13], and [14],

$$\tan (\alpha + \beta) = \frac{\sin (\alpha + \beta)}{\cos (\alpha + \beta)} = \frac{\sin \alpha \cos \beta + \cos \alpha \sin \beta}{\cos \alpha \cos \beta - \sin \alpha \sin \beta}.$$

Dividing both numerator and denominator by $\cos \alpha \cos \beta$, and applying [7],

$$\tan (\alpha + \beta) = \frac{\dfrac{\sin \alpha \cos \beta}{\cos \alpha \cos \beta} + \dfrac{\cos \alpha \sin \beta}{\cos \alpha \cos \beta}}{\dfrac{\cos \alpha \cos \beta}{\cos \alpha \cos \beta} - \dfrac{\sin \alpha \sin \beta}{\cos \alpha \cos \beta}} = \frac{\tan \alpha + \tan \beta}{1 - \tan \alpha \tan \beta}.$$

[17] $$\therefore \tan (\alpha + \beta) = \frac{\tan \alpha + \tan \beta}{1 - \tan \alpha \tan \beta}.$$

[18]   Similarly, **tan $(\alpha - \beta) = \dfrac{\tan \alpha - \tan \beta}{1 + \tan \alpha \tan \beta}$.**

Since formulas **[13]**, **[14]**, **[15]**, and **[16]** are true for all values of α and β, the formulas **[17]** and **[18]** are true in general. These formulas express the tangent of the sum or of the difference of two angles in terms of the tangents of the individual angles.

EXERCISES

1. Find tan 75° by using 75° = 45° + 30°.   *Ans.* 3.732.

2. Find tan 15° by using 15° = 45° − 30°.   *Ans.* 0.268.

3. Given $\tan \alpha = \frac{7}{24}$ and $\tan \beta = \frac{5}{12}$, α and β acute; find tan $(\alpha + \beta)$ and tan $(\alpha - \beta)$.   *Ans.* 0.8063; −0.1115.

4. Given $\sin \alpha = \frac{3}{4}$ and $\cos \beta = \frac{1}{3}$, α in the second quadrant and β in the first quadrant; find tan $(\alpha + \beta)$ and tan $(\alpha - \beta)$.   *Ans.* 0.4028; 1.7953.

5. Find tan $(\tan^{-1} \frac{4}{3} - \tan^{-1} \frac{1}{7})$, using the principal values of the angles.   *Ans.* 1.

6. Find tan $(\tan^{-1} \frac{1}{3} - \cos^{-1} \frac{2}{3})$, using the principal values of the angles.   *Ans.* −0.57166.

7. Find tan $(\tan^{-1} \frac{2}{11} + \cot^{-1} \frac{24}{7})$.   *Ans.* $\frac{1}{2}$.

8. Find cot $(\cot^{-1} \frac{24}{13} + \cot^{-1} \frac{15}{8})$.   *Ans.* $\frac{4}{1}$.

9. Prove that $\sec^{-1} \dfrac{5}{3} - \cot^{-1} 7 = \dfrac{\pi}{4}$.

10. Prove that $\tan^{-1} \frac{5}{7} + \tan^{-1} \frac{1}{6} = \frac{1}{4}\pi$.

11. Prove that $\tan^{-1} a \pm \tan^{-1} b = \tan^{-1} \dfrac{a \pm b}{1 \mp ab}$.

12. Prove that $\tan^{-1} \frac{3}{5} + \tan^{-1} \frac{3}{4} - \tan^{-1} \frac{8}{19} = \frac{1}{4}\pi$.

13. Derive formula **[18]**.

14. Derive the formula $\cot (\alpha + \beta) = \dfrac{\cot \alpha \cot \beta - 1}{\cot \alpha + \cot \beta}$.

15. Derive the formula $\cot (\alpha - \beta) = \dfrac{\cot \alpha \cot \beta + 1}{\cot \beta - \cot \alpha}$.

16. Prove that in any right triangle tan $(B - A) = \dfrac{(b + a)(b - a)}{2ab}$.

17. Derive the formula

$$\tan (\alpha + \beta + \gamma) = \frac{\tan \alpha + \tan \beta + \tan \gamma - \tan \alpha \tan \beta \tan \gamma}{1 - \tan \alpha \tan \beta - \tan \beta \tan \gamma - \tan \gamma \tan \alpha}.$$

18. Prove that $\tan \alpha + \dfrac{\tan \varphi \sec \alpha}{\cos \alpha - \tan \varphi \sin \alpha} = \tan (\alpha + \varphi)$.

84. Functions of an angle in terms of functions of half the angle.—Since the formulas for the sum of two angles are true for all values of α and β, they are true when $\beta = \alpha$.

Then, $\sin (\alpha + \beta) = \sin (\alpha + \alpha) = \sin \alpha \cos \alpha + \cos \alpha \sin \alpha$. That is,

[19] $\sin 2\alpha = 2 \sin \alpha \cos \alpha.$

This formula may be stated as follows:

The sine of any angle is equal to twice the product of the sine and cosine of the half angle.

Thus,
$$\sin 40° = 2 \sin 20° \cos 20°.$$
$$\sin \alpha = 2 \sin \tfrac{1}{2}\alpha \cos \tfrac{1}{2}\alpha.$$

And, conversely, $2 \sin 3\alpha \cos 3\alpha = \sin 2(3\alpha) = \sin 6\alpha.$

$$2 \sin 25° \cos 25° = \sin 2(25°) = \sin 50°.$$

Also

$$\cos (\alpha + \beta) = \cos (\alpha + \alpha) = \cos \alpha \cos \alpha - \sin \alpha \sin \alpha$$
$$= \cos^2 \alpha - \sin^2 \alpha = 1 - \sin^2 \alpha - \sin^2 \alpha = 1 - 2 \sin^2 \alpha,$$
or $\; = \cos^2 \alpha - (1 - \cos^2 \alpha) = 2 \cos^2 \alpha - 1.$

That is,

[20] $\qquad$ **$\cos 2\alpha = \cos^2 \alpha - \sin^2 \alpha = 1 - 2 \sin^2 \alpha = 2 \cos^2 \alpha - 1.$**

Thus, $\cos 30° = \cos^2 15° - \sin^2 15°$, or $1 - 2 \sin^2 15°$, etc.

$$\cos 3\theta = \cos^2 \frac{3\theta}{2} - \sin^2 \frac{3\theta}{2}.$$

Also, $\tan (\alpha + \beta) = \tan (\alpha + \alpha) = \dfrac{\tan \alpha + \tan \alpha}{1 - \tan \alpha \tan \alpha}.$

That is,

[21] $\qquad\qquad$ **$\tan 2\alpha = \dfrac{2 \tan \alpha}{1 - \tan^2 \alpha}.$**

Thus, $\tan 60° = \dfrac{2 \tan 30°}{1 - \tan^2 30°},\; \tan 100° = \dfrac{2 \tan 50°}{1 - \tan^2 50°},$

$$\tan \theta = \frac{2 \tan \tfrac{1}{2}\theta}{1 - \tan^2 \tfrac{1}{2}\theta}.$$

Example 1.—Given the functions of 30°, to find the functions of 60°.

Solution.—$\sin 60° = 2 \sin 30° \cos 30° = 2(\tfrac{1}{2})(\tfrac{1}{2}\sqrt{3}) = \tfrac{1}{2}\sqrt{3}.$

$$\cos 60° = 2 \cos^2 30° - 1 = 2(\tfrac{1}{2}\sqrt{3})^2 - 1 = \tfrac{3}{2} - 1 = \tfrac{1}{2},$$
or $\qquad = 1 - 2 \sin^2 30° = 1 - 2(\tfrac{1}{2})^2 = \tfrac{1}{2}.$

$$\tan 60° = \frac{2 \tan 30°}{1 - \tan^2 30°} = \frac{\tfrac{2}{3}\sqrt{3}}{1 - (\tfrac{1}{3}\sqrt{3})^2} = \sqrt{3}.$$

Example 2.—Prove that $\dfrac{2 \tan \alpha}{1 + \tan^2 \alpha} = \sin 2\alpha.$

Proof.—$\tan \alpha = \dfrac{\sin \alpha}{\cos \alpha}$ and $1 + \tan^2 \alpha = \sec^2 \alpha.$

Then $\dfrac{2 \tan \alpha}{1 + \tan^2 \alpha} = \dfrac{2 \dfrac{\sin \alpha}{\cos \alpha}}{\sec^2 \alpha} = \dfrac{2 \dfrac{\sin \alpha}{\cos \alpha}}{\dfrac{1}{\cos^2 \alpha}} = 2 \sin \alpha \cos \alpha = \sin 2\alpha.$

EXERCISES

Express the following in terms of functions of half the angle. Answer orally.

1. $\sin 4\alpha$.
2. $\sin \frac{1}{2}\alpha$.
3. $\sin 8\alpha$.
4. $\cos 4\alpha$.
5. $\cos \frac{1}{2}\alpha$.
6. $\sin 90°$.

7. $\sin 20°$.
8. $\cos 90°$.
9. $\tan \frac{1}{2}\theta$.
10. $\tan 4\theta$.
11. $\tan 80°$.
12. $\sin 3\theta$.

13. $\sin (90° + 2\alpha)$.
14. $\sin (2 \sin^{-1} a)$.
15. $\cos (2 \cos^{-1} a)$.
16. $\cos (2 \sin^{-1} a)$.
17. $\sin (2 \cos^{-1} a)$.
18. $\tan (2 \tan^{-1} a)$.

19. Given the functions of 75°; find sine, cosine, and tangent of 150°. *Note.*—See Exercise 19, page 112.

20. Given the functions of 150°; find sine, cosine, and tangent of 300°.

21. Given $\sin \theta = \frac{7}{25}$ and θ in the first quadrant; find sine, cosine and tangent of 2θ.   *Ans.* 0.5376; 0.8432; 0.6376.

22. Given $\cos \theta = \frac{1}{5}$; find $\cos 2\theta$.   *Ans.* −0.92.

23. Given $\sin \frac{1}{2}\theta = \frac{5}{13}$ and $\cos \frac{1}{2}\theta = -\frac{12}{13}$; find $\sin \theta$ and $\cos \theta$.   *Ans.* −0.7101; 0.7041.

24. Given $\tan 4\theta = \frac{5}{12}$; find $\tan 8\theta$.   *Ans.* 1.0084.

Find the value of the following, using the principal values of the angles:

25. $\sin (2 \cos^{-1} \frac{2}{5})$.   *Ans.* 0.7332.

26. $\cos (2 \sin^{-1} \frac{2}{5})$.   *Ans.* 0.68.

27. $\sin \left(2 \sin^{-1} \dfrac{1}{\sqrt{1 + x^2}} \right)$.   *Ans.* $\dfrac{2x}{1 + x^2}$.

28. $\cos (2 \text{ arc tan } \frac{1}{3})$.   *Ans.* 0.8.

29. $\tan (2 \text{ invsin } \frac{1}{3})$.   *Ans.* 0.8081.

30. If $\tan \dfrac{\theta}{2} = \dfrac{y}{x}$ show that $\sin \theta = \dfrac{2xy}{x^2 + y^2}$ and $\sin 2\theta = \dfrac{4xy(x^2 - y^2)}{(x^2 + y^2)^2}$.

31. If $\tan \theta = \dfrac{y}{x}$, show that $\sqrt{\dfrac{x + y}{x - y}} + \sqrt{\dfrac{x - y}{x + y}} = \dfrac{2 \cos \theta}{\sqrt{\cos 2\theta}}$.

32. Prove that $\tan \beta = \dfrac{\sin 2\beta}{1 + \cos 2\beta}$.

33. Prove that $\tan \theta - \cot \theta = -2 \cot 2\theta$.

34. Prove that $\dfrac{1 - \cos \alpha + \cos \beta - \cos (\alpha + \beta)}{1 + \cos \alpha - \cos \beta - \cos (\alpha + \beta)} = \left(\tan \dfrac{\alpha}{2} \right)\left(\cot \dfrac{\beta}{2} \right)$.

35. Prove that $\dfrac{1 + \tan^2 (45° - \theta)}{1 - \tan^2 (45° - \theta)} = \dfrac{1}{\sin 2\theta}$.

36. Prove that $\dfrac{\tan^2 2\alpha}{\sec^2 \alpha - 1} = (1 + \sec 2\alpha)^2$.

37. Prove that in any right triangle $\sin 2A = \sin 2B$.

38. Prove that in any right triangle $\cos 2A = \sin (B - A)$.

Derive the formulas given in Exercises 39 to 44.

39. $\sin 3\theta = 3 \sin \theta - 4 \sin^3 \theta$.

Suggestion.—In formula [13] let $\alpha = 2\theta$ and $\beta = \theta$.

40. $\cos 3\theta = 4 \cos^3 \theta - 3 \cos \theta$.

41. $\tan 3\theta = \dfrac{3 \tan \theta - \tan^3 \theta}{1 - 3 \tan^2 \theta}$.

42. $\sin 4\theta = 4 \cos^3 \theta \sin \theta - 4 \cos \theta \sin^3 \theta$.

43. $\cos 4\theta = \cos^4 \theta - 6 \cos^2 \theta \sin^2 \theta + \sin^4 \theta$.

44. $\tan 4\theta = \dfrac{4 \tan \theta (1 - \tan^2 \theta)}{1 - 6 \tan^2 \theta + \tan^4 \theta}$.

85. Functions of an angle in terms of functions of twice the angle.—By [20], $\cos 2\alpha = 1 - 2 \sin^2 \alpha$. Solving this for $\sin \alpha$, we have $\sin \alpha = \pm \sqrt{\dfrac{1 - \cos 2\alpha}{2}}$

Let $\alpha = \frac{1}{2}\theta$ and we have

$$[22] \qquad \sin \frac{1}{2}\theta = \pm \sqrt{\frac{1 - \cos \theta}{2}}.$$

That is, *the sine of an angle is equal to the square root of one-half of the quantity, one minus the cosine of twice the angle.*

Thus, $\sin 50° = \sqrt{\dfrac{1 - \cos 100°}{2}}$, $\sin 10° = \sqrt{\dfrac{1 - \cos 20°}{2}}$.

Also by [20], $\cos 2\alpha = 2 \cos^2 \alpha - 1$. Solving this for $\cos \alpha$ we have $\cos \alpha = \pm \sqrt{\dfrac{1 + \cos 2\alpha}{2}}$.

Let $\alpha = \frac{1}{2}\theta$ and we have

$$[23] \qquad \cos \frac{1}{2}\theta = \pm \sqrt{\frac{1 + \cos \theta}{2}}.$$

That is, *the cosine of an angle is equal to the square root of one-half of the quantity, one plus the cosine of twice the angle.*

Thus, $\cos 30° = \sqrt{\dfrac{1 + \cos 60°}{2}}$, $\cos 50° = \sqrt{\dfrac{1 + \cos 100°}{2}}$.

By dividing [22] by [23], we can derive

$$[24] \qquad \tan \frac{1}{2}\theta = \pm \sqrt{\frac{1 - \cos \theta}{1 + \cos \theta}} = \frac{1 - \cos \theta}{\sin \theta} = \frac{\sin \theta}{1 + \cos \theta}.$$

The last two forms given in [24] may be obtained as follows:

Multiplying numerator and denominator of $\sqrt{\dfrac{1 - \cos \theta}{1 + \cos \theta}}$ by $\sqrt{1 - \cos \theta}$,

$$\tan \frac{1}{2}\theta = \sqrt{\frac{1 - \cos \theta}{1 + \cos \theta} \cdot \frac{1 - \cos \theta}{1 - \cos \theta}} = \frac{\sqrt{(1 - \cos \theta)^2}}{\sqrt{1 - \cos^2 \theta}} = \frac{1 - \cos \theta}{\sin \theta}.$$

Again, multiplying numerator and denominator by $\sqrt{1 + \cos\,\theta}$,

$$\tan\frac{1}{2}\theta = \sqrt{\frac{1 - \cos\,\theta}{1 + \cos\,\theta} \cdot \frac{1 + \cos\,\theta}{1 + \cos\,\theta}} = \frac{\sqrt{1 - \cos^2\,\theta}}{\sqrt{(1 + \cos\,\theta)^2}} = \frac{\sin\,\theta}{1 + \cos\,\theta}.$$

Thus, $\tan 40° = \sqrt{\dfrac{1 - \cos 80°}{1 + \cos 80°}} = \dfrac{1 - \cos 80°}{\sin 80°} = \dfrac{\sin 80°}{1 + \cos 80°}.$

Example.—Find the value of $\sin\,(\frac{1}{2}\cos^{-1}\frac{3}{4})$.

Solution.—Let $\theta = \cos^{-1}\frac{3}{4}$. Then $\cos\,\theta = \frac{3}{4}$.

$$\sin\left(\frac{1}{2}\cos^{-1}\frac{3}{4}\right) = \sin\frac{1}{2}\theta = \sqrt{\frac{1 - \cos\,\theta}{2}} = \sqrt{\frac{1 - \frac{3}{4}}{2}} = \sqrt{\frac{1}{8}} = \frac{\sqrt{2}}{4}.$$

EXERCISES

Express the following in terms of functions of twice the angle. Answer orally.

1. $\sin 2\alpha$.
2. $\sin \frac{1}{4}\alpha$.
3. $\cos 4\alpha$.
4. $\cos 50°$.
5. $\sin 70°$.

6. $\tan 90°$.
7. $\tan 2\theta$.
8. $\tan \frac{1}{4}\theta$.
9. $\sin 3\theta$.
10. $\cos 80°$.

11. $\sin\,(45° + \frac{1}{2}\alpha)$.
12. $\cos\,(45° - \frac{1}{2}\alpha)$.
13. $\sin\,(135° + \frac{1}{2}\alpha)$.
14. $\cos\,(135° - \frac{1}{2}\alpha)$.
15. $\tan\,(135° - \frac{1}{2}\alpha)$.

16. Given $\cos 60° = \frac{1}{2}$; find $\sin 30°$ and $\cos 30°$.
17. Given $\cos 135° = -\frac{1}{2}\sqrt{2}$; find $\tan 67\frac{1}{2}°$.
18. Given $\cos 270° = 0$; find $\sin 135°$ and $\cos 135°$.
19. Given $\cos 30° = \frac{1}{2}\sqrt{3}$; find $\sin 15°$ and $\cos 15°$.
20. Given $\cos 2\theta = \frac{1}{5}$; find $\sin \theta$ and $\cos \theta$.   *Ans.* ±0.6325; ±0.7746.
21. Given $\cos \theta = 0.6$; find $\sin \frac{1}{2}\theta$ and $\cos \frac{1}{2}\theta$.   *Ans.* ±0.4462; ±0.8946.
22. Given $\cos 8\theta = -\frac{1}{2}\sqrt{2}$; find $\sin 4\theta$ and $\cos 4\theta$.

Ans. ±0.9239; ±0.3827.

23. Given $\sin \theta = -\frac{1}{4}$, θ in the third quadrant; find $\sin \frac{1}{2}\theta$, $\cos \frac{1}{2}\theta$, and $\tan \frac{1}{2}\theta$.   *Ans.* 0.9920; -0.1260.

24. Given $\cos \theta = \dfrac{b^2 + c^2 - a^2}{2bc}$, and $2s = a + b + c$; prove that

(a) $\sin^2\dfrac{1}{2}\theta = \dfrac{(s - b)(s - c)}{bc}$;

(b) $\cos^2\dfrac{1}{2}\theta = \dfrac{s(s - a)}{bc}$;

(c) $\tan^2\dfrac{1}{2}\theta = \dfrac{(s - b)(s - c)}{s(s - a)}$.

Find the value of the following, using the principal values of the angles:

25. $\cos\,(\frac{1}{2}\tan^{-1}\frac{16}{63})$.   *Ans.* 0.9923.
26. $\sin\,(\frac{1}{2}\cot^{-1}\frac{3}{4})$.   *Ans.* 0.4472.
27. $\tan\left[\dfrac{1}{2}\sin^{-1}\left(\dfrac{2\sqrt{x}}{1 + x}\right)\right]$.   *Ans.* $\sqrt{x}$, $0 < x < 1$; $\dfrac{1}{\sqrt{x}}$, $x > 1$.
28. $\sin\,(\pi + \frac{1}{2}\sin^{-1}\frac{7}{25})$.   *Ans.* -0.14142.
29. $\tan\,(60° + \frac{1}{2}\sec^{-1}\frac{5}{4})$.   *Ans.* 4.8867.
30. $\sin\,(120° + \frac{1}{2}\sin^{-1}\frac{1}{4})$.   *Ans.* 0.76901.
31. $\cos\,(90° - \frac{1}{2}\sin^{-1}\frac{1}{4})$.   *Ans.* 0.12597.

32. In any right triangle prove $\tan \frac{1}{2}A = \frac{c - b}{a}$, and $\sin \frac{1}{2}A = \sqrt{\frac{c - b}{2c}}$.

33. Prove that $\tan \frac{1}{2}\theta$ and $\cot \frac{1}{2}\theta$ are the roots of $x^2 - 2x \csc \theta + 1 = 0$.

Prove the following identities:

34. $1 + \tan \beta \tan \frac{\beta}{2} = \frac{1}{\cos \beta}$.

35. $\tan \left(\frac{\alpha + \beta}{2} \right) \cot \left(\frac{\alpha - \beta}{2} \right) = \frac{(\sin \alpha + \sin \beta)^2}{\sin^2 \alpha - \sin^2 \beta}$.

36. $\cot \beta = \frac{1}{2} \left(\cot \frac{\beta}{2} - \tan \frac{\beta}{2} \right)$.

37. In [24], show why the sign $\pm$ is not necessary before $\frac{1 - \cos \theta}{\sin \theta}$ and $\frac{\sin \theta}{1 + \cos \theta}$.

86. To express the sum and difference of two like trigonometric functions as a product.—In this article the following formulas are proved:

[25] $\sin \alpha + \sin \beta = 2 \sin \frac{1}{2}(\alpha + \beta) \cos \frac{1}{2}(\alpha - \beta)$.

[26] $\sin \alpha - \sin \beta = 2 \cos \frac{1}{2}(\alpha + \beta) \sin \frac{1}{2}(\alpha - \beta)$.

[27] $\cos \alpha + \cos \beta = 2 \cos \frac{1}{2}(\alpha + \beta) \cos \frac{1}{2}(\alpha - \beta)$.

[28] $\cos \alpha - \cos \beta = -2 \sin \frac{1}{2}(\alpha + \beta) \sin \frac{1}{2}(\alpha - \beta)$.

The object of these four relations is to express sums and differences of functions as products. In this manner formulas can be made suitable for logarithmic computations.

Proof of [25] *and* [26].—Let $\alpha = x + y$ and $\beta = x - y$.

Solving simultaneously for x and y,

$$x = \tfrac{1}{2}(\alpha + \beta) \text{ and } y = \tfrac{1}{2}(\alpha - \beta).$$

By [13], $\sin \alpha = \sin (x + y) = \sin x \cos y + \cos x \sin y$. (a)

By [15], $\sin \beta = \sin (x - y) = \sin x \cos y - \cos x \sin y$. (b)

By adding (a) and (b), $\sin \alpha + \sin \beta = 2 \sin x \cos y$.

Substituting the values of x and y, we have

$$\sin \alpha + \sin \beta = 2 \sin \tfrac{1}{2}(\alpha + \beta) \cos \tfrac{1}{2}(\alpha - \beta).$$

Subtracting (b) from (a) and substituting for x and y,

$$\sin \alpha - \sin \beta = 2 \cos x \sin y = 2 \cos \tfrac{1}{2}(\alpha + \beta) \sin \tfrac{1}{2}(\alpha - \beta).$$

Proof of [27] *and* [28].—

By [14], $\cos \alpha = \cos (x + y) = \cos x \cos y - \sin x \sin y$. (c)

By [16], $\cos \beta = \cos (x - y) = \cos x \cos y + \sin x \sin y$. (d)

Adding (c) and (d) and substituting for x and y,

$$\cos \alpha + \cos \beta = 2 \cos x \cos y = 2 \cos \tfrac{1}{2}(\alpha + \beta) \cos \tfrac{1}{2}(\alpha - \beta).$$

Subtracting (*d*) from (*c*) and substituting for *x* and *y*,

$$\cos \alpha - \cos \beta = -2 \sin x \sin y = -2 \sin \tfrac{1}{2}(\alpha + \beta) \sin \tfrac{1}{2}(\alpha - \beta).$$

Example 1.—Express $\dfrac{\cos 70° - \cos 30°}{\cos 70° + \cos 30°}$ as a product.

Solution.—

By [28], $\cos 70° - \cos 30° = -2 \sin \tfrac{1}{2}(70° + 30°) \sin \tfrac{1}{2}(70 - 30°)$
$$= -2 \sin 50° \sin 20°.$$

By [27], $\cos 70° + \cos 30° = 2 \cos \tfrac{1}{2}(70° + 30°) \cos \tfrac{1}{2}(70° - 30°)$
$$= 2 \cos 50° \cos 20°.$$

Then $\dfrac{\cos 70° - \cos 30°}{\cos 70° + \cos 30°} = \dfrac{-2 \sin 50° \sin 20°}{2 \cos 50° \cos 20°} =$
$$-\tan 50° \tan 20°.$$

Example 2.—Show that the following equality is true by using the tables to compute each side of the equality:

$$\sin 60° + \sin 40° = 2 \sin 50° \cos 10°.$$

Solution.—The right-hand member is best computed by logarithms.

$\sin 60° = 0.8660$	Let	$x = 2 \sin 50° \cos 10°$
$\sin 40° = 0.6428$		$\log 2 = 0.30103$
$\sin 60° + \sin 40° = 1.5088$		$\log \sin 50° = 9.88425$
		$\log \cos 10° = 9.99335$
		$\log x = 0.17863$
		$x = 1.5088$

The two results are found to agree.

Example 3.—If $\alpha + \beta + \gamma = 180°$, prove the identity:

$$\sin \alpha + \sin \beta + \sin \gamma = 4 \cos \tfrac{1}{2}\alpha \cos \tfrac{1}{2}\beta \cos \tfrac{1}{2}\gamma.$$

Proof.—

By [25], $\sin \alpha + \sin \beta = 2 \sin \tfrac{1}{2}(\alpha + \beta) \cos \tfrac{1}{2}(\alpha - \beta).$

Now $\gamma = 180° - (\alpha + \beta).$

$\therefore \sin \gamma = \sin [180° - (\alpha + \beta)] = \sin (\alpha + \beta)$ (**Art. 48**).

By [19], $\sin (\alpha + \beta) = 2 \sin \tfrac{1}{2}(\alpha + \beta) \cos \tfrac{1}{2}(\alpha + \beta).$

$\therefore \sin \alpha + \sin \beta + \sin \gamma$

$= 2 \sin \tfrac{1}{2}(\alpha + \beta) \cos \tfrac{1}{2}(\alpha - \beta) + 2 \sin \tfrac{1}{2}(\alpha + \beta) \cos \tfrac{1}{2}(\alpha + \beta)$
$= 2 \sin \tfrac{1}{2}(\alpha + \beta)[\cos \tfrac{1}{2}(\alpha - \beta) + \cos \tfrac{1}{2}(\alpha + \beta)].$

But $\cos \tfrac{1}{2}(\alpha - \beta) + \cos \tfrac{1}{2}(\alpha + \beta)$

$= 2 \cos \tfrac{1}{2}[\tfrac{1}{2}(\alpha - \beta) + \tfrac{1}{2}(\alpha + \beta)] \cos \tfrac{1}{2}[\tfrac{1}{2}(\alpha - \beta) - \tfrac{1}{2}(\alpha + \beta)]$
$= 2 \cos \tfrac{1}{2}\alpha \cos \tfrac{1}{2}\beta.$

$\therefore \sin \alpha + \sin \beta + \sin \gamma = 2 \sin \frac{1}{2}(\alpha + \beta)2 \cos \frac{1}{2}\alpha \cos \frac{1}{2}\beta$
$$= 4 \sin \frac{1}{2}(\alpha + \beta) \cos \frac{1}{2}\alpha \cos \frac{1}{2}\beta.$$

But $\frac{1}{2}(\alpha + \beta) = 90° - \frac{1}{2}\gamma$, and $\sin \frac{1}{2}(\alpha + \beta) = \cos \frac{1}{2}\gamma.$

$\therefore \sin \alpha + \sin \beta + \sin \gamma = 4 \cos \frac{1}{2}\alpha \cos \frac{1}{2}\beta \cos \frac{1}{2}\gamma.$

EXERCISES

Express the following sums and differences of functions as products. Answer orally.

1. $\sin 70° + \sin 50°.$
2. $\sin 70° - \sin 50°.$
3. $\cos 70° + \cos 50°.$
4. $\cos 70° - \cos 50°.$
5. $\sin 80° + \sin 140°.$
6. $\cos 140° - \cos 70°.$
7. $\sin 3\theta + \sin \theta.$
8. $\cos 5\theta - \cos 7\theta.$
9. $\cos 7\theta - \sin 3\theta.$
10. $\cos 2\alpha - \cos 2\beta.$
11. $\sin (\alpha + \beta) + \sin (\alpha - \beta).$
12. $\cos (\alpha + \beta) - \cos (\alpha - \beta).$

Express the following as products and simplify:

13. $\sin 80° - \sin 40°.$ *Ans.* $\sin 20°.$
14. $\cos 80° - \cos 40°.$ *Ans.* $-\sqrt{3} \sin 20°.$
15. $\cos 40° + \cos 20°.$ *Ans.* $\sqrt{3} \cos 10°.$
16. $\sin 40° + \sin 20°.$ *Ans.* $\cos 10°.$
17. $\sin 50° + \sin 70°.$ *Ans.* $\sqrt{3} \cos 10°.$
18. $\dfrac{\sin 50° - \sin 30°}{\cos 50° + \cos 30°}.$ *Ans.* $\tan 10°.$
19. $\dfrac{\sin 70° + \sin 50°}{\cos 70° - \cos 50°}.$ *Ans.* $-\cot 10°.$
20. $\dfrac{\cos 50° + \cos 10°}{\sin 50° + \sin 10°}.$ *Ans.* $\cot 30°.$
21. $\dfrac{\cos \alpha - \cos \beta}{\sin \alpha + \sin \beta}.$ *Ans.* $-\tan \frac{1}{2}(\alpha - \beta).$
22. $\dfrac{\cos 2\theta + \cos \theta}{\sin 2\theta + \sin \theta}.$ *Ans.* $\cot \frac{3}{2}\theta.$
23. $\cos (60° + \alpha) + \cos (60° - \alpha).$ *Ans.* $\cos \alpha.$
24. $\cos (\alpha + 30°) + \cos (\alpha - 30°).$ *Ans.* $\sqrt{3} \cos \alpha.$
25. $\sin (\alpha + 60°) + \sin (\alpha - 60°).$ *Ans.* $\sin \alpha.$
26. $\tan (\beta - \frac{1}{4}\pi) + \cot (\beta + \frac{1}{4}\pi).$ *Ans.* $0.$
27. Solve $\cos 3\theta + \sin 2\theta - \cos \theta = 0$ for values of $\theta < 360°.$
    Ans. $0°, 30°, 90°, 150°, 180°, 270°.$
28. Solve $\sin 3\theta + \sin 2\theta + \sin \theta = 0$ for values of $\theta < 360°.$
    Ans. $0°, 90°, 120°, 180°, 240°, 270°.$
29. Solve $\cos 3\theta - \sin 2\theta + \cos \theta = 0$ for values of $\theta < 360°.$
    Ans. $30°, 90°, 150°, 270°.$
30. Solve $\sin 5\theta - \sin 3\theta + \sin \theta = 0$ for values of $\theta < 360°.$
    Ans. $0°, 30°, 60°, 120°, 150°, 180°, 210°, 240°, 300°\ 330°.$

If $\alpha + \beta + \gamma = 180°$, prove the identities in the following exercises:

31. $\sin \alpha + \sin \beta - \sin \gamma = 4 \sin \frac{1}{2}\alpha \sin \frac{1}{2}\beta \cos \frac{1}{2}\gamma.$
32. $\cos \alpha + \cos \beta + \cos \gamma = 4 \sin \frac{1}{2}\alpha \sin \frac{1}{2}\beta \sin \frac{1}{2}\gamma + 1.$
33. $\cos 2\alpha + \cos 2\beta + \cos 2\gamma = -4 \cos \alpha \cos \beta \cos \gamma - 1.$
34. $\sin 2\alpha + \sin 2\beta + \sin 2\gamma = 4 \sin \alpha \sin \beta \sin \gamma.$

87. To change the product of functions of angles into the sum of functions.—From Art. 78,

$$\sin (\alpha + \beta) = \sin \alpha \cos \beta + \cos \alpha \sin \beta. \qquad (a)$$
$$\sin (\alpha - \beta) = \sin \alpha \cos \beta - \cos \alpha \sin \beta. \qquad (b)$$
$$\cos (\alpha + \beta) = \cos \alpha \cos \beta - \sin \alpha \sin \beta. \qquad (c)$$
$$\cos (\alpha - \beta) = \cos \alpha \cos \beta + \sin \alpha \sin \beta. \qquad (d)$$

Adding (a) and (b), $\sin (\alpha + \beta) + \sin (\alpha - \beta) = 2 \sin \alpha \cos \beta.$

[29] $\therefore$ **sin α cos β $= \frac{1}{2}$ sin (α + β) $+ \frac{1}{2}$ sin (α − β).**

Subtracting (b) from (a),

$$\sin (\alpha + \beta) - \sin (\alpha - \beta) = 2 \cos \alpha \sin \beta.$$

[30] $\therefore$ **cos α sin β $= \frac{1}{2}$ sin (α + β) $- \frac{1}{2}$ sin (α − β).**

Adding (c) and (d), $\cos (\alpha + \beta) + \cos (\alpha - \beta) = 2 \cos \alpha \cos \beta.$

[31] $\therefore$ **cos α cos β $= \frac{1}{2}$ cos (α + β) $+ \frac{1}{2}$ cos (α − β).**

Subtracting (d) from (c),

$$\cos (\alpha + \beta) - \cos (\alpha - \beta) = -2 \sin \alpha \sin \beta.$$

[32] $\therefore$ **sin α sin β $= -\frac{1}{2}$ cos (α + β) $+ \frac{1}{2}$ cos (α − β).**

Example 1.—Prove that $\sin 4\theta \cos 2\theta = \frac{1}{2} \sin 6\theta + \frac{1}{2} \sin 2\theta.$
Proof.—Applying [29], where $\alpha = 4\theta$ and $\beta = 2\theta$,

$$\sin 4\theta \cos 2\theta = \frac{1}{2} \sin (4\theta + 2\theta) + \frac{1}{2} \sin (4\theta - 2\theta)$$
$$= \frac{1}{2} \sin 6\theta + \frac{1}{2} \sin 2\theta.$$

It is often desirable to express the products and powers of sines and cosines as sums of functions that involve multiples of the angle. The formulas of this article and of **Art. 84** can be used for this purpose (see also **Art. 127**).

Example 2.—Prove that $\sin^2 \theta \cos \theta = -\frac{1}{4} \cos 3\theta + \frac{1}{4} \cos \theta.$
Proof.—By [19], $\sin 2\theta = 2 \sin \theta \cos \theta.$

Then $\sin \theta \cos \theta = \frac{1}{2} \sin 2\theta.$
Therefore, $\sin^2 \theta \cos \theta = \sin \theta (\sin \theta \cos \theta)$
$$= \frac{1}{2} \sin 2\theta \sin \theta$$
By [32], $= \frac{1}{2}[-\frac{1}{2} \cos (2\theta + \theta) + \frac{1}{2} \cos (2\theta - \theta)]$
$$= -\frac{1}{4} \cos 3\theta + \frac{1}{4} \cos \theta.$$

Example 3.—Prove that $\cos^5 \theta = \frac{1}{16} (10 \cos \theta + 5 \cos 3\theta + \cos 5\theta).$

Proof.—$\cos^5 \theta = (\cos^2 \theta)^2 \cos \theta = \left(\dfrac{1 + \cos 2\theta}{2} \right)^2 \cos \theta$ By [23].

$$= \frac{1}{4}(1 + 2 \cos 2\theta + \cos^2 2\theta) \cos \theta$$

$$= \tfrac{1}{4}\left(1 + 2\cos 2\theta + \frac{1 + \cos 4\theta}{2}\right)\cos \theta \quad \text{By [23]}.$$

$$= \tfrac{1}{8}(3 + 4\cos 2\theta + \cos 4\theta)\cos \theta$$

$$= \tfrac{1}{8}(3\cos \theta + 4\cos 2\theta \cos \theta + \cos 4\theta \cos \theta)$$

$$= \tfrac{1}{8}(3\cos \theta + 2\cos 3\theta + 2\cos \theta + \tfrac{1}{2}\cos 5\theta + \tfrac{1}{2}\cos 3\theta)$$

$$= \tfrac{1}{16}(10\cos \theta + 5\cos 3\theta + \cos 5\theta).$$

EXERCISES

Apply the formulas of this article to the following. Answer orally.

1. $\sin 50° \sin 40°$.

2. $\sin 40° \cos 20°$.

3. $\cos 20° \sin 50°$.

4. $\sin 70° \cos 10°$.

5. $\sin 6\phi \cos 4\phi$.

6. $\cos 4\phi \sin 8\phi$.

7. $\sin 20\phi \sin 12\phi$.

8. $\cos 10\phi \cos 16\phi$.

Prove the following identities:

9. $4\cos 2\phi \cos 4\phi \cos 6\phi = 1 + \cos 4\phi + \cos 8\phi + \cos 12\phi$.

10. $4\sin 2\phi \sin 4\phi \sin 6\phi = \sin 4\phi + \sin 8\phi - \sin 12\phi$.

11. $\dfrac{\sin 6\phi \cos 3\phi - \sin 8\phi \cos \phi}{\sin 4\phi \sin 3\phi - \cos 2\phi \cos \phi} = \tan 2\phi$.

12. $\sin 3\phi \sin \phi + \sin^2 \phi + \cos 3\phi \cos \phi - \cos^2 \phi = 0$.

13. $2\cos \dfrac{\pi}{13} \cos \dfrac{9\pi}{13} + \cos \dfrac{3\pi}{13} + \cos \dfrac{5\pi}{13} = 0$.

14. $\sin 160° \sin 120° \sin 80° \sin 40° = \tfrac{3}{16}$.

15. $\cos 160° \cos 120° \cos 80° \cos 40° = \tfrac{1}{16}$.

16. $\cos^2 \phi \sin^2 \phi = \tfrac{1}{8}(1 - \cos 4\phi)$.

17. $\sin^3 \phi \cos^3 \phi = \tfrac{1}{32}(3\sin 2\phi - \sin 6\phi)$.

18. $\sin^2 \phi \cos^3 \phi = \tfrac{1}{8}(\cos \phi - \tfrac{1}{2}\cos 3\phi - \tfrac{1}{2}\cos 5\phi)$.

19. $\sin^3 \phi = \tfrac{1}{4}(3\sin \phi - \sin 3\phi)$.

20. $\cos^3 \phi = \tfrac{1}{4}(3\cos \phi + \cos 3\phi)$.

21. $\sin^m \phi \cos^n \phi = \tfrac{1}{32}(2 - \cos 2\phi - 2\cos 4\phi + \cos 6\phi)$, if $m = 4, n = 2$.

22. Work out other combinations of m and n as illustrated in [21].

88. Important trigonometric series.—The trigonometric series given in this article and the following exercises are important, especially in certain problems in electricity. In the series, α and β are angles and n is an integer equal to the number of terms in a series. The two fundamental series with their sums are:

$$(1) \quad \sin \alpha + \sin (\alpha + \beta) + \sin (\alpha + 2\beta) + \cdots \sin [\alpha + (n - 1)\beta]$$

$$= \frac{\sin [\alpha + \tfrac{1}{2}(n - 1)\beta] \sin \tfrac{1}{2}n\beta}{\sin \tfrac{1}{2}\beta}.$$

$$(2) \quad \cos \alpha + \cos (\alpha + \beta) + \cos (\alpha + 2\beta) + \cdots \cos [\alpha + (n - 1)\beta]$$

$$= \frac{\cos [\alpha + \tfrac{1}{2}(n - 1)\beta] \sin \tfrac{1}{2}n\beta}{\sin \tfrac{1}{2}\beta}.$$

In both (1) and (2) $\sin \tfrac{1}{2}\beta \neq 0$.

Proof of (1).—Let S_n = the sum of n terms of the series.

Multiplying each term by $2 \sin \frac{1}{2}\beta$ and applying [32] to each product, we have the following equations, one equation resulting from each term:

$$2 \sin \alpha \sin \tfrac{1}{2}\beta = \cos (\alpha - \tfrac{1}{2}\beta) - \cos (\alpha + \tfrac{1}{2}\beta).$$
$$2 \sin (\alpha + \beta) \sin \tfrac{1}{2}\beta = \cos (\alpha + \tfrac{1}{2}\beta) - \cos (\alpha + \tfrac{3}{2}\beta).$$
$$2 \sin (\alpha + \beta) \sin \tfrac{1}{2}\beta = \cos (\alpha + \tfrac{3}{2}\beta) - \cos (\alpha + \tfrac{5}{2}\beta).$$

. . . .

$$2 \sin [\alpha + (n - 1)\beta] \sin \tfrac{1}{2}\beta = \cos \left(\alpha + \frac{2n - 3}{2}\beta\right) - \cos \left(\alpha + \frac{2n - 1}{2}\beta\right).$$

Adding these and noting that the sum of the first members is $S_n \cdot 2 \sin \frac{1}{2}\beta$,

$$S_n \cdot 2 \sin \tfrac{1}{2}\beta = \cos (\alpha - \tfrac{1}{2}\beta) - \cos \left(\alpha + \frac{2n - 1}{2}\beta\right).$$

Applying [28] to the second member of this,

$$S_n \cdot 2 \sin \tfrac{1}{2}\beta = 2 \sin [\alpha + \tfrac{1}{2}(n - 1)\beta \sin \tfrac{1}{2}n\beta.$$
$$\therefore S_n = \frac{\sin [\alpha + \tfrac{1}{2}(n - 1)\beta] \sin \tfrac{1}{2}n\beta}{\sin \tfrac{1}{2}\beta},$$

which is true if $\sin \frac{1}{2}\beta \neq 0$.

The proof of (2) can be carried out in an exactly similar manner multiplying by $2 \sin \frac{1}{2}\beta$ and applying [30].

EXERCISES

Prove the following, where, in each, the denominator of the sum must be different from zero:

1. $\sin \alpha + \sin 2\alpha + \sin 3\alpha + \cdots \sin n\alpha = \dfrac{\sin \frac{1}{2}(n + 1)\alpha \sin \frac{1}{2}n\alpha}{\sin \frac{1}{2}\alpha}.$

Suggestion.—In (1) put $\beta = \alpha$.

2. $\cos \alpha + \cos 2\alpha + \cos 3\alpha + \cdots \cos n\alpha = \dfrac{\cos \frac{1}{2}(n + 1)\alpha \sin \frac{1}{2}n\alpha}{\sin \frac{1}{2}\alpha}.$

3. $\sin \alpha + \sin 3\alpha + \sin 5\alpha + \cdots \sin (2n - 1)\alpha = \dfrac{\sin^2 n\alpha}{\sin \alpha}.$

4. $\cos \alpha + \cos 3\alpha + \cos 5\alpha + \cdots \cos (2n - 1)\alpha = \dfrac{\sin 2n\alpha}{2 \sin \alpha}.$

5. $\sin \alpha + \sin \left(\alpha + \dfrac{2\pi}{n}\right) + \sin \left(\alpha + \dfrac{4\pi}{n}\right) + \cdots \sin \left[\alpha + \dfrac{2(n - 1)\pi}{n}\right] = 0.$

6. $\cos \alpha + \cos \left(\alpha + \dfrac{2\pi}{n}\right) + \cos \left(\alpha + \dfrac{4\pi}{n}\right) + \cdots \cos \left[\alpha + \dfrac{2(n - 1)\pi}{n}\right] = 0.$

GENERAL EXERCISES

Prove the following identities by transforming the first member into the second:

1. $\cos 306° + \cos 234° + \cos 162° + \cos 18° = 0$.

2. $\dfrac{\tan x + \tan y}{\tan x - \tan y} = \dfrac{\sin (x + y)}{\sin (x - y)}$.

3. $\dfrac{1 - \tan x \tan y}{1 + \tan x \tan y} = \dfrac{\cos (x + y)}{\cos (x - y)}$.

4. $\tan (45° \pm y) = \dfrac{1 \pm \tan y}{1 \mp \tan y}$.

5. $\cot (45° \pm y) = \dfrac{\cot y \mp 1}{\cot y \pm 1}$.

6. $\cot x \pm \tan y = \dfrac{\cos (x \mp y)}{\sin x \cos y}$.

7. $\dfrac{1}{\sin 10°} - \dfrac{\sqrt{3}}{\cos 10°} = 4$.

8. $\frac{1}{2}[\cot \theta - \tan \theta] = \cot 2\theta$.

9. $4 \cot^2 2\alpha + 2 = \tan^2 \alpha + \cot^2 \alpha$.

10. $\dfrac{(2 - \sec^2 \alpha)(2 - \csc^2 \alpha)}{\sec^2 \alpha \csc^2 \alpha} = -\cos^2 2\alpha$.

11. $2\alpha + 4 \tan^{-1} (\sec \alpha - \tan \alpha) = \pi$.

12. $2\alpha + 4 \cot^{-1} (\sec \alpha + \tan \alpha) = \pi$.

13. $\dfrac{\tan \alpha + \tan \beta}{\cot \alpha + \cot \beta} = \tan \alpha \tan \beta$.

14. $\dfrac{\tan \alpha - \tan \beta}{\cot \alpha - \cot \beta} = - \tan \alpha \tan \beta$.

15. $\tan (45° + \theta) - \tan (45° - \theta) = 2 \tan 2\theta$.

16. $\dfrac{\sec^2 (\frac{1}{4}\pi + \frac{1}{2}\alpha)}{2 \tan (\frac{1}{4}\pi + \frac{1}{2}\alpha)} = \sec \alpha$.

17. $\dfrac{\sec^2 \frac{1}{2}\left(\dfrac{\pi}{2} + \alpha\right)}{\tan \left(\dfrac{\pi}{4} + \dfrac{1}{2}\alpha\right)} = \dfrac{2}{\cos \alpha}$.

18. $\dfrac{\tan \theta}{2 \cos \theta} + \dfrac{1}{4}\left(1 + \tan^2 \dfrac{1}{2}\theta\right)\cot \dfrac{1}{2}\theta = \dfrac{\sec^2 \theta}{2 \sin \theta}$.

19. $\dfrac{1 + \sin \theta - \cos \theta}{1 + \sin \theta + \cos \theta} = \tan \dfrac{1}{2}\theta$.

20. $\dfrac{2 \sin \theta - \sin 2\theta}{2 \sin \theta + \sin 2\theta} = \tan^2 \dfrac{1}{2}\theta$.

21. $8 \sin^4 \frac{1}{2}\theta - 8 \sin^2 \frac{1}{2}\theta + 1 = \cos 2\theta$.

22. $\sin (\alpha + \beta) \sin (\alpha - \beta) = \sin^2 \alpha - \sin^2 \beta = \cos^2 \beta - \cos^2 \alpha$.

23. $\cos (\alpha + \beta) \cos (\alpha - \beta) = \cos^2 \alpha - \sin^2 \beta = \cos^2 \beta - \sin^2 \alpha$.

24. $\dfrac{\cos (\alpha - \beta)}{\cos (\alpha + \beta)} = \dfrac{1 + \tan \alpha \tan \beta}{1 - \tan \alpha \tan \beta}$.

25. $\dfrac{4 \sin \alpha \sin (60° + \alpha)}{\csc (60° - \alpha)} = \sin 3\alpha$.

26. $\dfrac{\sin \alpha - \sqrt{1 + \sin 2\alpha}}{\cos \alpha - \sqrt{1 + \sin 2\alpha}} = \cot \alpha$.

27. $\dfrac{3 \sec^2 \theta}{3 \tan \theta + 1} - \dfrac{\sec^2 \theta}{\tan \theta + 3} = \dfrac{8}{3 + 5 \sin 2\theta}$.

In the two following exercises α, β, and γ are the angles of any triangle:

28. $\sin \alpha \cos \beta + \cos \alpha \sin \beta = \sin \gamma$.

29. $\tan \alpha + \tan \beta + \tan \gamma = \tan \alpha \tan \beta \tan \gamma$.

30. $\dfrac{\cos 6\theta + 6 \cos 4\theta + 15 \cos 2\theta + 10}{\cos 5\theta + 5 \cos 3\theta + 10 \cos \theta} = 2 \cos \theta$.

Suggestion.—Write the numerator in form $\cos 6\theta + \cos 4\theta + 5 \cos 4\theta + 5 \cos 2\theta + 10 \cos 2\theta + 10$.

Apply [**27**] and [**23**], and this becomes $2 \cos 5\theta \cos \theta + 10 \cos 3\theta \cos \theta + 20 \cos^2 \theta = 2 \cos \theta (\cos 5\theta + 5 \cos 3\theta + 10 \cos \theta)$.

31. $\sin 5\theta = 16 \sin^5 \theta - 20 \sin^3 \theta + 5 \sin \theta$.

32. $\cos 5\theta = 16 \cos^5 \theta - 20 \cos^3 \theta + 5 \cos \theta$.

33. $\tan \{\sin^{-1} [\cos (\tan^{-1} x)]\} = \dfrac{1}{x}$.

34. $3 \tan^{-1} a = \tan^{-1} \dfrac{3a - a^3}{1 - 3a^2}$.

35. $\tan^{-1} \dfrac{1}{1 - 2a + 4a^2} + \tan^{-1} \dfrac{1}{1 + 2a + 4a^2} = \tan^{-1} \dfrac{1}{2a^2}$.

36. $\tan^{-1} \dfrac{1}{3} + \tan^{-1} \dfrac{1}{5} + \tan^{-1} \dfrac{1}{7} + \tan^{-1} \dfrac{1}{8} = \dfrac{\pi}{4}$.

37. $\tan^{-1} \dfrac{bx}{a\sqrt{a^2 - b^2 - x^2}} = \sin^{-1} \dfrac{bx}{\sqrt{a^2 - x^2}\sqrt{a^2 - b^2}}$.

38. $2 \tan^{-1} (0.2) + \tan^{-1} \left(\dfrac{1}{7}\right) + 2 \tan^{-1} \left(\dfrac{1}{8}\right) = \dfrac{\pi}{4}$.

39. $\tan^{-1} \dfrac{1}{1 + a} + \tan^{-1} \dfrac{1}{1 - a} + \tan^{-1} \dfrac{2}{a^2} = n\pi$.

40. $\tan^{-1} \dfrac{2x - y}{y\sqrt{3}} + \tan^{-1} \dfrac{2y - x}{x\sqrt{3}} = \tan^{-1}\sqrt{3}$.

Solve the following equations for values of the angle less than 360°:

41. $\sin 2\theta + 2 \sin \frac{1}{2}\theta \cos \frac{1}{2}\theta = 0$.   *Ans.* 0°, 120°, 180°, 240°.

42. $\sin \theta \cos \theta - \sin \frac{1}{2}\theta \cos \frac{1}{2}\theta = 0$.   *Ans.* 0°, 60°, 180°, 300°.

43. $\sin 2\theta + \cos^2 \frac{1}{2}\theta - \sin^2 \frac{1}{2}\theta = 0$.   *Ans.* 90°, 210°, 270°, 330°.

44. $\sin^2 2\theta - \cos^2 2\theta = 0$.   *Ans.* $22\frac{1}{2}°$, $67\frac{1}{2}°$, $112\frac{1}{2}°$, etc.

45. $\cos 2\theta - \sin^2 \theta = 0$.

Ans. 35° 15.9′; 144° 44.1′; 215° 15.9′; 324° 44.1′.

46. $\sin 2\theta + \cos 2\theta + \sin \theta = 1$.   *Ans.* 0°, 65° 42.3′, 180°, 204° 17.7′.

47. $\sin 4\theta + \sin 2\theta + \cos \theta = 0$.

Ans. 70°, 90°, 110°, 190°, 230°, 270°, 310°, 350°.

48. $\theta = \sin^{-1} (\cos 2\theta) - 60°$.   *Ans.* 10°, 130°, 250°, 330°.

49. $\tan (80° - \frac{1}{2}\theta) = \cot \frac{2}{3}\theta$.   *Ans.* 60°.

50. $\cot (40° + \theta) = \tan \frac{1}{2}\theta$.   *Ans.* $33\frac{1}{3}°$, $153\frac{1}{3}°$, $273\frac{1}{3}°$.

51. $(\tan x + \sin x)(\tan x - \sin x) - \cos^2 x = 2(\sec^2 x - 3) \cot 2x$.

Ans. 116° 33.9′, 296° 33.9′.

52. $1 - \sin^2 x + \cos x = \sin 2x$.   *Ans.* 53° 7.8′, 90°, 180°, 270°.

53. $(4 \cos^2 \theta + 1) \tan^2 \theta = 6$.   *Ans.* 60°, 120°, 240°, 300°.

54. $\tan \theta - 1 + \tan (\theta - 45°) - \left(\dfrac{1 + \cos 2\theta}{2}\right) = \sin^2 \theta$.

Ans. 60°, 120°, 240°, 300°.

Solve the following equations, giving the values in general measure:

55. $\sin 2\theta + 1 = \tan (\theta + 45°)$.　　　　　*Ans.* $n\pi + \frac{3}{4}\pi$; $n\pi$.

56. $\cos 5\theta + \cos 3\theta + \cos \theta = 0$.　　*Ans.* $\frac{1}{6}(2n + 1)\pi$; $\frac{1}{3}(3n \pm 1)\pi$.

57. $\cos 7\theta - \cos \theta = 0$.　　　　　　　*Ans.* $\frac{1}{4}n\pi$; $\frac{1}{3}n\pi$.

58. $\sin 5\theta + \sin 3\theta = 0$.　　　　　*Ans.* $\frac{1}{4}n\pi$; $(2n + 1)\frac{1}{2}\pi$.

59. $\cos 7\theta + \cos 5\theta + \cos 3\theta = 0$.

　　　　　　　　Ans. $(2n + 1)\frac{1}{10}\pi$; $(2n + 1)\frac{1}{2}\pi \pm \frac{1}{6}\pi$.

60. $\tan (\frac{1}{4}\pi + \theta) + \tan (\frac{1}{4}\pi - \theta) = 4$.　　　*Ans.* $n\pi \pm \frac{1}{6}\pi$.

Solve the following equations for x:

61. $\sin^{-1} 2x - \sin^{-1} \sqrt{3}x = \sin^{-1} x$.

Solution.—Taking the sine of both members of the equation,

$$2x\sqrt{1 - 3x^2} - \sqrt{1 - 4x^2} \cdot \sqrt{3}x = x.$$

Transposing and factoring, $\quad x(2\sqrt{1 - 3x^2} - \sqrt{3}\sqrt{1 - 4x^2} - 1) = 0$.

Equating each factor to 0, $x = 0$, $2\sqrt{1 - 3x^2} - \sqrt{3}\sqrt{1 - 4x^2} - 1 = 0$.

Solving these equations, $\quad x = 0$, and $x = \pm \frac{1}{2}$.

All of these values satisfy the equation when principal values of the angles are used.

62. $\tan (\cos^{-1} x) = \sin \left(\cot^{-1} \frac{1}{2}\right)$.　　　　*Ans.* $\dfrac{\sqrt{5}}{3}$.

63. $\sin^{-1} \left(\dfrac{5}{x}\right) + \sin^{-1} \left(\dfrac{12}{x}\right) = \dfrac{\pi}{2}$.　　　*Ans.* 0; 13.

64. $\tan^{-1} 2x + \tan^{-1} 3x = \frac{1}{4}\pi$.　　　　　*Ans.* $\frac{1}{6}$.

65. $\tan^{-1} x + 2 \cot^{-1} x = 135°$.　　　　　*Ans.* 1.

66. $\sin \left(\dfrac{1}{2}\pi - 2 \tan^{-1}\sqrt{\dfrac{1 - x}{1 + x}}\right) = a$.　　*Ans.* a.

67. $\cos^{-1} \left(\dfrac{x^2 - 1}{x^2 + 1}\right) + \tan^{-1} \left(\dfrac{2x}{x^2 - 1}\right) = \dfrac{2}{3}\pi$.　　*Ans.* $\sqrt{3}$.

68. $\sin^{-1} (\frac{1}{4}x) + \sin^{-1} (\frac{1}{2}x) = \frac{1}{4}\pi$.　　　*Ans.* $\sqrt{1.022}$.

69. $\cot^{-1} (x - 1) - \cot^{-1} (x + 1) = \frac{1}{12}\pi$.　　*Ans.* $\pm (1 + \sqrt{3})$.

70. $\cot^{-1} (x) - \cot^{-1} (x + 2) = 15°$.　　*Ans.* $\sqrt{3}, -\sqrt{3} - 2$.

71. Given $a \sin \theta + b \cos \theta = c$, and $a \cos \theta - b \sin \theta = d$; eliminate θ.

　　　　　　　　　　　Ans. $a^2 + b^2 = c^2 + d^2$.

72. Eliminate φ from the following equations:

$$x = a \cos \varphi, \quad y = b \sin \varphi.$$　　　*Ans.* $\dfrac{x^2}{a^2} + \dfrac{y^2}{b^2} = 1$.

73. Eliminate φ from the following equations:

$a \cos \varphi + b \sin \varphi = c$, $b \cos \varphi + c \sin \varphi = a$.

　　　Ans. $(bc - a^2)^2 + (c^2 - ab)^2 = (ac - b^2)^2$.

Suggestion.—Solve for $\sin \varphi$ and $\cos \varphi$, then square and add.

74. Given $P \cos \theta - W \sin \alpha = 0$ and $R + P \sin \theta - W \cos \alpha = 0$; solve for R.　　　　　*Ans.* $R = \dfrac{W \cos (\alpha + \theta)}{\cos \theta}$.

75. Eliminate θ from the following equations:

$\csc \theta - \sin \theta = a$, $\sec \theta - \cos \theta = b$.　　*Ans.* $a^{\frac{2}{3}}b^{\frac{2}{3}}(a^{\frac{2}{3}} + b^{\frac{2}{3}}) = 1$.

Suggestion.—From the first $a = \dfrac{\cos^2 \theta}{\sin \theta}$. From the second $b = \dfrac{\sin^2 \theta}{\cos \theta}$.

Find $a^{\frac{2}{3}}b^{\frac{2}{3}} (a^{\frac{2}{3}} + b^{\frac{2}{3}})$.

76. Eliminate θ and φ from the following equations:

$\sin \theta + \sin \varphi = a.$
$\cos \theta + \cos \varphi = b.$
$\cos (\theta - \varphi) = c.$ $\qquad$ *Ans.* $a^2 + b^2 - 2c = 2.$

77. Eliminate θ from the following equations:

$$x \sin \theta - y \cos \theta = \sqrt{x^2 + y^2}.$$
$$\frac{\sin^2 \theta}{a^2} + \frac{\cos^2 \theta}{b^2} = \frac{1}{x^2 + y^2}. \qquad Ans.\ \frac{x^2}{a^2} + \frac{y^2}{b^2} = 1.$$

Suggestion.—Square the first equation and collect the terms in x^2 and y^2. This gives the square of $x \cos \theta + y \sin \theta = 0$. Then $\tan \theta = -\dfrac{x}{y}$. From this find $\sin \theta$ and $\cos \theta$ and substitute in the second equation.

78. Show that if $\tan (\theta - \alpha) \tan (\theta - \beta) = \tan^2 \theta$, $\theta = \dfrac{1}{2} \tan^{-1} \dfrac{2 \sin \alpha \sin \beta}{\sin (\alpha + \beta)}$

Suggestion.—Write the equation in the form

$$\frac{\sin (\theta - \alpha) \sin (\theta - \beta)}{\cos (\theta - \alpha) \cos (\theta - \beta)} = \frac{\sin^2 \theta}{\cos^2 \theta}.$$

Applying [**32**] and [**31**],

$$\frac{-\frac{1}{2} \cos (2\theta - \alpha - \beta) + \frac{1}{2} \cos (\alpha - \beta)}{\frac{1}{2} \cos (2\theta - \alpha - \beta) + \frac{1}{2} \cos (\alpha - \beta)} = \frac{\sin^2 \theta}{\cos^2 \theta}.$$

Clearing of fractions and uniting, or by composition and division,

$$\cos [2\theta - (\alpha + \beta)] = \cos 2\theta \cos (\alpha - \beta).$$

Applying [**16**],

$$\cos 2\theta \cos (\alpha + \beta) + \sin 2\theta \sin (\alpha + \beta) = \cos 2\theta \cos (\alpha - \beta).$$

Then $\qquad \tan 2\theta = \dfrac{\cos (\alpha - \beta) - \cos (\alpha + \beta)}{\sin (\alpha + \beta)}.$

Applying [**28**], $\quad \tan 2\theta = \dfrac{2 \sin \alpha \sin \beta}{\sin (\alpha + \beta)}.$

79. Given $aI^2 \cos \theta + bI \cos \theta = c\theta$, and $an^2 I^2 - bnI = c \dfrac{\theta}{\cos \theta}$; prove that $anI^2 = c \dfrac{\theta}{\cos \theta}.$

Suggestion.—Multiply the first by $\dfrac{n}{\cos \theta}$ and add the second.

80. Show that if $\tan \varphi = \dfrac{B}{A}$,

$$A \sin \theta + B \cos \theta = \sqrt{A^2 + B^2} \sin \left(\theta + \tan^{-1} \frac{B}{A} \right).$$

81. Given $I = W \sin \theta$, and $P \cos \theta = W \sin \theta$; show that

$$\frac{1}{I^2} = \frac{1}{P^2} + \frac{1}{W^2}.$$

82. Solve the following equations for x and y:

$x \cos \theta + y \sin \theta = a.$ *Ans.* $x = a \cos \theta + b \sin \theta.$

$x \sin \theta - y \cos \theta = b.$ $y = a \sin \theta - b \cos \theta.$

83. Show that

$$\frac{k \sin \theta}{\sin \cot^{-1}\left(-\dfrac{2 \cot \theta + RC\omega}{\omega\sqrt{4LC - R^2C^2}} \right)}$$

$$= \frac{2k}{\omega\sqrt{4LC - R^2C^2}}\sqrt{(LC\omega^2 - 1)\sin^2 \theta + \tfrac{1}{2}RC\omega \sin 2\theta + 1}.$$

CHAPTER IX

OBLIQUE TRIANGLES

89. General statement.—In the present chapter methods for solving any triangle will be developed. As pointed out in **Art. 38,** it is possible to solve a triangle whenever there are enough parts given so that the triangle can be constructed. The constructions and, likewise, the solutions fall under four cases, depending upon the parts given and required:

CASE I.   *Given one side and two angles.*

CASE II.   *Given two sides and an angle opposite one of them.*

CASE III.   *Given two sides and the included angle.*

CASE IV.   *Given the three sides.*

Since there are *six* parts to a triangle, and, in each of the four cases, *three* parts are given, then, in general, there are *three* unknown parts to be found in solving a triangle. Also, since

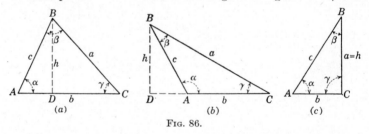

Fig. 86.

three independent equations are necessary and sufficient to determine three unknowns, it is necessary to have three independent formulas or relations connecting the parts of a triangle.

These three relations are:

(1) *The sum of the angles of a triangle is equal to* 180°.

(2) *The sine theorem, or the law of sines.*

(3) *The cosine theorem, or the law of cosines.*

For greater convenience in carrying out the numerical work of the solutions, various other relations are derived from the formulas growing out of the sine theorem and cosine theorem.

90. Law of sines.—*In any triangle the sides are proportional to the sines of the opposite angles.*

130

First Proof.—In Fig. 86, let ABC be any triangle, and let h be the perpendicular from B to AC. The following applies to each of the triangles (a), (b), and (c); but note that in triangle (c) $h = a$.

(1)
$$\sin \alpha = \frac{h}{c}.$$

(2)
$$\sin \gamma = \frac{h}{a}.$$

Dividing (1) by (2), there results

(3)
$$\frac{\sin \alpha}{\sin \gamma} = \frac{a}{c}, \text{ or } \frac{a}{\sin \alpha} = \frac{c}{\sin \gamma}.$$

Similarly, drawing perpendiculars from A to CB,

(4)
$$\frac{\sin \beta}{\sin \gamma} = \frac{b}{c}, \text{ or } \frac{b}{\sin \beta} = \frac{c}{\sin \gamma}.$$

Hence, uniting (3) and (4), there results

[33]
$$\frac{a}{\sin \alpha} = \frac{b}{\sin \beta} = \frac{c}{\sin \gamma}.$$

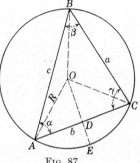

FIG. 87.

Second Proof.—In Fig. 87, let ABC be any triangle. About the triangle circumscribe a circle. Let O be the center. Draw the radii OA, OB, and OC. Draw OD perpendicular to AC.

Then $\angle AOD = \beta$ or is the supplement of β.

In triangle AOD,
$$AD = AO \sin \angle AOD.$$
$$\therefore \tfrac{1}{2}b = R \sin \beta.$$

In a similar manner,
$$\tfrac{1}{2}c = R \sin \gamma,$$

and
$$\tfrac{1}{2}a = R \sin \alpha.$$

These give
$$\frac{a}{\sin \alpha} = \frac{b}{\sin \beta} = \frac{c}{\sin \gamma}.$$

Corollary.—*The constant ratio of a side of the triangle to the sine of the opposite angle is equal to the diameter of the circumscribed circle.*

EXERCISES

1. Derive the proportion $\dfrac{b}{\sin \beta} = \dfrac{c}{\sin \gamma}$.

2. Derive $2R = \dfrac{a}{\sin \alpha}$, also $2R = \dfrac{c}{\sin \gamma}$.

3. Solve $\dfrac{a}{\sin \alpha} = \dfrac{b}{\sin \beta}$ for each part involved.

4. What does the law of sines become when one of the angles, say γ, is a right angle?

91. Law of cosines.—*In any triangle the square of a side equals the sum of the squares of the other sides minus twice the product of these sides by the cosine of their included angle.*

Proof.—In each triangle of Fig. 86,

$$a^2 = h^2 + \overline{DC}^2.$$

But $\qquad h^2 = c^2 - \overline{AD}^2 \text{ and } \overline{DC}^2 = (b - AD)^2.$

(Notice that in (a) AD is positive, in (b) negative, and in (c) DC is zero because D falls on C.)

$$\therefore a^2 = c^2 - \overline{AD}^2 + (b - AD)^2$$
$$= c^2 - \overline{AD}^2 + b^2 - 2b \cdot AD + \overline{AD}^2$$
$$= c^2 + b^2 - 2b \cdot AD.$$

But $AD = c \cos \alpha,$

[34₁] $\qquad\qquad \therefore\ \boldsymbol{a^2 = b^2 + c^2 - 2bc \cos \alpha}.$

By similar proofs or by cyclic changes we have,

[34₂] $\qquad\qquad \boldsymbol{b^2 = a^2 + c^2 - 2ac \cos \beta}.$

[34₃] $\qquad\qquad \boldsymbol{c^2 = a^2 + b^2 - 2ab \cos \gamma}.$

The cyclic changes of letters is carried out as follows:

a changes to b.	α changes to β.
b changes to c.	β changes to γ.
c changes to a.	γ changes to α.

EXERCISES

1. Are the formulas [34₁], [34₂], and [34₃] adapted to solving by logarithms?

2. Derive [34₂] and [34₃] independently.

3. Solve each of the three formulas for the angles in terms of the sides.

4. Solve $a^2 = b^2 + c^2 - 2bc \cos \alpha$ for b.

$\qquad\qquad\qquad$ *Ans.* $b = c \cos \alpha \pm \sqrt{a^2 - c^2 \sin^2 \alpha}.$

5. What does the law of cosines become when one of the angles, say γ, is a right angle?

92. Case I.   The solution of a triangle when one side and two angles are given.—In this case, it is evident that the third angle can always be found from the equation

$$\alpha + \beta + \gamma = 180°.$$

The sides can then be found by using the relations stated in the law of sines, namely,

$$\frac{a}{\sin \alpha} = \frac{b}{\sin \beta}, \frac{a}{\sin \alpha} = \frac{c}{\sin \gamma}, \text{ and } \frac{b}{\sin \beta} = \frac{c}{\sin \gamma}.$$

In each of these there are four parts of the triangle involved; therefore, if any three of these parts are known, the fourth can be found. That is, any one of these equations can be solved for any one of the four parts.

Any formula not used in the solution of a triangle may be used in checking the work. One should be certain, however, that the check formula was not involved in the formulas used in solving. For instance, when two equations from the law of sines have been used to find the parts of a triangle, the third equation from the law of sines cannot be used as a check, since the first two equations involve the third.

Two particularly convenient equations for checking the accuracy of the numerical solutions of triangles are the following, known as **Mollweide's equations,** from the German astronomer Karl Brandon Mollweide (1774–1825), though why they should bear his name is not clear, since they were known long before his time, and were used by Newton and others.

(1)
$$\frac{a - b}{c} = \frac{\sin \frac{1}{2}(\alpha - \beta)}{\cos \frac{1}{2}\gamma}.$$

(2)
$$\frac{a + b}{c} = \frac{\cos \frac{1}{2}(\alpha - \beta)}{\sin \frac{1}{2}\gamma}.$$

The certainty of these equations as a check lies in the fact that each contains all six parts of a triangle.

Mollweide's equations are readily derived from the law of sines. *Derivation of* (1).—From the law of sines,

$$a = \frac{c \sin \alpha}{\sin \gamma}, \qquad b = \frac{c \sin \beta}{\sin \gamma}.$$

Then
$$\frac{a - b}{c} = \frac{\dfrac{c \sin \alpha}{\sin \gamma} - \dfrac{c \sin \beta}{\sin \gamma}}{c} = \frac{\sin \alpha - \sin \beta}{\sin \gamma}.$$

By [19], [26],
$$= \frac{2 \cos \frac{1}{2}(\alpha + \beta) \sin \frac{1}{2}(\alpha - \beta)}{2 \sin \frac{1}{2}\gamma \cos \frac{1}{2}\gamma}.$$

Now $\sin \frac{1}{2}\gamma = \sin \frac{1}{2}[180° - (\alpha + \beta)] = \sin [90° - \frac{1}{2}(\alpha + \beta)]$
$$= \cos \frac{1}{2}(\alpha + \beta).$$

$$\therefore \frac{a - b}{c} = \frac{\sin \frac{1}{2}(\alpha - \beta)}{\cos \frac{1}{2}\gamma}.$$

Equation (2) can be derived in a very similar manner.

The same suggestions as were given in **Art. 41** for the solution of right triangles should be carried out here. Draw the triangle, state the formulas, make out a careful scheme for all the work, and, *lastly*, fill in the numerical part by the use of the **Tables.** Remember that in computations *time* and *accuracy* are of very great importance. Time will be saved by carefully planning the arrangement of the work. Accuracy can be secured by checking the work at every step. Verify at every step the additions, subtractions, multiplications, and divisions. Check interpolations when using **Tables,** by repeating the work at each step.

From geometry, the area of a triangle equals one-half the product of the base and altitude. Using b for base, h for altitude, and K for area, $K = \frac{1}{2}bh$. But $h = c \sin \alpha$, and $c = \dfrac{b \sin \gamma}{\sin \beta}$.

[**35**] $$\therefore K = \frac{b^2 \sin \alpha \sin \gamma}{2 \sin \beta}.$$

Since any side of the triangle can be used as base, or the given side, two other forms for [**35**] can be found. These may be written from the formula given by making the cyclic changes in the parts of the triangle.

Example.—Given $\alpha = 53° 23.7'$, $\gamma = 75° 46.3'$, and $a = 27.64$; find β, b, and c.

Solution.   *Construction*

$$\text{Given} \begin{cases} \alpha = 53° 23.7'. \\ \gamma = 75° 46.3'. \\ a = 27.64. \end{cases}$$

$$\text{To find*} \begin{cases} \beta = 50° 50'. \\ b = 26.695. \\ c = 33.375. \end{cases}$$

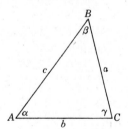

Formulas

$$\alpha + \beta + \gamma = 180° \qquad \therefore \beta = 180° - (\alpha + \gamma).$$

$$\frac{a}{\sin \alpha} = \frac{b}{\sin \beta} \qquad \therefore b = \frac{a \sin \beta}{\sin \alpha}.$$

* Values to be put in after solving.

$$\frac{a}{\sin \alpha} = \frac{c}{\sin \gamma} \qquad \therefore c = \frac{a \sin \gamma}{\sin \alpha}.$$

Logarithmic formulas

$\log b = \log a + \log \sin \beta + \text{colog} \sin \alpha.$
$\log c = \log a + \log \sin \gamma + \text{colog} \sin \alpha.$

Computation

$\beta = 180° - (53° 23.7' + 75° 46.3') = 50° 50'.$

$\log a = 1.44154$	$\log a = 1.44154$
$\log \sin \beta = 9.88948$	$\log \sin \gamma = 9.98647$
$\text{colog} \sin \alpha = 0.09541$	$\text{colog} \sin \alpha = 0.09541$
$\log b = 1.42643$	$\log c = 1.52342$
$b = 26.695$	$c = 33.375$

Check by Mollweide's equation:

$$\frac{c - b}{a} = \frac{\text{s n } \frac{1}{2}(\gamma - \beta)}{\cos \frac{1}{2}\alpha}, \text{ or } c - b = \frac{a \sin \frac{1}{2}(\gamma - \beta)}{\cos \frac{1}{2}\alpha},$$

$$c - b = 6.680 \qquad\qquad \log a = 1.44154$$

Note. Use Mollweide's equation with the middle-sized side in the denominator.

$a = 27.64$	$\log \sin \frac{1}{2}(\gamma - \beta) = 9.33426$
$\frac{1}{2}(\gamma - \beta) = 12° 28.1'$	$\text{colog} \cos \frac{1}{2}\alpha = 0.04896$
$\frac{1}{2}\alpha = 26° 41.8'$	$\log (c - b) = 0.82476$
	$c - b = 6.680$

EXERCISES

1. Given β, γ, and a; to find α, b, and c. Give formulas and scheme for solution.

2. Give the formula for area when b is the given side. When c is the given side.

3. Given $\alpha = 40° 5.5'$, $\beta = 28° 34.4'$, $c = 267.95$; find $a = 185.26$, $b = 137.58$, $\gamma = 111° 20.1'$.

4. Given $\alpha = 58° 9'$, $\beta = 41° 41.2'$, $c = 108.85$; find $a = 93.84$, $b = 73.472$, $\gamma = 80° 9.8'$.

5. Given $\alpha = 23° 4' 8''$, $\gamma = 33° 9' 22''$, $c = 5.94$; find $a = 4.256$, $b = 9.028$, $\beta = 123° 46' 30''$, $K = 5.265$.

6. Given $\beta = 34° 47.3'$, $\gamma = 109° 26.3'$, $a = 322.4$; find $b = 314.66$, $c = 520.09$, $\alpha = 35° 46.4'$, $K = 47,833$.

7. Given $\beta = 56° 21.3'$, $\gamma = 55° 17' 37''$, $b = 89.042$; find $a = 99.42$, $c = 87.93$, $\alpha = 68° 21.1'$, $K = 3,638.7$.

8. Given $\alpha = 144° 8.4'$, $\beta = 25° 19.2'$, $b = 430.10$; find $a = 589.14$, $c = 183.96$, $\gamma = 10° 32.4'$, $K = 23,174$.

Solve the following and check by Mollweide's equations:

9. Given $\alpha = 47° 16.2'$, $\beta = 75° 41.4'$, $c = 23.53$; find a, b, γ, and K.

10. Given $\alpha = 96° 41.4'$, $\gamma = 23° 13.3'$, $a = 2.458$; find b, c, β and K.

11. Given $\beta = 40°\ 13'\ 20''$, $\gamma = 60°\ 12'\ 13''$, $b = 22.659$; find a, c, and α.

12. Given $\beta = 18°\ 22'\ 26''$, $\gamma = 99°\ 15'\ 27''$, $a = 35.863$; find b, c, and α.

13. Given $\alpha = 68°\ 42'\ 28''$, $\beta = 35°\ 42'\ 18''$, $a = 27.423$; find b, c, and γ,

14. The distance between two points P and Q in a horizontal plane cannot be measured directly. In order to find the distance, a line $PA = 238$ ft. is measured in the same plane, and the angles $APQ = 128°\ 38'$ and $PAQ = 35°\ 58'$ are measured. Find PQ.   *Ans.* 526.37 ft.

15. To find the width of a river, a line $AB = 600$ ft. is measured on one side parallel to the bank of the stream. A tree C stands on the opposite bank. The angles $ABC = 65°\ 30'$, and $BAC = 81°\ 10'$ are measured. Find the width of the stream if line AB is 30 ft. from the bank of the stream.
          Ans. 951.8 ft.

16. Find the area of a triangular plot of ground one side of which is 130 rd., and the angles adjacent to this side are $47°\ 15'$ and $55°\ 45'$.
          Ans. 5264 sq. rods.

17. In a triangle, given c, α, and β; prove that

$$a = \frac{c \sin \alpha}{\sin\ (\alpha + \beta)}, \text{ and } b = \frac{c \sin \beta}{\sin\ (\alpha + \beta)}.$$

18. The points A and B are on opposite sides of a river, and the distance AB cannot be measured directly. A point C is chosen on the same side of the river as A and the following measurements made: $AC = 600$ ft., $\angle CAB = 80°\ 45'$, and $\angle ACB = 60°\ 10'$. Compute the distance AB.
          Ans. 825.6 ft.

93. Case II.   The solution of a triangle when two sides and an angle opposite one of them are given.—It is known from geometry that when two sides and an angle opposite one of them are given the triangle *may not* be uniquely determined.

With these parts given: (1) It may not be possible to construct any triangles; (2) it may be possible to construct just one triangle; (3) it may be possible to construct *two* triangles—the *ambiguous case.*

EXERCISES

Construct carefully the following triangles:

1. (a) $a = 1$ in., $c = 3$ in., and $\alpha = 40°$.

  (b) $a = 2$ in., $c = 3$ in., and $\alpha = 140°$.

2. (a) $a = 1$ in., $c = 2$ in., and $\alpha = 30°$.

  (b) $a = 3$ in., $c = 2$ in., and $\alpha = 35°$.

  (c) $a = 3$ in., $c = 2$ in., and $\alpha = 120°$.

3. $a = 2$ in., $c = 3$ in., and $\alpha = 30°$.

Corresponding to Exercises 1, 2 and 3 above, we have the following, which should be compared with the corresponding constructions in Fig. 88

(1) No solution when:

  (a) Angle is acute and opposite side less than adjacent side times the sine of the angle.

(b) Angle is obtuse and opposite side not greater than adjacent side.

(2) One solution when:

    (a) Angle is acute and opposite side is equal to adjacent side times the sine of the angle. This gives a right triangle.

    (b) Angle of any size and opposite side greater than adjacent side.

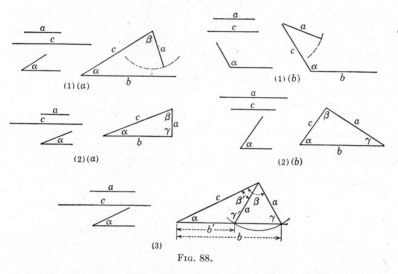

Fig. 88.

(3) Two solutions when angle is acute and the opposite side greater than the adjacent side times the sine of the angle, and less than the adjacent side.

The ambiguity of (3) is also apparent from the solution of γ found from the relation $\sin \gamma = \dfrac{c \sin \alpha}{a}$. This equation has two values of γ less than 180° each of which may enter into the triangle when α is acute. With each of these values of γ there may be found values of β and b, thus making two triangles.

When logarithms are used, proper conclusions can be drawn from the following, where a, b, and α are given. For other given parts, the proper change can easily be made.

If $\log \sin \beta = 0$, $\sin \beta = 1$, $\beta = 90°$; hence a right triangle.

If $\log \sin \beta > 0$, $\sin \beta > 1$, which is impossible; hence no solution.

If $\log \sin \beta < 0$ and $b < a$, and therefore $\beta < \alpha$, only the acute value of β can be used; hence there is one solution.

If $\log \sin \beta < 0$ and $b > a$, both acute value of β and its supplement may be used; hence there are two solutions.

If the given parts are a, c, and α, with α acute and $a < c$, the formulas for the solution are:

$$\frac{a}{\sin \alpha} = \frac{c}{\sin \gamma}, \text{ which gives two values for } \gamma, \text{ say, } \gamma \text{ and } \gamma';$$

$$\beta = 180° - (\alpha + \gamma); \beta' = 180° - (\alpha + \gamma');$$

$$\frac{b}{\sin \beta} = \frac{a}{\sin \alpha} \text{ gives } b; \frac{b'}{\sin \beta'} = \frac{a}{\sin \alpha} \text{ gives } b';$$

or $\dfrac{b}{\sin \beta} = \dfrac{c}{\sin \gamma}$ gives b; $\dfrac{b'}{\sin \beta'} = \dfrac{c}{\sin \gamma'}$ gives b'.

The area K can be determined as follows: suppose b, c, and γ are given. Then $K = \frac{1}{2}bh = \frac{1}{2}bc \sin \alpha$, and $\alpha = 180° - (\beta + \gamma)$, where β can be determined from $\sin \beta = \dfrac{b \sin \gamma}{c}$.

Example.—Solve the triangle when $a = 11.75$, $c = 15.61$, and $\alpha = 34° 15.3'$.

Solution.—Here α is acute, $a < c$, and $a > c \sin \alpha$; hence there are two solutions.

Construction

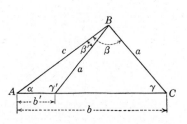

$$\text{Given} \begin{cases} a = 11.75. \\ c = 15.61. \\ \alpha = 34° 15.3'. \end{cases}$$

$$\text{To find} \begin{cases} \gamma = 48° 23.9'. \\ \beta = 97° 20.8'. \\ b = 20.704. \\ \gamma' = 131° 36.1'. \\ \beta' = 14° 8.6'. \\ b' = 5.1008. \end{cases}$$

Formulas

$$\frac{a}{\sin \alpha} = \frac{c}{\sin \gamma} \qquad \therefore \sin \gamma = \frac{c \sin \alpha}{a} = \sin \gamma'.$$

$$\beta = 180° - (\alpha + \gamma); \beta' = 180° - (\alpha + \gamma').$$

$$\frac{b}{\sin \beta} = \frac{a}{\sin \alpha} \qquad \therefore b = \frac{a \sin \beta}{\sin \alpha}.$$

$$\frac{b'}{\sin \beta'} = \frac{a}{\sin \alpha} \qquad \therefore b' = \frac{a \sin \beta'}{\sin \alpha}.$$

Logarithmic formulas

$$\log \sin \gamma = \log c + \log \sin \alpha + \text{colog } a = \log \sin \gamma'.$$
$$\log b = \log a + \log \sin \beta + \text{colog } \sin \alpha.$$
$$\log b' = \log a + \log \sin \beta' + \text{colog } \sin \alpha.$$

Computation

$\log c = 1.19340$
$\log \sin \alpha = 9.75041$
$\operatorname{colog} a = 8.92996$
$\log \sin \gamma = \overline{9.87377}$
$\gamma = 48° \ 23.9'$

$\gamma' = 131° \ 36.1'$
$\therefore \ \beta = 97° \ 20.8'$
$\underline{\beta' = 14° \ 8.6'}$

$\log a = 1.07004$
$\log \sin \beta = 9.99642$
$\operatorname{colog} \sin \alpha = 0.24959$
$\log b = \overline{1.31605}$
$\underline{b = 20.704}$

$\log a = 1.07004$
$\log \sin \beta' = 9.38801$
$\operatorname{colog} \sin \alpha = 0.24959$
$\log b' = \overline{0.70764}$
$\underline{b' = 5.1008}$

EXERCISES

Apply the tests and determine the number of solutions in Exercises 1 to 5.

1. Given $a = 4$, $c = 5$ and $\alpha = 55°$.

2. Given $a = 25$, $b = 45$ and $\beta = 117°$.

3. Given $b = 72$, $c = 28$ and $\gamma = 21°$.

4. Given $b = 22.5$, $c = 55.3$, and $\beta = 24° \ 0.5'$.

5. Given $a = 49.7$, $b = 55.3$, and $\alpha = 132°, \ 20.5'$.

6. Given $a = 78.291$, $c = 111.98$, $\alpha = 38° \ 21.3'$;
find $\qquad \gamma = 62° \ 34.1'$, $\beta = 79° \ 4.6'$, $b = 123.88$.
$\qquad \gamma' = 117° \ 25.9'$, $\beta' = 24° \ 12.8'$, $b' = 51.74$.

7. Given $a = 84.675$, $b = 94.423$, $\beta = 69° \ 11' \ 28''$;
find $\qquad \gamma = 53° \ 51' \ 2''$, $\alpha = 56° \ 57' \ 30''$, $c = 81.564$.

8. Given $a = 16.1$, $b = 18.7$, and $\alpha = 22° \ 18' \ 23''$;
find $\qquad \beta = 26° \ 9' \ 29''$, $\gamma = 131° \ 32' \ 8''$, $c = 31.752$.
$\qquad \beta' = 153° \ 50' \ 31''$, $\gamma' = 3° \ 51' \ 6''$, $c' = 2.849$.

9. Given $a = 58.345$, $b = 47.654$, and $\beta = 18° \ 15' \ 46''$;
find $\qquad \alpha = 22° \ 33.7'$, $\gamma = 139° \ 10.5'$, $c = 99.415$.
$\qquad \alpha' = 157° \ 26.3'$, $\gamma' = 4° \ 17.9'$, $c' = 11.4$.

10. Given $a = 248.4$, $b = 96.1$, $\alpha = 66° \ 31'$;
find $\qquad c = 270.5$, $\beta = 20° \ 47'$, $\gamma = 92° \ 42'$.

11. Given $a = 462.3$, $b = 535.9$, $\alpha = 42° \ 32'$;
find $\qquad c = 682.07$, $\beta = 51° \ 35.7'$, $\gamma = 85° \ 52.3'$.
$\qquad c' = 107.7$, $\beta' = 128° \ 24.3'$, $\gamma' = 9° \ 3.7'$.

12. Given $b = 160$, $c = 180$, $\beta = 20° \ 18' \ 23''$;
find $\qquad a = 316.1$, $\alpha = 136° \ 42' \ 47''$, $\gamma = 22° \ 58' \ 50''$.
$\qquad a' = 21.51$, $\alpha' = 2° \ 40' \ 27''$, $\gamma' = 157° \ 1' \ 10''$.

13. Given $b = 32.597$, $c = 43.465$, and $\beta = 28° \ 43.6'$;
find $\qquad a = 63.14$, $\alpha = 111° \ 25'$, $\gamma = 39° \ 51.4'$.
$\qquad a' = 13.092$, $\alpha' = 11° \ 7.8'$, $\gamma' = 140° \ 8.6'$.

14. Given $b = 46.342$, $c = 65.899$, and $\beta = 21° \ 15' \ 18''$;
find $\qquad a = 101.13$, $\alpha = 127° \ 42' \ 50''$, $\gamma = 31° \ 1' \ 52''$.
$\qquad a' = 21.706$, $\alpha' = 9° \ 46' \ 34''$, $\gamma' = 148° \ 58' \ 8''$.

15. Given $a = 24.897$, $b = 33.543$, $\alpha = 26° \ 44.9'$; find c, β, and γ. Check by Mollweide's equations.

16. Given $a = 25.34$, $c = 45.76$, $\alpha = 35°\ 43.8'$; find b, β, and γ.   Check.

17. Given $b = 366.62$, $c = 621.35$, $\beta = 154°\ 38'$; find a, α, and γ.   Check.

18. Given $a = 322.22$, $c = 847.36$, $\alpha = 17°\ 34'\ 48''$; find b, β, and γ. Check.

94. Case III.   The solution of a triangle when two sides and the included angle are given.   First method.—Let the given parts be a, b, and γ.   Then, from the law of cosines,

$$c = \sqrt{a^2 + b^2 - 2ab\ \cos\ \gamma},$$

and α and β may be found from

$$\sin\ \alpha = \frac{a\ \sin\ \gamma}{c} \text{ and } \sin\ \beta = \frac{b\ \sin\ \gamma}{c}, \text{ respectively.}$$

As a check, $\alpha + \beta + \gamma = 180°$ may be used, or use Mollweide's equations.

The area $K = \frac{1}{2}hb = \frac{1}{2}ab\ \sin\ \gamma$; or, in words, *the area equals one-half the product of the two sides and the sine of the included angle.*

[36] $$K = \tfrac{1}{2}ab\ \sin\ \gamma.$$

It is evident that the formula for finding c is not adapted to the use of logarithms.   This method is often convenient, however, when the numbers expressing the sides contain few figures or when only the third side is to be found.

EXERCISES

Solve the following by the first method and check:

1. Given $a = 2$, $b = 3$, $\gamma = 41°\ 39.8'$; find c, α, β, and K.

2. Given $a = 4$, $c = 8$, $\beta = 105°\ 32.3'$; find b, α, γ, and K.

3. Given $b = 27$, $c = 80$, $\alpha = 64°\ 45'\ 34''$; find a, β, γ, and K.

4. Given $a = 19$, $b = 29$, $\gamma = 76°\ 24'$; find c, α, β, and K.

5. Given $b = 14$, $c = 16$, $\alpha = 125°\ 18.9'$; find a, β, γ, and K.

95. Case III.   Second method.—For a solution by logarithms when two sides and the included angle are given, the following theorem, known as the law of tangents, is needed.

LAW OF TANGENTS.—*In any triangle the difference of any two sides is to their sum as the tangent of half the difference of the opposite angles is to the tangent of half their sum.*

Proof.— $\dfrac{a}{b} = \dfrac{\sin\ \alpha}{\sin\ \beta}$, from the law of sines.

Then $\dfrac{a - b}{a + b} = \dfrac{\sin\ \alpha - \sin\ \beta}{\sin\ \alpha + \sin\ \beta}$, by a theorem of proportion.

By [25] and [26], $= \dfrac{2 \cos \frac{1}{2}(\alpha + \beta) \sin \frac{1}{2}(\alpha - \beta)}{2 \sin \frac{1}{2}(\alpha + \beta) \cos \frac{1}{2}(\alpha - \beta)}$

$$= \tan \tfrac{1}{2}(\alpha - \beta) \cot \tfrac{1}{2}(\alpha + \beta) = \dfrac{\tan \frac{1}{2}(\alpha - \beta)}{\tan \frac{1}{2}(\alpha + \beta)}.$$

[37] $\qquad \therefore \dfrac{a - b}{a + b} = \dfrac{\tan \frac{1}{2}(\alpha - \beta)}{\tan \frac{1}{2}(\alpha + \beta)}.$

This can be put in another form for

$$\alpha + \beta = 180° - \gamma \text{ and } \tfrac{1}{2}(\alpha + \beta) = 90° - \tfrac{1}{2}\gamma,$$
$$\therefore \tan \tfrac{1}{2}(\alpha + \beta) = \tan (90° - \tfrac{1}{2}\gamma) = \cot \tfrac{1}{2}\gamma.$$

Substituting this in [37] gives

[38] $\qquad \tan \dfrac{1}{2}(\alpha - \beta) = \dfrac{a - b}{a + b} \cot \dfrac{1}{2}\gamma.$

Formula [37] or [38] makes it possible to find $\frac{1}{2}(\alpha - \beta)$ when a, b, and γ are given, while $\frac{1}{2}(\alpha + \beta)$ can readily be found because $\frac{1}{2}(\alpha + \beta) = 90° - \frac{1}{2}\gamma$, therefore α and β can be found from the relations:

$$\alpha = \tfrac{1}{2}(\alpha + \beta) + \tfrac{1}{2}(\alpha - \beta),$$
and $\qquad \beta = \tfrac{1}{2}(\alpha + \beta) - \tfrac{1}{2}(\alpha - \beta).$

It is evident that the other side can be found by the law of sines, which may also be used as a check, together with $\alpha + \beta + \gamma = 180°$ after finding $\frac{1}{2}\gamma$. A more certain check formula is one of Mollweide's equations.

A discussion similar to the above can be given when any two sides and the included angle are given. The other formulas can also readily be written by a cyclic change in the letters.

A convenient set of formulas for solving the triangle when a, b, and γ are given is

$$\tfrac{1}{2}(\alpha + \beta) = 90° - \tfrac{1}{2}\gamma.$$
$$\tan \dfrac{1}{2}(\alpha - \beta) = \dfrac{a - b}{a + b} \cot \dfrac{1}{2}\gamma.$$
$$\alpha = \tfrac{1}{2}(\alpha + \beta) + \tfrac{1}{2}(\alpha - \beta).$$
$$\beta = \tfrac{1}{2}(\alpha + \beta) - \tfrac{1}{2}(\alpha - \beta).$$
$$c = \dfrac{a \sin \gamma}{\sin \alpha} = \dfrac{b \sin \gamma}{\sin \beta}.$$

It should be noted that negatives are avoided if the larger angle and side come first in [38]. Thus, if $\beta > \alpha$ and hence $b > a$, write [38] in form $\tan \dfrac{1}{2}(\beta - \alpha) = \dfrac{b - a}{b + a} \cot \dfrac{1}{2}\gamma.$

Example.—Solve the triangle when $a = 42.367$, $c = 58.964$, and $\beta = 79° 31' 44''$.

Solution.

Construction

Given $\begin{cases} a = 42.367. \\ c = 58.964. \\ \beta = 79° 31' 44''. \end{cases}$

To find $\begin{cases} b = 66.057. \\ \alpha = 39° 6' 1''. \\ \gamma = 61° 22' 15''. \end{cases}$

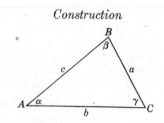

Formulas

$$\frac{1}{2}(\gamma + \alpha) = 90° - \frac{1}{2}\beta, \quad \tan\frac{1}{2}(\gamma - \alpha) = \frac{c - a}{c + a}\cot\frac{1}{2}\beta,$$

$$b = \frac{a\sin\beta}{\sin\alpha}, \quad \text{and, for a check,} \quad \frac{c - a}{b} = \frac{\sin\frac{1}{2}(\gamma - \alpha)}{\cos\frac{1}{2}\beta}.$$

Computation

$$\begin{aligned} c &= 58.964 \\ a &= 42.367 \\ c - a &= 16.597 \\ c + a &= 101.331 \\ \tfrac{1}{2}\beta &= 39°45'52'' \end{aligned}$$

$$\begin{aligned} \log a &= 1.62703 \\ \log\sin\beta &= 9.99270 \\ \text{colog}\sin\alpha &= 0.20019 \\ \log b &= 1.81992 \\ b &= 66.057 \end{aligned}$$

Check

$$\begin{aligned} \log(c - a) &= 1.22003 \\ \text{colog}(c + a) &= 7.99426 \\ \log\cot\tfrac{1}{2}\beta &= 0.07981 \\ \log\tan\tfrac{1}{2}(\gamma - \alpha) &= 9.29410 \\ \tfrac{1}{2}(\gamma - \alpha) &= 11° 8' 7'' \\ \tfrac{1}{2}(\gamma + \alpha) &= 50° 14' 8'' \\ \gamma &= 61° 22' 15'' \\ \alpha &= 39° 6' 1'' \end{aligned}$$

$$\begin{aligned} \log b &= 1.81992 \\ \log\sin\tfrac{1}{2}(\gamma - \alpha) &= 9.28585 \\ \text{colog}\cos\tfrac{1}{2}\beta &= 0.11426 \\ \log(c - a) &= 1.22003 \\ c - a &= 16.597 \end{aligned}$$

EXERCISES

1. Derive formulas like [38] for finding $\tan\frac{1}{2}(\alpha - \gamma)$; for $\tan\frac{1}{2}(\gamma - \beta)$.

2. Given $a = 50.35$, $b = 36.54$, $\gamma = 125° 12.3'$;
find $c = 77.405$, $\alpha = 32° 6.4'$, $\beta = 22° 41.3'$.

3. Given $a = 26.548$, $c = 41.654$, $\beta = 61° 0' 33''$;
find $b = 36.986$, $\alpha = 38° 53' 29''$, $\gamma = 80° 5' 57''$.

4. Given $a = 51.455$, $b = 27.345$, and $\gamma = 51° 19.8'$;
find $c = 40.461$, $\alpha = 96° 49.3'$, $\beta = 31° 50.9'$, $K = 549.29$.

5. Given $a = 285.6$; $b = 171.4$, and $\gamma = 65° 41' 10''$;
find $c = 265.78$, $\alpha = 78° 19' 9''$, $\beta = 35° 59' 41''$, $K = 22,305$.

6. Given $b = 248.65$, $c = 471.69$, and $\alpha = 139° 8' 46''$;
find $a = 679.52$, $\beta = 13° 50' 55''$, $\gamma = 27° 0' 19''$, $K = 38,361$.

7. Given $a = 43.5$, $b = 38.1$, $\gamma = 57° 14.9'$; find c, α, and β. Check by Mollweide's equations.

8. Given $a = 26$, $c = 25$, $\beta = 42° 56.8'$; find b, α, γ, and K. Check.

9. Given $b = 569.59$, $c = 543.76$, $\alpha = 71° 56'$;
find $a = 654.21$, $\beta = 55° 51.9'$, $\gamma = 52° 12.1'$.

10. In an isosceles triangle each of the two equal sides is 23 in. and the included angle is $58° 40'$. Find the third side. *Ans.* 22.5 in.

11. The two diagonals of a parallelogram are, respectively, 30 and 25 in., and one of the angles formed by them is $71° 25'$. Find the sides of the parallelogram. *Ans.* 16.18 in.; 22.38 in.

12. To find the distance AB through a swamp, a point C was chosen and the following measurements made: $CA = 163$ rd., $CB = 145$ rd., and angle $ACB = 36° 37'$. Compute the distance AB. *Ans.* 98.25 rd.

13. At a certain point the length of a lake subtends an angle of $53° 44.5'$, and the distances from this point to the extremities of the lake are 144 and 86.3 rd., respectively. Find the length of the lake. *Ans.* 116.1 rd.

14. Two railroad tracks intersect at an angle of $85° 30'$. At a certain time a train going 32 miles an hour passes the point of intersection; 2 min. later a train going 55 miles an hour on the other track passes this point. Write a formula showing their distance apart t min. after the first train passes the intersecting point. How far will they be apart in 25 min.? *Ans.* 24.045 miles, or 25.815 miles.

15. Two headlands P and Q are separated by water. In order to find the distance between them a third point A is chosen from which both P and Q are visible, and the following measurements are made: $AP = 1160$ ft., $AQ = 1945$ ft., and angle $PAQ = 60° 30'$. Find the distance PQ.
Ans. 1705 ft.

96. Case IV. The solution of a triangle when the three sides are given.—In this case the angles can be found by means of the law of cosines, from which the following formulas are derived:

$$\cos \alpha = \frac{b^2 + c^2 - a^2}{2bc}.$$

$$\cos \beta = \frac{a^2 + c^2 - b^2}{2ac}.$$

$$\cos \gamma = \frac{a^2 + b^2 - c^2}{2ab}.$$

These formulas give the cosines of the angles and, therefore, the angles; but they are not adapted to logarithms. They are convenient when the sides are expressed in numbers of few figures, or when tables of squares and products are at hand

A very good check formula is $\alpha + \beta + \gamma = 180°$.

EXERCISES

Find the angles when the sides are given as follows:

1. $a = 3$, $b = 4$, and $c = 5$.   5. $a = 10$, $b = 8$, and $c = 7$.
2. $a = 4$, $b = 3$, and $c = 6$.   6. $a = 200$, $b = 300$, and $c = 400$.
3. $a = 15$, $b = 19$, and $c = 21$.   7. $a = 12$, $b = 17$, and $c = 14$.
4. $a = 12$. $b = 13$, and $c = 16$.   8. $a = 12$, $b = 5$, and $c = 13$.

97. Case IV.   Formulas adapted to the use of logarithms.—

(1) Start with the equation $\cos \alpha = \dfrac{b^2 + c^2 - a^2}{2bc}$ and subtract each member of it from 1.   This gives

$$1 - \cos \alpha = 1 - \frac{b^2 + c^2 - a^2}{2bc}.$$

$$\therefore 2 \sin^2 \frac{1}{2}\alpha = \frac{a^2 - (b^2 - 2bc + c^2)}{2bc} = \frac{(a - b + c)(a + b - c)}{2bc}$$

Let $a + b + c = 2s$.   Then $a - b + c = 2(s - b)$, and $a + b - c = 2(s - c)$.

Substituting these values in the above,

$$2 \sin^2 \frac{1}{2}\alpha = \frac{2(s - b)2(s - c)}{2bc}.$$

[39₁] $$\therefore \sin \frac{1}{2}\alpha = \sqrt{\frac{(s - b)(s - c)}{bc}}.$$

In like manner are obtained the following:

[39₂] $$\sin \frac{1}{2}\beta = \sqrt{\frac{(s - a)(s - c)}{ac}}.$$

[39₃] $$\sin \frac{1}{2}\gamma = \sqrt{\frac{(s - a)(s - b)}{ab}}.$$

(2) By adding each member of the equation $\cos \alpha = \dfrac{b^2 + c^2 - a^2}{2bc}$ to 1, and carrying out the work in a manner similar to the above, there are obtained the following:

[40₁] $$\cos \frac{1}{2}\alpha = \sqrt{\frac{s(s - a)}{bc}}.$$

[40₂] $$\cos \frac{1}{2}\beta = \sqrt{\frac{s(s - b)}{ac}}.$$

[40₃] $$\cos \frac{1}{2}\gamma = \sqrt{\frac{s(s - c)}{ab}}.$$

(3) By dividing each formula of the set under (1) by the corresponding formula of the set under (2), there results:

[41₁]
$$\tan \frac{1}{2}\alpha = \sqrt{\frac{(s - b)(s - c)}{s(s - a)}}.$$

[41₂]
$$\tan \frac{1}{2}\beta = \sqrt{\frac{(s - a)(s - c)}{s(s - b)}}.$$

[41₃]
$$\tan \frac{1}{2}\gamma = \sqrt{\frac{(s - a)(s - b)}{s(s - c)}}.$$

These last three can be put in a form slightly more convenient.

Since
$$\sqrt{\frac{(s - b)(s - c)}{s(s - a)}} = \sqrt{\frac{(s - a)(s - b)(s - c)}{s(s - a)^2}}$$
$$= \frac{1}{s - a}\sqrt{\frac{(s - a)(s - b)(s - c)}{s}},$$

by writing
$$r = \sqrt{\frac{(s - a)(s - b)(s - c)}{s}},$$

[42₁]
$$\tan \frac{1}{2}\alpha = \frac{r}{s - a}.$$

Similarly, the following are obtained:

[42₂]
$$\tan \frac{1}{2}\beta = \frac{r}{s - b}.$$

[42₃]
$$\tan \frac{1}{2}\gamma = \frac{r}{s - c}.$$

In using any of these sets of formulas, the work may be checked by

$$\tfrac{1}{2}\alpha + \tfrac{1}{2}\beta + \tfrac{1}{2}\gamma = 90°.$$

The area can be found from

$$K = \tfrac{1}{2}bh = \tfrac{1}{2}bc \sin \alpha = bc \sin \tfrac{1}{2}\alpha \cos \tfrac{1}{2}\alpha$$
$$= bc\sqrt{\frac{(s - b)(s - c)}{bc}}\sqrt{\frac{s(s - a)}{bc}} = \sqrt{s(s - a)(s - b)(s - c)}.$$

[43]
$$\therefore K = \sqrt{s(s - a)(s - b)(s - c)}.*$$

Since the sine varies most rapidly for small angles, and the cosine most rapidly for angles near 90°, formulas [39] should be used when the angles are small, and [40] when the angles are near 90°. In all cases the tangent varies more rapidly than either sine or cosine. Hence, formulas [41] or [42] are always more nearly accurate than [39] or [40].

* Formula [43] was discovered by Hero (or Heron) of Alexandria about the beginning of the Christian era.

Again, formulas [**41**] or [**42**] are more convenient, since, for a complete solution of the triangle, they require only *four* logarithms to be taken from the table; while [**39**] and [**40**] require, respectively, six and seven.

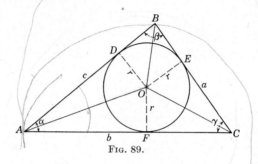

Fig. 89.

Formulas [**42**] may be derived by taking from geometry the fact that the area of a triangle, when the three sides are given, is

$$K = \sqrt{s(s-a)(s-b)(s-c)};$$

and, from Fig. 89, $K = sr$, where r is the radius of the inscribed circle.

$$\therefore sr = \sqrt{s(s-a)(s-b)(s-c)},$$

and

$$r = \sqrt{\frac{(s-a)(s-b)(s-c)}{s}}.$$

Also

$$AF + EC + EB = s.$$

$$\therefore AF = s - (EC + EB) = s - a.$$

But

$$\tan \frac{1}{2}\alpha = \frac{r}{AF}.$$

$$\therefore \tan \frac{1}{2}\alpha = \frac{r}{s-a}.$$

It should be noted that r in the formulas of this article is the radius of the inscribed circle, and the formula given for r is a simple formula for finding the radius of the inscribed circle.

Example.—Solve for the angles when $a = 23.764$, $b = 42.376$, and $c = 31.166$.

Solution.—Use formulas [**42**] with that for r.

$a = 23.764$	$\log (s-a) = 1.39600$
$b = 42.376$	$\log (s-b) = 0.79775$
$c = 31.166$	$\log (s-c) = 1.24272$
$2s = 97.306$	$\text{colog } s = 8.31289$

$$s = 48.653$$
$$s - a = 24.889$$
$$s - b = 6.277$$
$$s - c = 17.487$$
$$2s = 97.306$$

A check.

$$\log r^2 = 1.74936$$
$$\log r = 0.87468$$
$$\log \tan \tfrac{1}{2}\alpha = 9.47868$$
$$\therefore \tfrac{1}{2}\alpha = 16° 45' 21''$$
$$\log \tan \tfrac{1}{2}\beta = 0.07693$$
$$\therefore \tfrac{1}{2}\beta = 50° 2' 53''$$
$$\log \tan \tfrac{1}{2}\gamma = 9.63196$$
$$\therefore \tfrac{1}{2}\gamma = 23° 11' 45''$$

Check.—$\tfrac{1}{2}\alpha + \tfrac{1}{2}\beta + \tfrac{1}{2}\gamma = 89° 59' 59''$.

Remark.—The sum of s, $(s - a)$, $(s - b)$, and $(s - c)$ is $2s$, and hence is a check on the additions and subtractions.

To facilitate the subtractions, write the values of s on the margin of a slip of paper, when it can be placed above the values a, b, and c, successively. In like manner $\log r$ can be written on a margin and placed above logs of $(s - a)$, $(s - b)$, and $(s - c)$.

EXERCISES

1. Derive $\sin \dfrac{1}{2}\gamma = \sqrt{\dfrac{(s - a)(s - b)}{ab}}$ from the law of cosines.

2. Derive $\cos \dfrac{1}{2}\beta = \sqrt{\dfrac{s(s - b)}{ac}}$ from the law of cosines.

3. Derive $K = \sqrt{s(s - a)(s - b)(s - c)}$ by geometry.

4. What is the tabular difference for each of log sine, log cosine, and log tangent when the angle is near $11°$? How accurately can the angle be found from each?

5. Answer the same questions for $82°$ and $46°$.

6. In Fig. 89, show that $BE = s - b$.

7. Can $s - a$ be less than 0. Show why.

8. How many values of α will satisfy $\sin \dfrac{1}{2}\alpha = \sqrt{\dfrac{(s - b)(s - c)}{bc}}$?

9. In solving the triangle, when two sides and an angle opposite one of them are given, an ambiguity was introduced because from the sine of the angle two values of the angle were found. Why is there not an ambiguity when formulas [**39**] are used?

10. Given $a = 72.392$, $b = 55.678$, $c = 42.364$;
find $\qquad \tfrac{1}{2}\alpha = 47° 6' 10''$, $\tfrac{1}{2}\beta = 25° 2' 42''$, $\tfrac{1}{2}\gamma = 17° 51' 11''$.

11. Given $a = 43.294$, $b = 40.526$, $c = 39.945$;
find $\qquad \tfrac{1}{2}\alpha = 32° 32' 45''$, $\tfrac{1}{2}\beta = 29° 3' 2''$, $\tfrac{1}{2}\gamma = 28° 24' 11''$.

12. Given $a = 610$, $b = 363$, $c = 493$;
find $\qquad \alpha = 89° 33' 50''$, $\beta = 36° 31' 2''$, $\gamma = 53° 55' 6''$.

13. Given $a = 16.47$, $b = 25.49$, $c = 33.77$;
find $\qquad \alpha = 28° 5' 2''$, $\beta = 46° 46' 4''$, $\gamma = 105° 8' 51''$.

14. Solve the example in **Art. 97** by using formulas [**39**]. By using formulas [**40**]. Compare the work with that in the solution of the example.

15. Given $a = 98.34$, $b = 353.26$, $c = 276.49$;
find $\alpha = 11°\ 16'\ 58''$, $\beta = 135°\ 20'\ 27''$, $\gamma = 33°\ 22'\ 32''$, $K = 9{,}554.5$.

16. Given $a = 8.363$, $b = 5.473$, $c = 10.373$;
find $\alpha = 53°\ 27'\ 12''$, $\beta = 31°\ 43'\ 8''$, $\gamma = 94°\ 49'\ 40''$, $K = 22.804$.

17. Given $a = 49.63$, $b = 39.65$, $c = 67.54$; find α, β, γ, and K. Check.

18. Given $a = 2.374$, $b = 4.375$, $c = 5.73$; find α, β, and γ. Check.

19. Given $a = 70$, $b = 40$, $c = 35$; find the area of the triangle and the radius of the inscribed circle. *Ans.* $K = 470$, $r = 6.483$.

20. The sides of a triangle are, respectively 28, 16, and 25 ft. Find the area of the triangle and the area of the inscribed circle.
Ans. 198.52 sq. ft., 104.02 sq. ft.

21. Find the radius of the largest circular gas tank that can be constructed on a triangular lot whose sides are 75, 85, and 95 ft., respectively, and locate the center by giving the distance from the ends of the 85-ft. side to the point of tangency on the other sides. *Ans.* $r = 23.85$ ft., 52.5 ft., 32.5 ft.

GENERAL EXERCISES

1. Find the area of a triangle with sides 13.6 and 16.39 ft. and included angle $163°\ 36'\ 16''$. *Ans.* 31.459 sq. ft.

2. Find the area of a triangle with the three sides, respectively, 47.45, 36.4, and 36.65 ft. *Ans.* 658.85 sq. ft.

3. Two sides of a parallelogram are 46.3 and 46.36 rd., respectively, and the included angle is $56°\ 35'$. Find the area. *Ans.* 1791.6 sq. rd.

4. The base of a triangle is 62.53 ft. and the two angles at the base are, respectively, $109°\ 53'$, and $36°\ 16'$; find the other two sides and the area of the triangle. *Ans.* 66.407 ft., 105.57 ft., 1952.5 sq. ft.

5. Two angles of a triangle are, respectively, $57°\ 47'\ 14''$ and $59°\ 47'\ 43''$. If the included side is 14.63 in., find the area. *Ans.* 88.286 sq. in.

6. In a triangle an angle is $52°\ 16'$ and the opposite side is 36 in.; find the diameter of the circumscribed circle. *Ans.* 45.52 in.

7. If the sides of triangle are 4, 6, 7, find the radius of the inscribed circle. *Ans.* 1.41.

8. If the sides of triangle are 4, 6, 5, find the radius of the circumscribed circle. *Ans.* 3.024.

9. The three sides of a triangle are 8, 12, 15; find the length of median drawn to the side 12. *Ans.* 10.42.

10. In a triangle ABC, angle A is $126°\ 47'$, and AD is the bisector of angle A with D on the side BC. If $b = 24$, and $c = 15$, find AD, BD, and DC. *Ans.* $AD = 8.27$, $BD = 13.5$, $DC = 21.6$.

11. The angles of a triangle are in the ratio of $3:5:7$; and the longest side is 154 ft. Solve the triangle. *Ans.* Angles, $36°$, $60°$, $84°$; sides 91.02, 134.1.

12. The sides of a triangle are in the ratio of $7:4:8$; find the sine of the smallest angle. The cosine of the largest angle. *Ans.* 0.49992, 0.01786.

13. Solve the following triangle for the parts not given: $K = 7934.2$, $\alpha = 36°$, and $\beta - \gamma = 16°$. *Ans.* $a = 102.65$, $b = 171.99$, $c = 156.97$, $\beta = 80°$, $\gamma = 64°$.

14. The sides of a triangular field of which the area is 13 acres are in the ratio of $3:4:6$. Find the length of the shortest side. *Ans.* 59.248 rds.

15. Prove that in any triangle $K = \dfrac{b^2 \sin \alpha \sin \gamma}{2 \sin (\alpha + \gamma)}$.

16. Use the corollary of Art. 90, and the formula $K = \frac{1}{2}ab \sin \gamma$, and show that the radius of the circumscribed circle is given by $R = \dfrac{abc}{4K}$. Also show that $K = \dfrac{abc}{4R}$.

17. In a parallelogram given a diagonal $d = 15.36$, and the angles $\alpha = 26° 36.4'$, and $\beta = 36° 32.4'$ which this diagonal makes with the sides; find the sides. *Ans.* 10.25, 7.711.

18. In a parallelogram are given a side a, a diagonal d, and the angle θ between the diagonals; find the other diagonal and side.

19. If one side of a parallelogram is 13.52 in., one diagonal is 19.23 in., and one angle between the diagonals is 35° 32' 35", find the other diagonal. *Ans.* 40.27 or 8.974 in.

20. The two parallel sides of a trapezoid are a and b, and the angles formed by the nonparallel sides at the two ends of one of the parallel sides are, respectively, α and β. Find the lengths of the nonparallel sides.

$$Ans. \quad \frac{(a - b) \sin \alpha}{\sin (\alpha + \beta)} \text{ and } \frac{(a - b) \sin \beta}{\sin (\alpha + \beta)}.$$

21. The two parallel sides of a trapezoid are, respectively, 17.5 and 9.3 ft., and the angles formed by the nonparallel sides at the ends of the first side are respectively 31° 25', and 52° 36'. Find the lengths of the nonparallel sides. *Ans.* 4.298 ft., 6.55 ft.

22. Show that the area of any quadrilateral is equal to one-half the product of its diagonals and the sine of the included angle.

23. One side of a parallelogram is 46.4 rd., and the angles which the diagonals make with that side are 57° 34' and 36° 34'. Find the length of the other side. *Ans.* 49.67 rd.

24. Two circles whose radii are 28 and 36 in. intersect. The angle between the tangents at a point of intersection is 36° 35'. Find the distance between their centers. *Ans.* 60.82 in., 21.47 in.

25. B is 48 miles from A in the direction N 71° W, and C is 75 miles from A in the direction N 15° E. What is the position of C relative to B? *Ans.* 86.18 miles, N 48° 45' 16" E.

26. Given a parallelogram $ABCD$ with $AD = m$, $AC = d$, $AB = n$, $\angle BAD = \phi$, and $\angle DAC = \alpha$; prove that $\dfrac{\sin (\phi - \alpha)}{\sin \phi} = \dfrac{m}{d}$ and that

$$\cot \phi = \cot \alpha - \frac{m}{d \sin \alpha} \cdot \text{ If } AD = AB = m,$$

prove that $d = 2m \cos \frac{1}{2}\phi$.

27. Given two triangles with data shown in Fig. 90; prove that $p = w \tan 50°$. If $w = 200$, find the values of p, r_1, r_2, and r_3. *Ans.* $p = 238.36$, $r_1 = 178.46$, $r_2 = 300.56$, $r_3 = 254.87$.

EXERCISES, APPLICATIONS

1. Two streets intersect at an angle of 86° 36'. The corner lot fronts 100 ft. on one street and 146 ft. on the other, and the other two sides are perpendicular to the streets. Find the area of the lot. *Ans.* 13,696 sq. ft.

2. Along a bank of a river, a line 500 ft. in length is measured. The angles between this line and the lines drawn from its extremities to a point P on the opposite bank of the river are, respectively, 62° 35′ and 55° 44′. Find the width of the river.   *Ans.* 416.7 ft.

3. A bridge is to be constructed over a valley.   If the length of the bridge is l and the inclinations of the two sides of the valley are respectively α and β, find the height of a pier erected at the lowest point of the valley to support the bridge.   *Ans.* $\dfrac{l \sin \alpha \sin \beta}{\sin (\alpha + \beta)}$.

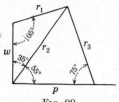

Fig. 90.

4. A ship at a point Q observes two capes A and B; the bearing of A is N 36° 35′ E, and the bearing of B is N 16° 36′ W.   Find the distance the ship is from each cape if it is known that the distance between the capes is 23.8 miles, and the bearing of B from A is N 58° 40′ W.   *Ans.* 19.92 miles from A; 29.61 miles from B.

5. In Fig. 91, find the height $DC = x$, and the distance $AC = y$ of an inaccessible object, having measured on a horizontal plane the distance a in the line CAB, and the angles α and β.

Suggestion.–

$$AD = \frac{a \sin \beta}{\sin (\alpha - \beta)}.$$

$$CD = AD \sin \alpha = \frac{a \sin \alpha \sin \beta}{\sin (\alpha - \beta)}.$$

$$AC = AD \cos \alpha = \frac{a \cos \alpha \sin \beta}{\sin (\alpha - \beta)}.$$

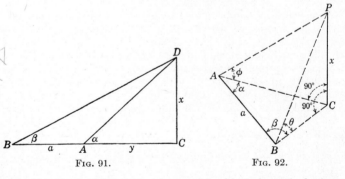

Fig. 91.   Fig. 92.

6. In Fig. 92, the point P is an inaccessible object above the horizontal plane ABC.   The straight line $AB = a$ is measured, also the angles α, β, θ, and ϕ.   Find the height x of the point P above the plane, giving two solutions which will check each other.   State the result in the form

$$x = \frac{a \sin \beta \tan \phi}{\sin (\alpha + \beta)} = \frac{a \sin \alpha \tan \theta}{\sin (\alpha + \beta)}.$$

7. In Exercise 6, given $a = 465$ ft., $\alpha = 49° 51′ 47″$, $\beta = 52° 46′ 30″$, $\phi = 39° 16′ 14″$, and $\theta = 40° 25′ 5″$; find x.   Could this exercise be solved if θ were not given?   *Ans.* 310.26 ft.

8. Two observers at A and B, 125 rd. apart on a horizontal plane, observe at the same instant an aviator. His angle of elevation at A is 72° 25′, and at B 64° 34.8′. The angles made by the projections of the lines of sight cn that horizontal plane with the line AB are 40° 27′ at A and 25° 38′ at B. Find the height of the aviator. *Ans.* 3080 ft.

9. Compute the inaccessible distance PQ (Fig. 93) when given the line $AB = a$ and the angles α, β, γ, and δ. Are the data sufficient for a check?

10. In Exercise 9, given $a = 330$ ft., $\alpha = 41° 36.5′$, $\beta = 64° 47.5′$, $\gamma = 30° 46.5′$, and $\delta = 35° 53.5′$; find PQ. *Ans.* 271.8 ft.

11. To find the distance between two inaccessible points A and B, a base line $CD = 800$ ft. is measured in the same plane as A and B, and the angles $DCA = 106°$, $DCB = 39°$, $CDB = 122°$ and $CDA = 41°$ are measured. Compute the distance AB. *Ans.* 1924 ft.

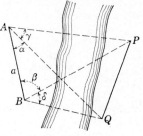

Fig. 93.

12. Two points P and Q are on opposite sides of a stream and invisible from each other on account of an island in the stream. A straight line AB is run through Q and the following measurements taken: $AQ = 824$ ft., $QB = 662$ ft., and $QAP = 42° 34.4′$, and angle $QBP = 57° 45′$. Compute QP. *Ans.* 872.1 ft.

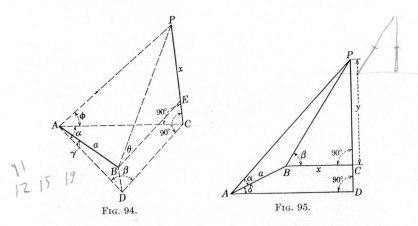

Fig. 94.   Fig. 95.

13. Two points P and Q on the same side of a river are inaccessible. They are both visible from a single point A only, on the opposite side of the river. From other points on this side of the river only P or only Q can be seen. Show what measurements can be made to compute PQ, and outline the solution.

14. A statue, of height $2h$, standing on the top of a pillar, subtends an angle α at a point on the ground distant d from the foot of the pillar. Prove that the height of the pillar is $\sqrt{h^2 + 2hd \cot \alpha - d^2} - h$.

15. A flagstaff 50 ft. tall stands on the top of the end of a building 105 ft. high.   At what distance from the base of the building will the flagstaff subtend an angle of 9°?   *Ans.* 251 ft. or 64.9 ft.

16. In taking measurements for finding the height of P (Fig. 94) above the horizontal line AC, a line $AB = a$ was measured in a plane making an angle $DAB = \gamma$ with the horizontal.   Other angles measured were $\angle DAC = \alpha$, $\angle ADC = \beta$, $\angle CAP = \phi$, and $\angle EBP = \theta$.   Find the height x that P is above C, and put in the form

$$x = \frac{a \cos \gamma \sin \beta \tan \phi}{\sin (\alpha + \beta)} = \frac{a \cos \gamma \sin \alpha \tan \theta}{\sin (\alpha + \beta)} + a \sin \gamma.$$

17. In Exercise 16, given $a = 145$ ft., $\alpha = 47° 60' 33''$, $\beta = 60° 44' 20''$, $\phi = 59° 35' 12''$, $\gamma = 4° 15' 31''$, and $\theta = 63° 45' 43''$; find x.
                                                                        Ans. 226.94 ft.

18. From the data given in Fig. 95; find x and y in the forms:

$$x = \frac{a \sin \alpha \cos \beta}{\sin (\beta - \alpha - \delta)}, \quad y = \frac{a \sin \alpha \sin \beta}{\sin (\beta - \alpha - \delta)}.$$

19. From the top of a hill 720 ft. high, the angles of depression of the top and the base of a tower are, respectively, 38° 30' and 51° 25'.   Find the height of the tower.   *Ans.* 263.1 ft.

20. A tower 120 ft. high casts a shadow 148 ft. long upon a plane which slopes downward from the base of the tower at the rate of 1 ft. in 12 ft. What is the angle of elevation of the sun?   *Ans.* 41° 53.5'.

21. A flagstaff 40 ft. high stands on the top of a wall 29 ft. high.   At a point P on the level with the base of the wall and on a line perpendicular to the wall below the flagstaff, the height of the wall and the flagstaff subtend equal angles.   Find the distance of P from the wall.   *Ans.* 72.63 ft.

22. A tower stands on the top of a hill whose side has a uniform inclination of θ with the horizontal.   At a distance of d from the foot of the tower measured down the hill the tower subtends an angle ϕ.   Find the height h of the tower.   *Ans.* $h = \dfrac{d \sin \phi}{\cos (\phi + \theta)}$.

23. In the preceding exercise, find the height of the tower if $\theta = 18° 45'$, $\phi = 23° 45'$, and $d = 410$ ft.   *Ans.* 224 ft.

24. From a point 250 ft. above the level of a lake and to one side, an observer finds the angles of depression of the two ends of the lake to be 4° 15' and 3° 30', respectively.   The angle between the two lines of sight is 48° 20'.   Find the length of the lake.   *Ans.* 3128 ft.

25. A man is on a bluff 300 ft. above the surface of a lake.   From his position the angles of depression of the two ends of the lake are 10° 30' and 6° 45', respectively.   The angle between the two lines of sight is 98° 40'. Find the length of the lake.   *Ans.* 3239 ft.

26. From a point h ft. above the surface of a lake the angle of elevation of a cloud is observed to be α, and the angle of depression of its reflection in the lake is β.   Find that the height of the cloud above the surface of the lake is $h \dfrac{\sin (\beta + \alpha)}{\sin (\beta - \alpha)}$ ft.

27. A kite K, sent up and fastened to the ground at a point A, drifted so that it stands directly over the point B in the same horizontal plane as A

and separated from it by water so that AB cannot be measured directly. To find the height of the kite, a line AC 1000 ft. long is laid off on the horizontal, and the angles $BAK = 46° \; 35' \; 52''$, $KAC = 67° \; 54' \; 39''$, and $ACK = 65°$ are measured. Compute the vertical height of the kite.

Ans. 899 ft.

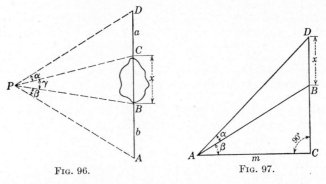

Fig. 96. Fig. 97.

28. Given the data as shown in Fig. 96; find the distance x in form:

$$(a + x)(b + x) \sin \alpha \sin \beta = ab \sin (\alpha + \gamma) \sin (\beta + \gamma).$$

After numerical values are substituted, this can be solved as a quadratic equation in x.

29. Given data as shown in Fig. 97; solve for x and state the result in a formula. *Ans.* $x = m[\tan (\alpha + \beta) - \tan \beta]$.

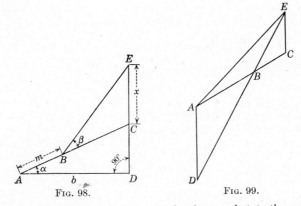

Fig. 98. Fig. 99.

30. Given data as shown in Fig. 98; solve for x and state the result in a formula. *Ans.* $x = \dfrac{(b \sec \alpha - m) \sin \beta}{\cos (\alpha + \beta)}$.

31. A flagstaff of known height c stands on the top at the end of a building. At a point P on the level with the base of the building, the building and the flagstaff each subtend an angle α. Find the distance of the point P from the base of the building.

Ans. $\dfrac{c}{\tan 2\alpha - \tan \alpha}$.

32. At each end of a horizontal base line of length $2a$, the angle of elevation of a mountain peak is β, and at the middle of the base line it is α. Show that the height of the peak above the plane of the base line is

$$\frac{a \sin \alpha \sin \beta}{\sqrt{\sin (\alpha + \beta) \sin (\alpha - \beta)}}.$$

33. Two railway tracks intersect making an angle of 70°. The tracks are connected by a circular Y that is tangent to each of the tracks at points 700 ft. from the intersection. Find the radius of the Y and its length. Neglect the width of the tracks.   *Ans.* 490.16 ft., 941.02 ft.

34. In Fig. 99, CE is parallel to DA, $DA = 10$ ft. $AB = 10$ ft., $BC = 5$ ft. and angle $DAB = 120°$. Find AE and angle AEC.
Ans. 18.03 ft., 46° 6.2′.

35. Two forces of 75 and 92 lb., respectively, are acting on a body. What is the resultant force if the angle between the forces is 54° 36′?
Ans. 148.6 lb.

36. Resolve a force of 250 lb. acting along the positive x-axis into two components of 170 and 180 lb., and find the directions of the components with respect to the x-axis.   *Ans.* 46° 2′ 23″; −42° 50′.

37. Two forces of 35 lb. each are acting on a body. One is directed downward and the other at a positive angle of 47° with the horizontal. Find the magnitude of the resultant and its direction with reference to the horizontal.
Ans. 25.655 lb.; −21° 30′.

38. Three forces of 18, 22, and 27 lb. respectively, and in the same plane are in equilibrium. Find the angles they make with each other. Check by noting the sum of the angles is 360°.

39. Four forces are acting on the origin of a system of rectangular axes. One of 300 lb. acts along the negative x-axis, one of 175 lb. acts along the positive x-axis, one of 60 lb. acts at an angle of 50° with the x-axis, and one of r lb. acts at an angle θ with the x-axis. If the forces are in equilibrium, find r and θ.   *Ans.* −28° 0′ 10″; 97.9 lb.

40. Five forces in equilibrium are acting at the origin of a system of rectangular axes. One of 4000 lb. acts along the negative y-axis, one of 1700 lb. acts along the negative x-axis, one of 1400 lb. acts at an angle of 135° with the x-axis, one of r_1 lb. acts at an angle of 60° with the x-axis, and one of r_2 lb. acts along the positive x-axis. Find r_1 and r_2.
Ans. 3475.8 lb.; 952.1 lb.

41. An automobile is traveling N. 45° W. at 40 miles per hour, and the wind is blowing from the northeast at 30 miles per hour. What velocity and direction does the wind appear to have to the chauffeur?
Ans. 50 miles per hour N 8° 7.8′ W.

42. A train is running at the rate of 40 miles per hour in the direction S. 55° W., and the engine leaves a steam track in the direction N. 80° E. The wind is known to be blowing from the northeast; find its velocity.
Ans. 29.47 miles per hour.

43. In a river flowing due south at 3 miles per hour a boat is drifted by a wind blowing from the southwest at the rate of 15 miles per hour. Determine the position of the boat after 60 minutes if resistance reduces the effect of the wind 60 per cent.   *Ans.* 4.42 miles N, 73° 40.8′ E.

44. A ship S is 12 miles to the north of a ship Q. S sails 10 miles per hour and Q 15 miles per hour.   Find the distance and direction Q should sail in order to intercept S which is sailing in a northeasterly direction.

Ans. 29.23 miles, N 28° 7.5′ E.

45. A tug that can steam 13 miles per hour is at a point P.   It wishes to intercept a steamer as soon as possible that is due east at a point Q and making 21 miles per hour in a direction S. 58° W.   Find the direction the tug must steam and the time it will take if Q is 3 miles from P.

Ans. S 31° 7′ 44″ E; 7′ 20.3″.

46. Two poles are 42 ft. apart and one is 6 ft. taller than the other.   A cable 48 ft. long is fastened to the tops of the poles and supports a weight of 400 lb. hanging from it by a trolley.   When the trolley is at rest find the two segments of the cable and the angle each makes with the horizontal. Suppose the trolley has no friction and that the two segments of the cable are straight lines.   *Ans.* 30.2 ft., 17.8 ft.; each angle = 28° 57.3′.

Suggestion.—Tension in cable is same throughout, and horizontal components are equal.

47. An airplane, which is at an altitude of 1800 ft. and moving at the rate of 100 miles per hour in a direction due east, drops a bomb.   Disregarding the resistance of the air, where will the bomb strike the ground?

Ans. 1551.7 ft. east of point where bomb was dropped.

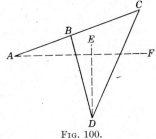

S u g g e s t i o n.—To find the number of seconds it is falling, use the equation

$$\tfrac{1}{2}gt^2 = 1600.$$

Fig. 100.

48. In a dredge derrick (Fig. 100) the following measurements are made: AF is perpendicular to DE, $AB = 20$ ft., $BC = 25$ ft., $DB = 30$ ft., $\angle FAC = 20°$, $\angle BDE = 15°$.   Find $\angle DBC$ and DC.

Ans. $\angle DBC = 95°$; $DC = 40.69$ ft.

49. $ABCD$ is the ground plan of a barn of known dimensions $AB = a$ and $AD = b$.   A surveying party, wishing to locate a point P in the same horizontal plane with the barn, measure the angles $DPC = \alpha$ and $BPC = \beta$. Determine the lengths of the lines $PB = x$, $PC = y$, and $PD = z$.

Ans. $x = -\dfrac{b \cos \phi}{\sin \beta}$; $y = \dfrac{a \sin (\phi + \alpha)}{\sin \alpha} = -\dfrac{b \cos (\phi - \beta)}{\sin \beta}$; $z = \dfrac{a \sin \phi}{\sin \alpha}$,

and $\tan \phi = -\dfrac{a + b \cot \beta}{b + a \cot \alpha}$, where $\phi =$ angle DCP.

50. The jib of a crane makes an angle of 35° with the vertical.   If the crane swings through a right angle about its vertical axis, find the angle between the first and the last positions of the jib.   *Ans.* 47° 51′ 18″.

51. If the jib of a crane makes an angle ϕ with the vertical and swings about the vertical axis through an angle θ, show that the angle α between the first and last positions of the jib is given by the equation

$$\sin \tfrac{1}{2}\alpha = \sin \phi \sin \tfrac{1}{2}\theta.$$

52. An umbrella is partly open and has n straight ribs each inclined at an angle ϕ with the center stick of the umbrella. Show that the angle θ between consecutive ribs is given by the equation $\sin \frac{1}{2}\theta = \sin \frac{\pi}{n} \sin \phi$.

53. To lay out a pentagon in a circle, draw two perpendicular diameters AB and CD (Fig. 101) and bisect AO at E. With E as a center and ED

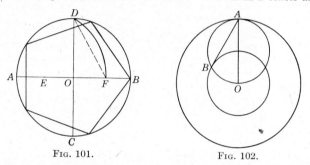

Fig. 101.	Fig. 102.

as a radius, draw the arc DF. The length of the chord DF is the side of the inscribed pentagon. Prove this.

54. To lay out a regular heptagon in a circle, make a construction as shown in Fig. 102. AB is very nearly the side of the inscribed regular heptagon. Determine the error in one side for a circle with a radius of 10 in. and determine the per cent of error. Determine the angle at the center intercepting the chord found by this process.

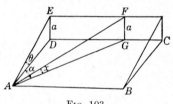

Fig. 103.

Ans. 0.2 per cent too small.

55. If the angle of slope of a plane is θ, find the angle of slope x of the line of intersection of this plane with a vertical plane making an angle α with the vertical plane containing the line of greatest slope. (Note the difference between this exercise and Exercise 18, page 99.)

Suggestion.—In Fig. 103, $AD = a \cot \theta$, $AG = a \cot x$.

$$\therefore \cos \alpha = \frac{a \cot \theta}{a \cot x}, \text{ and } \tan x = \tan \theta \cos \alpha.$$

56. Two vertical faces of rock at right angles to each other show sections of a geological stratum which have dips (angles with the horizontal) of α and β respectively. If δ is the true dip (angle between the stratum and a horizontal plane), show that

$$\tan^2 \delta = \tan^2 \alpha + \tan^2 \beta.$$

57. Two vertical planes at right angles to each other intersect a third plane that is inclined at an unknown angle θ to a horizontal plane. If the intersections of the vertical planes with the third plane make angles of α and β, respectively, with the horizontal plane, find the secant of θ.

Ans. $\sec \theta = \sqrt{1 + \tan^2 \alpha + \tan^2 \beta}$.

Note.—The answer to the above is an important formula used in calculus.

58. To determine the dip of a stratum that is under ground, three holes are bored at three angular points of a horizontal square of side a. The depths at which the stratum is struck are, respectively, p, q, and r ft. Show that the dip δ of the stratum is given by the equation

$$\tan \delta = \frac{\sqrt{(p - q)^2 + (q - r)^2}}{a}.$$

CHAPTER X

MISCELLANEOUS TRIGONOMETRIC EQUATIONS

98. Types of equations.—In this chapter equations of the following types will be considered:

(1) Where there is one unknown angle involved in trigonometric functions.

(2) Where the unknown is not an angle but is involved in inverse trigonometric functions.

(3) Where there are other unknowns, as well as unknown angles, involved in simultaneous equations; but only the angle involved trigonometrically.

(4) Where the unknown angle is involved both algebraically and trigonometrically.

It is not possible to give general solutions of equations of all these types. They offer algebraic as well as trigonometric difficulties. Methods of solution are best shown by examples.

EXERCISES

1. Given $\tan 2\theta = \frac{24}{7}$; find $\sin \theta$ and $\cos \theta$ without finding θ, for values in the first and second quadrants.

Solution.—By [21], $\tan 2\theta = \dfrac{2 \tan \theta}{1 - \tan^2 \theta}$.

$$\therefore \frac{2 \tan \theta}{1 - \tan^2 \theta} = \frac{24}{7}, \text{ or } 12 \tan^2 \theta + 7 \tan \theta - 12 = 0.$$

Solving for $\tan \theta$, $\tan \theta = \dfrac{-7 \pm \sqrt{49 + 576}}{24} = -\dfrac{4}{3} \text{ or } \dfrac{3}{4}$.

When $\tan \theta = \frac{3}{4}$, $\sin \theta = \frac{3}{5}$ and $\cos \theta = \frac{4}{5}$.

When $\tan \theta = -\frac{4}{3}$, $\sin \theta = \frac{4}{5}$ and $\cos \theta = -\frac{3}{5}$.

The student can easily verify these by triangles or formulas.

2. Given $\tan^{-1}(a + 1) + \tan^{-1}(a - 1) = \tan^{-1} 2$; find a.

Solution.—Let $\theta = \tan^{-1}(a + 1)$; then $\tan \theta = a + 1$.

Let $\beta = \tan^{-1}(a - 1)$; then $\tan \beta = a - 1$.

$$\tan(\theta + \beta) = \frac{\tan \theta + \tan \beta}{1 - \tan \theta \tan \beta} = \frac{a + 1 + a - 1}{1 - (a + 1)(a - 1)} = \frac{2a}{2 - a^2}.$$

$$\therefore \theta + \beta = \tan^{-1} \frac{2a}{2 - a^2} = \tan^{-1} 2.$$

That is, $\dfrac{2a}{2 - a^2} = 2$, whence $a^2 + a - 2 = 0$,

or $\qquad\qquad (a + 2)(a - 1) = 0$, whence $a = -2$ or 1.

Check.—When $a = -2$, $\tan^{-1}(-1) + \tan^{-1}(-3) = \tan^{-1}\dfrac{-1 - 3}{1 - (-1)(-3)}$

$$= \tan^{-1}\dfrac{-4}{-2} = \tan^{-1} 2.$$

3. Given $\sin 2\theta = 2 \sin \theta$; find $\theta < 360°$. *Ans.* $0, \pi$.

Suggestion.—Use $\sin 2\theta = 2 \sin \theta \cos \theta$ and factor.

4. Given $\tan 2\theta = \frac{12}{5}$; find $\sin \theta$ and $\cos \theta$ for θ in quadrants I and II.

$$Ans.\ \dfrac{2}{\sqrt{13}}, \pm\dfrac{3}{\sqrt{13}}.$$

5. $2 \cos^2 2\theta + \cos 2\theta - 1 = 0$; find θ. *Ans.* $(n \pm \frac{1}{6})\pi$, $(2n + 1)\dfrac{\pi}{2}$.

6. $\sin 2\theta + \sin 4\theta + \sin 6\theta = 0$; find θ. *Ans.* $\dfrac{n\pi}{4}$, $(2n + 1 \pm \frac{1}{3})\pi$.

Suggestion.—Apply [**25**] to $\sin 2\theta + \sin 6\theta$. Factor the resulting equation and equate each factor to zero.

7. $\cos 2\theta = \sin \theta$; find θ. *Ans.* $(2n + \frac{1}{2} \pm \frac{1}{3})\pi$, $(2n + \frac{3}{2})\pi$.

8. Given $\tan^{-1}(a + 1) + \tan^{-1}(a - 1) = \tan^{-1}(-\frac{7}{24})$; solve for a. *Ans.* 7.137 or -0.280.

9. Given $r \sin \theta = 2$ and $r \cos \theta = 4$; solve for r and θ. *Ans.* $r = 2\sqrt{5}$; $\theta = 26° \ 33' \ 53''$, $206° \ 33' \ 53''$.

Suggestion.—Square both equations and add, to obtain r. Divide the first by the second to obtain θ.

10. Given $\tan^{-1}(x + 1) + \tan^{-1}(x - 1) = \tan^{-1}\frac{3}{4}$; find x. *Ans.* 0.610 or -3.277.

11. Given $\cos^{-1}(1 - a) + \cos^{-1} a = \cos^{-1}(-a)$; solve for a. *Ans.* 0 or $\frac{1}{2}$.

12. Given $r \sin(\theta - \tan^{-1}\frac{1}{4}) = 3$, and $r \cos(\theta - \tan^{-1}\frac{1}{4}) = 6$; find r and θ. *Ans.* $r = 3\sqrt{5}$; $\theta = 40° \ 36' \ 5''$, $220° \ 36' \ 5''$.

Suggestion.—Obtain r as in Exercise 9. To obtain θ, divide one equation by the other; expand the functions and solve for $\tan \theta$.

13. $\sin 4\theta = 2 \cos 2\theta$; find θ. *Ans.* $(n + \frac{1}{2})\dfrac{\pi}{2}$.

14. $\tan^{-1}\dfrac{a + 1}{a - 1} + \tan^{-1}\dfrac{a - 1}{a} = \tan^{-1} x$. Find a when (a) $x = 1$, (b) $x = 2$, (c) $x = -7$. *Ans.* (a) $a = 0$, (b) $a = \frac{1}{2}$ or -1, (c) $a = 2$.

15. $\tan 2\alpha \tan \alpha = 1$; find α. *Ans.* $(n \pm \frac{1}{6})\pi$.

16. $\sin(120° - x) - \sin(120° + x) = \frac{1}{2}\sqrt{3}$; find x. *Ans.* $60°, 120°$.

17. $\cos(30° + \theta) - \sin(60° + \theta) = -\frac{1}{2}\sqrt{3}$; find θ. *Ans.* $60°, 120°$.

18. $\sqrt{1 - \sqrt{\sin^4 x + \sin^2 x}} = \sin x - 1$; solve for x.

19. $\sqrt{7 \sin \alpha - 5} + \sqrt{4 \sin \alpha - 1} = \sqrt{7 \sin \alpha - 4} + \sqrt{4 \sin \alpha - 2}$; solve for α. *Ans.* $(2n + \frac{1}{2})\pi$.

20. Given $\tan(80° - \frac{1}{2}\theta) = \cot \frac{2}{3}\theta$; find θ. *Ans.* $60°$.

21. Given $3 \sin^{-1} x + 2 \cos^{-1} x = 240°$; solve for x. *Ans.* $\frac{1}{2}\sqrt{3}$.

22. Given $\tan^{-1} x + 2 \cot^{-1} x = 135°$; solve for x. *Ans.* 1.

23. Given $\tan 2x\ (\tan^2 x - 1) = 2\sec^2 x - 6$; solve for x.

$\qquad\qquad$ *Ans.* 45°, 225°, 116° 33′ 56″, 296° 33′ 56″.

24. Given $10 \cos \theta - 5 \sin \theta = 2$; show that $\theta = 2 \tan^{-1} \frac{1}{2}$.

99. To solve $r \sin \theta + s \cos \theta = t$, for θ, when r, s, and t are known. *Solution.*—Either $\sin \theta$ or $\cos \theta$ can be eliminated by means of the relation $\sin^2 \theta + \cos^2 \theta = 1$, but logarithms are not applicable to this solution. A solution will now be given in which the computations may be done by logarithms.

(1) Let $\qquad\qquad m \sin \gamma = r$, and $m \cos \gamma = s$,

where m is a positive constant, and γ an auxiliary angle.

Such an assumption is always permissible, for, squaring both equations of (1) and adding,

$m^2 \sin^2 \gamma + m^2 \cos^2 \gamma = r^2 + s^2$, or $m^2 = r^2 + s^2$, or $m = \sqrt{r^2 + s^2}$.

Then m is real if r and s are real quantities.

Dividing the first equation of (1) by the second,

$$(2) \qquad\qquad \tan \gamma = \frac{r}{s}.$$

Since the tangent may have any real value from $-\infty$ to $+\infty$, when r and s are real, the angle γ will always exist.

Substituting (1) in the original equation,

$m \sin \gamma\, \theta + m \cos \gamma \cos \theta = t$, which, by **[16]**, gives

$$(3) \qquad\qquad m \cos (\theta - \gamma) = t.$$

Now m and γ can be determined from (1) and (2), and then $\theta - \gamma$ from (3). From this θ is determined.

Example.—Given $3 \sin \theta + 4 \cos \theta = 2$; find θ.

Solution.—This is of the form given in this article, and $r = 3$, $s = 4$, and $t = 2$. $\therefore m = \sqrt{r^2 + s^2} = \sqrt{9 + 16} = 5$.

$\tan \gamma = \dfrac{r}{s} = \dfrac{3}{4} = 0.75$, and $\gamma = 36° 52′ 12″$ or $216° 52′ 12″$.

Since r and s are both positive, $\sin \gamma$ and $\cos \gamma$ are positive. Therefore, γ is in the first quadrant, and so must be $36° 52′ 12″$ only.

$\cos (\theta - \gamma) = \dfrac{t}{m} = \dfrac{2}{5} = 0.4$, by equation (3).

$\qquad \theta - \gamma = 66° 25′ 18″$ or $293° 34′ 42″$.

$\qquad \therefore \theta = 66° 25′ 18″ + 36° 52′ 12″ = 103° 17′ 30″$,

and $\qquad\qquad \theta = 293° 34′ 42″ + 36° 52′ 12″ = 330° 26′ 54″$.

The method given in this article enables one to combine two simple harmonic motions of the same period into a single simple harmonic motion of the same period.

Thus, $r \sin \theta \pm s \cos \theta$ becomes $m \cos (\theta \mp \gamma)$.

100. Equations in the form $\begin{cases} \varrho \sin \alpha \cos \beta = a \\ \varrho \sin \alpha \sin \beta = b \\ \varrho \cos \alpha = c \end{cases}$

where ϱ, α, and β are variables. *Solution.*—Squaring all three equations and adding,

$$\rho^2 \sin^2 \alpha \cos^2 \beta + \rho^2 \sin^2 \alpha \sin^2 \beta + \rho^2 \cos^2 \alpha = a^2 + b^2 + c^2.$$
$$\rho^2 \sin^2 \alpha (\cos^2 \beta + \sin^2 \beta) + \rho^2 \cos^2 \alpha = a^2 + b^2 + c^2.$$
$$\rho^2 (\sin^2 \alpha + \cos^2 \alpha) = \rho^2 = a^2 + b^2 + c^2.$$

From the third equation,

$$\cos \alpha = \frac{c}{\rho} = \frac{c}{\pm \sqrt{a^2 + b^2 + c^2}}, \text{ or } \alpha = \cos^{-1} \frac{c}{\pm \sqrt{a^2 + b^2 + c^2}}.$$

Dividing the second equation by the first, $\dfrac{\rho \sin \alpha \sin \beta}{\rho \sin \alpha \cos \beta} = \dfrac{b}{a}.$

Whence, $\tan \beta = \dfrac{b}{a}; \beta = \tan^{-1} \dfrac{b}{a}.$

101. Equations in the form $\sin (\alpha + \beta) = c \sin \alpha$, where β and c are known. *Solution.*—Dividing by $\sin \alpha$,

$$\frac{\sin (\alpha + \beta)}{\sin \alpha} = \frac{c}{1}.$$

Taking the proportion by composition and division,

$$\frac{\sin (\alpha + \beta) + \sin \alpha}{\sin (\alpha + \beta) - \sin \alpha} = \frac{c + 1}{c - 1}.$$

By **[25]** and **[26]**, $\dfrac{2 \sin (\alpha + \frac{1}{2}\beta) \cos \frac{1}{2}\beta}{2 \cos (\alpha + \frac{1}{2}\beta) \sin \frac{1}{2}\beta} = \dfrac{c + 1}{c - 1}.$

Applying **[7]**, $\dfrac{\tan (\alpha + \frac{1}{2}\beta)}{\tan \frac{1}{2}\beta} = \dfrac{c + 1}{c - 1},$

or $\tan \left(\alpha + \dfrac{1}{2}\beta \right) = \dfrac{c + 1}{c - 1} \tan \dfrac{1}{2}\beta.$

From which, since β and c are known, α may be found.

Example.—Solve $\sin (\alpha + 50°) = 2 \sin \alpha.$

Solution.—Substituting 50° for β and 2 for c in the above formula, we have

$$\tan (\alpha + 25°) = \frac{2 + 1}{2 - 1} \tan 25° = 3 \tan 25°.$$

$$\log 3 = 0.47712$$
$$\log \tan 25° = 9.66867$$
$$\log \tan (\alpha + 25°) = \overline{0.14579}$$
$$\alpha + 25° = 54° \; 26' \; 29'' \text{ or } 234° \; 26' \; 29''.$$
$$\alpha = 29° \; 26' \; 29'' \text{ or } 209° \; 26' \; 29''.$$

102. Equations in the form tan $(\alpha + \beta) = c$ tan α, where β and c are known. *Solution.*—Dividing by $\tan \alpha$ and taking the resulting proportion by composition and division,

$$\frac{\tan (\alpha + \beta)}{\tan \alpha} = \frac{c}{1}.$$

$$\frac{\tan (\alpha + \beta) + \tan \alpha}{\tan (\alpha + \beta) - \tan \alpha} = \frac{c + 1}{c - 1}.$$

$$\frac{\dfrac{\sin (\alpha + \beta)}{\cos (\alpha + \beta)} + \dfrac{\sin \alpha}{\cos \alpha}}{\dfrac{\sin (\alpha + \beta)}{\cos (\alpha + \beta)} - \dfrac{\sin \alpha}{\cos \alpha}} = \frac{\sin (2\alpha + \beta)}{\sin [(\alpha + \beta) - \alpha]} = \frac{c - 1}{c + 1}.$$

$$\therefore \sin (2\alpha + \beta) = \frac{c + 1}{c - 1} \sin \beta.$$

Since c and β are known, α may be found.

Example.—Given $\tan (\alpha + 24°) = 4 \tan \alpha$; find α.

Solution.—Substituting 24° for β and 4 for c in the above formula, we have

$$\sin (2\alpha + 24°) = \tfrac{5}{3} \sin 24°.$$
$$\log 5 = 0.69897$$
$$\log \sin 24° = 9.60931$$
$$\text{colog } 3 = 9.52288$$
$$\log \sin (2\alpha + 24°) = \overline{9.83116}$$
$$2\alpha + 24° = 42° \; 40.7', \; 137° \; 19.3', \; 402° \; 40.7', \; 497° \; 19.3'.$$
$$2\alpha = 18° \; 40.7', \; 113° \; 19.3', \; 378° \; 40.7', \; 473° \; 19.3'.$$
$$\therefore \alpha = 9° \; 20.4', \; 56° \; 39.6', \; 189° \; 20.4', \; 236° \; 39.6'.$$

103. Equations of the form $t = \theta + \phi \sin t$, where θ and ϕ are given angles.—First express θ and ϕ in radians if not already so given. Then t must satisfy the relation $t - \theta = \phi \sin t$.

Let
$$y_1 = t - \theta \text{ and } y_2 = \phi \sin t.$$

Plot the straight line with equation $y_1 = t - \theta$, and the sine curve $y_2 = \phi \sin t$. An approximate value of t can be determined from the value of t where the line and the curve intersect. The more nearly accurate the sine curve is plotted the more nearly will the value of t come to the solution of the equation.

Example.—Given $t = 2 + \pi \sin t$.

Let $y_1 = t - 2$ and $y_2 = \pi \sin t$.

Now plot $y_1 = t - 2$, giving the line AB, as in Fig. 104. Also plot the modified sine curve with equation $y_2 = \pi \sin t$.

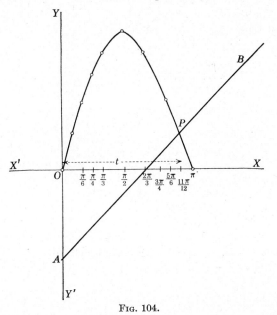

Fig. 104.

By measurement, the abscissa t for the point P of intersection is found to be 2.86 radians, or 164°. This is, therefore, an approximate solution for the equation.

Substituting for t in the original equation,

$$2.86 = 2 + \pi \sin 164° = 2 + 0.8659 = 2.8659.$$

This result shows the value of t to be too small.

Substituting $t = 165°$, $2.88 = 2 + \pi \sin 165° = 2.813$.

This result shows that 165° is too large, which the intersection of the curves also verifies. The correct value may now be approximated by assuming values of t between 164 and 165°, say 164° 10', etc.

EXERCISES

1. Change $3 \cos \theta + 4 \sin \theta$ to the form $m \cos (\theta - \gamma)$.

Ans. $5 \cos (\theta - 53° 7' 45'')$.

2. Change $a \cos \omega t + b \sin \omega t$ to the form $m \cos (\omega t - \gamma)$.

$$Ans. \; \sqrt{a^2 + b^2} \cos \left(\omega t - \tan^{-1} \frac{b}{a} \right).$$

3. Given $5 \sin \theta - 2 \cos \theta = 3$; find θ. $Ans.$ 55° 39′ 20″, 167° 56′ 50″.

Suggestion.—sin γ is $+$ and cos γ is $-$; therefore, γ will be in second quadrant.

4. Given $2 \sin \theta + 5 \cos \theta = -3$; find θ.

$$Ans. \; 145° \; 39′ \; 20″, \; 257° \; 56′ \; 50″.$$

5. Given $1.31 \sin \theta - 3.58 \cos \theta = 1.885$; find θ.

$$Ans. \; 99° \; 32′ \; 10″, \; 220° \; 16′.$$

Suggestion.—Use logarithms in the solution.

6. Given $\rho \sin \alpha \cos \beta = 3,$
$\rho \sin \alpha \sin \beta = 2,$
    $\rho \cos \alpha = 1$; find α, β, and ρ.

$$Ans. \; \rho = \sqrt{14}; \; \alpha = 74° \; 29′ \; 56″; \; \beta = 33° \; 41′ \; 24″.$$

7. Given $\rho \sin \theta \cos \phi = 6,$
$\rho \sin \theta \sin \phi = 2,$
    $\rho \cos \theta = 0$; find θ, ϕ, and ρ.

$$Ans. \; \rho = 2\sqrt{10}; \; \theta = 90°; \; \phi = 18° \; 26′ \; 5″.$$

8. Given $\sin (x + 32° 16′) = 4 \sin x$; find x.

$$Ans. \; 9° \; 36′ \; 23″, \; 189° \; 36′ \; 23″.$$

9. Given $\sin (y - 75°) = 3 \sin y$; find y. $Ans.$ 160° 35.3′, 340° 35.3′.

10. Given $\tan (r + 40°) = 5 \tan r$; find r.

$$Ans. \; 17° \; 18.6′, \; 32° \; 41.4′, \; 197° \; 18.6′, \; 212° \; 41.4.$$

11. Given $\tan (s - 60° 20′) = 2 \tan s$; find s.

12. Given $x = 1 + 30° \sin x$; find x approximately.

13. Given $S = 60° + \dfrac{\pi}{3} \sin S$; find S approximately.

CHAPTER XI

COMPLEX NUMBERS, DEMOIVRE'S THEOREM, SERIES

104. Imaginary numbers.—If the equation $x^2 + 1 = 0$ is solved, we obtain the symbol $\sqrt{-1}$, and from its derivation the square of this symbol must be -1. The symbol $\sqrt{-1}$ is commonly represented by i, and is called the **unit of imaginaries.** It follows that, if i is a number, it is such a number that $i^2 = -1$. This is taken as the definition of i.

As the only property attached to i by its definition is that its square is -1, it may be multiplied by any real number a. The product ai is called an **imaginary number.**

In contradistinction to imaginary numbers, the rational and irrational numbers, including positive and negative integers and fractions, are called **real numbers.**

The name "imaginary number" suggests an unreality that does not exist, for in the present state of the development of mathematics the imaginary number in comparison with whole numbers is no more unreal in the ordinary sense than is the fraction or the irrational number.

The system of numbers created by accepting the imaginary unit is an entirely new system of numbers distinct from the system of real numbers. The operations upon these numbers and their combinations with real numbers present various applications of trigonometry; and, further, the method developed in this field can be used to advantage in deriving various formulas in trigonometry.

105. Square root of a negative number.—By definition, the square root of a number is such a number that, when multiplied by itself, will give the original number. If c is a positive real number, no real number can equal $\sqrt{-c}$, for, by the definition of square root,

$$\sqrt{-c} \cdot \sqrt{-c} = -c.$$

But the square of every real number is positive. Hence, the square root of a negative real number is not a real number. That it is an imaginary number can be shown as follows:

$i^2 = -1$, by definition of unit of imaginaries.

$\sqrt{c} \cdot \sqrt{c} = c$, by definition of square root.

Then $\sqrt{ci} \cdot \sqrt{ci} = c(-1) = -c$, by multiplying.

$\therefore \sqrt{ci} = \sqrt{-c}$, taking the square root of each member.

Therefore, $\sqrt{-c}$ is an imaginary number, being of the form *ai* of **Art. 104.**

It follows that any number of the form $\sqrt{-c}$, where *c* is a positive real number can be put in the form $\sqrt{c}i$, which will be called the **proper imaginary form.** It is always best to write an imaginary number in the proper form before performing an operation.

Thus,
$$\sqrt{-4} = \sqrt{4}i = 2i.$$
$$\sqrt{-6} = \sqrt{6}i.$$

106. Operations with imaginary numbers.—It can be shown that, with proper definitions for combining imaginary numbers, they act like real numbers and obey all the laws of algebra, with the exception of the law

$$\sqrt{a}\sqrt{b} = \sqrt{ab}.$$

This law is excepted because it conflicts with the definition of the unit of imaginaries, and a definition is always fundamental.

Thus, if this law did apply, we should have

$$\sqrt{-1}\sqrt{-1} = \sqrt{(-1)(-1)} = \sqrt{1} = 1,$$

whereas, by definition, $\sqrt{-1}\sqrt{-1} = i^2 = -1$.

It, therefore, contradicts the definition of the unit of imaginaries to say

$$\sqrt{-2}\sqrt{-3} = \sqrt{(-2)(-3)} = \sqrt{6}.$$

If the imaginary numbers are first put in the proper form, no trouble will occur.

Thus, $\sqrt{-2}\sqrt{-3} = \sqrt{2}i \cdot \sqrt{3}i = \sqrt{6}i^2 = -\sqrt{6}.$

107. Complex numbers.—In order to solve the general quadratic equation $mx^2 + nx + l = 0$, it is necessary to have numbers of the form $a + bi$. These numbers are formed by adding a real number to an imaginary number.

Thus, the solution of $x^2 - 4x + 13 = 0$ gives the two values for *x*, $2 + 3i$ and $2 - 3i$.

Numbers of the form $a + bi$, where a and b are real numbers and $i^2 = -1$, are called **complex numbers.**

It should be noted that a real number is a special case of the complex number $a + bi$ where $b = 0$, and an imaginary number is a special case where $a = 0$.

108. Conjugate complex numbers are complex numbers which differ only in the signs of their imaginary parts. Thus, $3 - 4i$ and $3 + 4i$ are conjugate complex numbers. Also $+2i$ and $-2i$ are conjugate.

EXERCISES

Write the complex numbers conjugate to the following:

1. $2 - 3i$.   3. $1 + \sqrt{3}i$.   5. $-7 - \sqrt{-1}$.   7. $\sqrt{6}i$.

2. $3 + i$.   4. $\sqrt{2} - \sqrt{-3}$.   6. $3\sqrt{-1}$.   8. $\sqrt{-4}$.

109. Graphical representation of complex numbers.—Long after imaginary numbers presented themselves in algebraic work, they were rejected by mathematicians as impossible. Indeed, this was the case with any new kind of number. The negative number was disregarded for centuries after it appeared, and was generally accepted only after its graphical representation was introduced by Descartes (1596–1650). The system of representing complex numbers graphically was discovered independently by

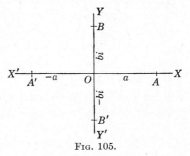

Fig. 105.

Wessel, a Norwegian, in 1797; by Argand, a Frenchman, in 1806; and by Gauss, a German, in 1831. More recently the practical importance of complex numbers as graphically represented has been recognized by physicists and engineers. In the field of electricity they have been put to important uses by Steinmetz and others. The system for representing these numbers is as follows:

Draw the rectangular coordinate axes $X'OX$ and $Y'OY$ (Fig. 105). The real numbers can be represented by points on the line $X'OX$ as follows: The point A, corresponding to the positive number a, is taken a units to the right of O. The point A', corresponding to the negative number $-a$, is taken a units to the left of O. The number a can also be considered as represented by the line segment OA, and the number $-a$ by the line segment OA'.

If the point A represents the number 5, the point A', representing the number -5, can be obtained by rotating OA through 180°. It seems, then, that multiplying a number by -1 acts as if the multiplication rotated the line segment representing the number through 180°.

Multiplying a number twice by i, as $5ii$, is the same as multiplying it by -1. In other words, it rotates the line segment, representing the number 5, through 180°, but does not change the length of the line segment. This suggests that multiplying a number by i should rotate the line segment, representing the number, through 90°. Then an imaginary number like bi would be represented by a point B on the positive y-axis and b units above the x-axis. Likewise, the imaginary number $-bi$ would be represented by a point B' on the negative y-axis and b units below the x-axis. The imaginary number bi can also be considered as represented by the line segment OB, and the imaginary number $-bi$, by the line segment OB'.

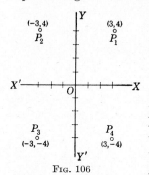

Fig. 106

The line on which the real numbers are represented is called the **axis of reals.** The line on which the imaginary numbers are represented is called the **axis of imaginaries.**

By this system it is easy to represent complex numbers graphically. In Fig. 106, the complex number $3 + 4i$ is represented by the point $(3, 4)$, 3 units to the right of the y-axis and 4 units above the x-axis. Likewise, the complex number $3 - 4i$ is represented by the point $(3, -4)$; the complex number $-3 + 4i$ by the point $(-3, 4)$; and the complex number $-3 - 4i$ by the point $(-3, -4)$.

The figure on which the complex numbers are plotted is called the **Argand diagram.**

EXERCISES

Plot the following complex numbers:

1. $2 + 3i$; $-2 + 3i$; $2 - 3i$; $-2 - 3i$.

2. $4 - i$; $4 + i$; $6i$; $-5i$; $-6 + 3i$; $-3 - 5i$; 4.

3. $\pi + i$; $\pi + \pi i$; $-1 - \pi i$; $e + \pi i$; $\pi - ei$; $e - i$; $-1 - ei$.

4. i; i^2; i^3; i^4; i^5; i^6; i^7; i^8.

Plot the following complex numbers and their conjugates:

5. $1 - i$, $2 + i$; $2i$; $3 - 2i$; $2i - 4$.

110. Powers of i.—It is a very easy matter to compute any power of i.

$i^1 = i$, by the definition of an exponent.
$i^2 = -1$, by the definition of the unit of imaginaries.
$i^3 = i^2 i = (-1)i = -i$.
$i^4 = (i^2)^2 = (-1)^2 = 1$.
$i^5 = (i^2)^2 i = (-1)^2 i = i$.
$i^6 = (i^2)^3 = (-1)^3 = -1$.

. . . .

By continuing this process, it is found that the integral powers of i recur in a cycle of the four different values i, -1, $-i$, and 1.

The powers of i can, perhaps, be made clearer by referring to Fig. 107, where each multiplication by i rotates the line segment of unit length through 90°.

The value of any integral power of i can be readily found as illustrated in the following examples:

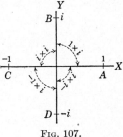

Fig. 107.

$i^{17} = (i^2)^8 i = (-1)^8 i = i$.
$i^{18} = (i^2)^9 = (-1)^9 = -1$.

EXERCISES

Compute the following powers of i:

1. i^7.	**6.** i^{20}.	**11.** $(-i)^{10}$.	**16.** i^{120}.
2. i^9.	**7.** i^{25}.	**12.** $(-i)^{11}$.	**17.** i^{202}.
3. i^{13}.	**8.** i^{30}.	**13.** $-i^6$.	**18.** $-i^{300}$.
4. i^{17}.	**9.** i^{35}.	**14.** $-i^8$.	**19.** $-i^{1000}$.
5. i^{18}.	**10.** $(-i)^8$.	**15.** i^{101}.	**20.** $(-i)^{567}$.

111. Operations on complex numbers.—Complex numbers, under proper definitions for the four fundamental operations, obey all the laws of algebra, with the exception of the law mentioned in **Art. 106**. In fact, complex numbers act the same as real numbers.

The four fundamental operations are defined as follows:

Addition. $(a + bi) + (c + di) = (a + c) + (b + d)i$.
Subtraction. $(a + bi) - (c + di) = (a - c) + (b - d)i$.
Multiplication. $(a + bi)(c + di) = ac + adi + bci + bdi^2$
$$= ac - bd + (ad + bc)i.$$

Division. $\dfrac{a + bi}{c + di} = \dfrac{(a + bi)(c - di)}{(c + di)(c - di)} = \dfrac{ac + bd + (bc - ad)i}{c^2 + d^2}$

$$= \dfrac{ac + bd}{c^2 + d^2} + \dfrac{(bc - ad)i}{c^2 + d^2}.$$

Note that division cannot be defined if $c^2 + d^2 = 0$, that is, $c = 0$ and $d = 0$. In this case it will be seen in the next article that the complex number $c + di = 0$. Hence, in the field of complex numbers, division by zero is impossible.

Note also that the four fundamental operations on complex numbers always yield complex numbers.

EXERCISES*

Simplify the following by performing the operations indicated:

1. $(3 + 2i) + (6 - 7i)$.

2. $(1 + i) - (3 + 4i)$.

3. $(7 - i) + (3 + 4i)$.

4. $(1 - 6i) - (-7 + 3i)$.

5. $(3 + 2i)(1 + 5i)$.

6. $(-3 + 2i)(-3 - i)$.

7. $\dfrac{4 - i}{2 + i}$.

8. $\dfrac{5 + 2i}{3 + 4i}$.

9. $\dfrac{6 - 3i}{7 - i}$.

10. $\dfrac{8 + 2i}{1 - 2i}$.

11. $\dfrac{\sqrt{2} + 3i}{1 - \sqrt{2}i}$.

12. $\dfrac{3 - \sqrt{6}i}{6 + \sqrt{3}i}$.

13. $\dfrac{2 + 3i}{\sqrt{2} - \sqrt{3}i}$.

14. $\dfrac{5}{\sqrt{2} + \sqrt{3}i}$.

15. $\dfrac{6 - 7i}{i}$.

16. $\dfrac{1 + 3i}{5i}$.

17. $(1 + \sqrt{5}i) \div \sqrt{5}i$.

18. $1 \div (1 - i)$.

19. $(1 - i)^2$.

20. $(1 + i)^3$.

21. $(3 - 4i)^2$.

22. $(\sqrt{3} - \sqrt{-2})^3$.

23. $\left(\dfrac{-1 + \sqrt{-3}}{2}\right)^3$.

24. $\left(\dfrac{1 + \sqrt{-3}}{2}\right)^3$.

25. $\dfrac{\sqrt{-a} + \sqrt{-b}}{\sqrt{-a} - \sqrt{-b}}$.

26. $\dfrac{a + i\sqrt{1 - a^2}}{a - i\sqrt{1 - a^2}}$.

27. $\dfrac{a + i\sqrt{1 + a^2}}{a - i\sqrt{1 - a^2}}$.

28. $(i^9 + i^{10} + i^{11} + i^{12})^7$.

29. $(i^7 + i^8 + i^9)^{12}$.

30. $(i^6 + i^9 + i^{12})^5$.

31. $\left(2a^{-2} - \dfrac{a}{\sqrt{-2}}\right)^3$.

32. $\left(\dfrac{a}{\sqrt{3}} + \dfrac{\sqrt{-3}}{a}\right)^3$.

33. Prove that $1 + i$ is a root of the equation
$$2x^3 - x^2 - 2x + 6 = 0.$$

34. Find the value of $x^3 - 2x^2 + 9x + 13$ when $x = 2 + 3i$.

* Answers to above problems will be found at the end of this chapter.

35. Find the value of $(x^2 + 5x)^2 + x(x + 5)$ when $x = \dfrac{-5 + i\sqrt{3}}{2}$.

36. Find the value of $\dfrac{3x^2 - 4x + 12}{x^2 + x + 1}$ when $x = 3 + i$.   *Ans.* 2.

37. Find the value of $\dfrac{5x^2 - 6x + 9}{2x^2 - x + 2}$ when $x = 2 + i$.   *Ans.* 2.

38. Prove that the sum and the product of two conjugate complex numbers are both real.

39. Prove that, if the sum and the product of two complex numbers are real, the numbers are conjugate complex numbers.

112. Properties of complex numbers. THEOREM I.—*If the complex number $a + bi = 0$, then $a = 0$ and $b = 0$.*

Proof.—Since the laws of algebra for real numbers hold with one exception for complex numbers, if bi is transposed to the right-hand side, then $a = -bi$. Squaring both sides of this equation gives $a^2 = -b^2$. But a positive number cannot equal a negative number unless both are zero. Hence $a = 0$ and $b = 0$.

THEOREM II.—*If $a + bi$ and $c + di$ are two complex numbers such that $a + bi = c + di$, then $a = c$ and $b = d$.*

Proof.—If $c + di$ is transposed to the left-hand side of the equation, $a - c + (b - d)i = 0$. Then, by Theorem I, $a - c = 0$ and $b - d = 0$. Hence, $a = c$ and $b = d$.

THEOREM III.—*If the product of two complex numbers vanishes, at least one of the factors must vanish, and conversely.*

The proof of this theorem is to be given as an exercise.

EXERCISES

Find the real values of x and y for which the following equations are true.

1. $x + y + (2x + 3y)i = 3 + i$.   *Ans.* $x = 8, y = -5$.

Suggestion.—Apply Theorem II, which gives

$$x + y = 3, \text{ and } 2x + 3y = 1.$$

2. $3x - 2 + (-2)i = y(1 - i)$.   *Ans.* $x = 1\frac{1}{3}; y = 2$.

3. $y + 16 + 2(y + 1)i = 2x(2 - i)$.   *Ans.* $x = 3; y = -4$.

4. $x(1 + i) + y(1 - i) = 2$.   *Ans.* $x = 1; y = 1$.

5. $x^2 + 2xyi + y^2 = 25 + 24i$.   *Ans.* $x = \pm 4$ and $\pm 3; y = \pm 3$ and ± 4.

6. $x(x + i) + y(y + i) = 5 + 3i$.   *Ans.* $x = 1$ and $2; y = 2$ and 1.

7. The product of two complex numbers is $5 - i$, the sum of their real parts is 3, and the product of their real parts is 2. Find the numbers.   *Ans.* $1 + i$ and $2 - 3i$, or $1 - \frac{3}{2}i$ and $2 + 2i$.

8. Find two conjugate complex numbers whose product is 13, and the product of whose imaginary parts is 9.   *Ans.* $2 + 3i$ and $2 - 3i$.

113. Complex numbers and vectors.—By means of the Argand diagram the general complex number $a + bi$ is represented by the point P (Fig. 108), with coordinates (a, b). In **Art. 109,**

it was seen that a real number or a pure imaginary number can be represented by either a point or a line segment. This notion can be extended to complex numbers by representing the complex number $a + bi$ by the line segment OP. For, if the segment OP is given, a, the real part of the complex number, equals the projection of OP on the x-axis, and b, the coefficient of i, equals the projection of OP on the y-axis.

Definition.—A quantity that has magnitude as well as direction is called a **vector.**

The line segment OP begins at the origin and ends at P. It, therefore, has a magnitude and a direction. Hence the complex number P can be represented by the vector OP. Hereafter, the word "vector" will be used in place of "line segment."

114. Polar form of complex numbers.—The vectorial representation of a complex number enables it to be written in another form, called the "polar form" of the complex number. Let

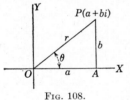

Fig. 108.

θ be the angle through which the positive portion of the x-axis would have to be revolved in order to coincide with the vector OP (Fig. 108). The angle θ is called the **amplitude,** or **argument,** of the complex number $a + bi$. Let r be the length, or magnitude, of the vector OP. The number r is called the **modulus** of the complex number $a + bi$, and is always taken *positive*. From the right triangle whose sides are a, b, and r,

$$a = r \cos \theta, \text{ and } b = r \sin \theta.$$

Note that these equations hold no matter in what quadrant θ lies. The complex number $a + bi$ can now be written

$$a + bi = r(\cos \theta + i \sin \theta).$$

The expression $r(\cos \theta + i \sin \theta)$ is called the **polar form** of a complex number.

The expression $a + bi$ is called the **rectangular form** of a complex number.

If θ is increased, or decreased, by multiples of 360°, the sine and the cosine are not changed, then the polar form of a complex number can be written

$$r[\cos (\theta + k \cdot 360°) + i \sin (\theta + k \cdot 360°)],$$

where k is any positive or negative integer. This is called the **complete polar form** of a complex number.

The values of r and θ in terms of a and b can be obtained immediately from Fig. 108. They are

$$r = \sqrt{a^2 + b^2}, \text{ and } \theta = \sin^{-1}\frac{b}{r} = \cos^{-1}\frac{a}{r} = \tan^{-1}\frac{b}{a}.$$

Example 1.—Write $2 + 2\sqrt{3}i$ in the polar form. Plot.

$$r = \sqrt{2^2 + (2\sqrt{3})^2} = 4.$$

$$\theta = \tan^{-1}\frac{2\sqrt{3}}{2} = \tan^{-1}\sqrt{3} = 60°.$$

$$\therefore 2 + 2\sqrt{3}i = 4(\cos 60° + i \sin 60°).$$

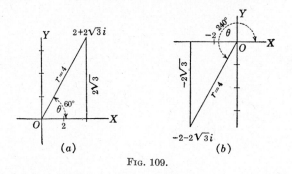

Fig. 109.

The plotting is shown in Fig. 109a.

Example 2.—Write $-2 - 2\sqrt{3}i$ in the polar form. Plot.

$$r = \sqrt{(-2)^2 + (-2\sqrt{3})^2} = 4.$$

$$\theta = \tan^{-1}\frac{-2\sqrt{3}}{-2} = \tan^{-1}\sqrt{3} = 240°.$$

Here 240° is taken because both a and b are negative and θ is, therefore, in the third quadrant.

$$\therefore -2 - 2\sqrt{3}i = 4(\cos 240° + i \sin 240°).$$

The plotting is shown in Fig. 109b.

Note that, while a and b may be negative numbers, r is always *positive*, and that the signs in front of cos θ and sin θ are always *plus*.

The complete polar forms of the complex numbers in the preceding examples are

$$2 + 2\sqrt{3}i = 4[\cos (60° + k \cdot 360°) + i \sin (60° + k \cdot 360°)],$$

and

$$-2 - 2\sqrt{3}i = 4[\cos (240° + k \cdot 360°) + i \sin (240° + k \cdot 360°)].$$

Suggestion.—In changing from rectangular form to polar form, it is better first to plot the complex number, and then check the results obtained by computation with those indicated on the graph. Thus, the common error of writing for θ a first-quadrant angle when θ is an angle in some other quadrant may be avoided. Often the values of r and θ can be obtained directly from the figure.

EXERCISES*

Write the following complex numbers in the polar form:

1. $1 + i$.   *Ans.* $\sqrt{2}$ (cos 45° + i sin 45°).

2. $-1 + i$.   *Ans.* $\sqrt{2}$ (cos 135° + i sin 135°).

3. $-1 - i$.   *Ans.* $\sqrt{2}$ (cos 225° + i sin 225°).

4. $1 - i$.   *Ans.* $\sqrt{2}$ (cos 315° + i sin 315°).

5. $-\sqrt{3} + 3i$.   **9.** $-3\sqrt{2} - 3\sqrt{6}i$.

6. $\sqrt{3} - 3i$.   **10.** $\sqrt{2} + \sqrt{6}i$.

7. $\sqrt{6} + 3\sqrt{2}i$.   **11.** $\sqrt{5} + \sqrt{15}i$.

8. $-\sqrt[3]{2} + \sqrt[3]{2}i$.   **12.** $-\sqrt{21} + \sqrt{7}i$.

13. 4.	**18.** $-i$.	**23.** $2i^2$.
14. $4i$.	**19.** 1.	**24.** $3i^3$.
15. -6.	**20.** -1.	**25.** $1 + 3i$.
16. $-6i$.	**21.** $\sqrt{2}$.	**26.** $4 - 2i$.
17. i.	**22.** $\sqrt{-3}$.	**27.** $-4 + 3i$.

28. cos 30° − i sin 30°.   **31.** cos 30° + i sin 60°.

29. −cos 75° + i sin 75°.   **32.** sin 30° + i sin 240°.

30. −3(cos 10° + i sin 10°).   **33.** −sin 210° − i sin 120°.

Write the following complex numbers in the complete polar form:

34. $3 + 3i$.   **35.** $-\sqrt{3} - 3i$.   **36.** $-1 + \sqrt{3}i$.   **37.** $3i$.

Write the following complex numbers in the rectangular form:

38. 3 (cos 30° + i sin 30°).   **46.** 2 (cos 150° + i sin 150°).

39. $\sqrt{2}$ (cos 45° + i sin 45°).   **47.** 2 (cos 510° + i sin 510°).

40. 4(cos $\frac{1}{3}\pi$ + i sin $\frac{1}{3}\pi$).   **48.** cos (−210°) + i sin (−210°).

41. 2 (cos $\frac{1}{2}\pi$ + i sin $\frac{1}{2}\pi$).   **49.** cos (−570°) + i sin (−570°).

42. 4 (cos $\frac{1}{4}\pi$ + i sin $\frac{1}{4}\pi$).   **50.** cos 100° + i sin 100°.

43. 4 (cos $\frac{7}{6}\pi$ + i sin $\frac{7}{6}\pi$).   **51.** 2 (cos 200° + i sin 200°).

44. 10 (cos $\frac{2}{3}\pi$ + i sin $\frac{2}{3}\pi$).   **52.** 3 (cos 300° + i sin 300°).

45. 6 (cos 720° + i sin 720°).   **53.** 4 (cos 1000° + i sin 1000°).

115. Graphical representation of addition.—Let the vector OP (Fig. 110), represent the complex number $a + bi$, and let the vector OS represent the complex number $c + di$.

* Answers to some of the above problems will be found at the end of this chapter.

In order to represent graphically the sum of $a + bi$ and $c + di$, complete the parallelogram $OPTS$ by drawing PT parallel to OS and ST parallel to OP. Then the vector OT represents the complex number $(a + bi) + (c + di)$.

Proof.—Drop perpendiculars from P and T to the x-axis, and call the feet of these perpendiculars P_1 and T_1, respectively. Also drop perpendiculars from S and T to the y-axis, and call the feet of these perpendiculars S_2 and T_2, respectively.

Then the real part of the complex number represented by the vector OT is $OT_1 = OP_1 + P_1T_1 = a + c$.

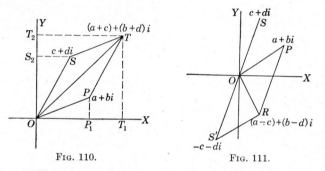

FIG. 110. FIG. 111.

The coefficient of i for the complex number represented by the vector OT is $OT_2 = OS_2 + S_2T_2 = b + d$.

Therefore, OT represents the complex number $a + c + (b + d)i$.

116. Graphical representation of subtraction.—In order to represent graphically $(a + bi) - (c + di)$, write the expression in the form $(a + bi) + (-c - di)$. In Fig. 111, produce the line OS through the origin to a point S', so that $S'O = OS$. The vector OS' represents the complex number $-c - di$. Then add the vector OS' to OP precisely as was done in the case of addition.

EXERCISES

Perform the following operations graphically, and check the results algebraically:

1. $(3 + 4i) + (5 + 2i)$.   5. $(3 + 4i) - (5 + 2i)$.
2. $(-3 + 2i) + (6 - 3i)$.   6. $(-3 + 2i) - (8 - 3i)$.
3. $(2 + i) + i$.   7. $(2 + i) - i$.
4. $2 + (3 - i)$.   8. $(1 - i) + (-2 + 3i) + (4 + i)$.
9. $2 (\cos 45° + i \sin 45°) + (\cos 135° + i \sin 135°)$.
10. $(\cos 30° + i \sin 30°) + (\cos 60° + i \sin 60°)$.
11. $(\cos 0° + i \sin 0°) + 4 (\cos 90° + i \sin 90°)$.
12. $(\cos 60° + i \sin 60°) + (\cos 180° + i \sin 180°) + (\cos 300° + i \sin 300°)$.
13. $2 (\cos 120° + i \sin 120°) - 3 (\cos 135° + i \sin 135°)$.

117. Multiplication of complex numbers in polar form.
THEOREM.—*The modulus of the product of two complex numbers equals the product of their moduli, and the amplitude of their product equals the sum of their amplitudes.*

Proof.—Let $r_1(\cos \theta_1 + i \sin \theta_1)$, and $r_2 (\cos \theta_2 + i \sin \theta_2)$ be two complex numbers. Then their product is

$$[r_1(\cos \theta_1 + i \sin \theta_1)][r_2(\cos \theta_2 + i \sin \theta_2)]$$
$$= r_1r_2[(\cos \theta_1 \cos \theta_2 - \sin \theta_1 \sin \theta_2) + i(\sin \theta_1 \cos \theta_2 + \cos \theta_1 \sin \theta_2)]$$
$$= r_1r_2[\cos (\theta_1 + \theta_2) + i \sin (\theta_1 + \theta_2)]. \qquad \text{By [13] and [14].}$$

It is evident that this theorem can be generalized to include the product of any number of complex numbers. Thus,

$$[r_1(\cos \theta_1 + i \sin \theta_1)][r_2(\cos \theta_2 + i \sin \theta_2)] \cdots [r_n(\cos \theta_n + i \sin \theta_n)]$$
$$= r_1r_2 \cdots r_n[\cos (\theta_1 + \theta_2 + \cdots \theta_n) + i \sin (\theta_1 + \theta_2 + \cdots \theta_n)].$$

Example.—$[5(\cos 15° + i \sin 15°)][6(\cos 20° + i \sin 20°)]$
$= 30(\cos 35° + i \sin 35°)$.

If the result is required in the rectangular form, find the value $\cos 35°$ and $\sin 35°$ in trigonometric tables.

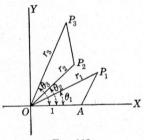

FIG. 112.

Thus, $30(\cos 35° + i \sin 35°) = 24.575 + 17.207i$.

118. Graphical representation of multiplication.—Let the vectors OP_1 and OP_2 (Fig. 112) represent the complex numbers $r_1(\cos \theta_1 + i \sin \theta_1)$ and $r_2(\cos \theta_2 + i \sin \theta_2)$, respectively. Let the point A on the positive axis of reals be 1 unit distant from the origin. Join P_1 to A. Construct a triangle OP_2P_3 similar to the triangle OAP_1 and similarly situated. Then the vector OP_3 represents $r_3(\cos \theta_3 + i \sin \theta_3)$, the required product.

Proof.—$\theta_3 = \angle AOP_2 + \angle P_2OP_3 = \angle AOP_2 + \angle AOP_1 = \theta_2 + \theta_1$.
Since corresponding sides of similar triangles are in proportion,

$$\frac{OP_3}{OP_2} = \frac{OP_1}{OA}. \quad \text{Whence } \frac{r_3}{r_2} = \frac{r_1}{1}, \text{ or } r_3 = r_2r_1.$$

Therefore,

$$r_3(\cos \theta_3 + i \sin \theta_3) = r_1r_2[\cos (\theta_1 + \theta_2) + i \sin (\theta_1 + \theta_2)].$$

119. Division of complex numbers in polar form. THEOREM.
The modulus of the quotient of two complex numbers equals the modulus of the dividend divided by the modulus of the divisor,

and the amplitude of the quotient equals the amplitude of the dividend minus the amplitude of the divisor.

Proof.—

$$\frac{r_1(\cos \theta_1 + i \sin \theta_1)}{r_2(\cos \theta_2 + i \sin \theta_2)} = \frac{r_1(\cos \theta_1 + i \sin \theta_1)(\cos \theta_2 - i \sin \theta_2)}{r_2(\cos \theta_2 + i \sin \theta_2)(\cos \theta_2 - i \sin \theta_2)}$$

$$= \frac{r_1}{r_2} \frac{(\cos \theta_1 \cos \theta_2 + \sin \theta_1 \sin \theta_2) + i(\sin \theta_1 \cos \theta_2 - \cos \theta_1 \sin \theta_2)}{\cos^2 \theta_2 + \sin^2 \theta_2}$$

$$= \frac{r_1}{r_2}[\cos (\theta_1 - \theta_2) + i \sin (\theta_1 - \theta_2)].$$

Example.—$16(\cos 157° + i \sin 157°) \div 8(\cos 22° + i \sin 22°)$
$$= 2(\cos 135° + i \sin 135°) = -\sqrt{2} + \sqrt{2}i.$$

120. Graphical representation of division.—To divide graphically the complex number represented by the vector OP_3 by the complex number represented by the vector OP_1 (Fig. 112), construct a triangle OP_3P_2 similar to the triangle OP_1A and similarly situated. Then the complex number represented by the vector OP_2 is the required quotient. The proof is left as an exercise.

EXERCISES

Perform the following operations and express the results in rectangular form:

1. $[3(\cos 15° + i \sin 15°)][6(\cos 75° + i \sin 75°)]$.   *Ans.* $18i$.
2. $[4(\cos 127° + i \sin 127°)][3(\cos 203° + i \sin 203°)]$.   *Ans.* $6\sqrt{3} - 6i$.
3. $[2(\cos \frac{1}{5}\pi + i \sin \frac{1}{5}\pi)][5(\cos \frac{2}{15}\pi + i \sin \frac{2}{15}\pi)]$.   *Ans.* $5 + 5\sqrt{3}i$.
4. $[3(\cos \frac{1}{12}\pi + i \sin \frac{1}{12}\pi)][5(\cos \frac{5}{12}\pi + i \sin \frac{5}{12}\pi)]$.   *Ans.* $15i$.
5. $\dfrac{4(\cos 47° + i \sin 47°)}{2(\cos 17° + i \sin 17°)}$.   *Ans.* $\sqrt{3} + i$.
6. $\dfrac{12 (\cos 26° + i \sin 26°)}{3(\cos 206° + i \sin 206°)}$.   *Ans.* -4.

Perform the following multiplications and divisions graphically and check the results algebraically:

7. $(1 + i)(2 + 3i)$.   9. $(2 + i)(1 - 2i)$.
8. $(10 + 11i) \div (4 + i)$.   10. $(3i - 1) \div (1 + i)$.

11. Plot $a + bi$ and $i(a + bi)$. Does multiplying a complex number by i rotate the vector representing the complex number through 90°? Prove.

121. Involution of complex numbers.—If all the factors of the generalized theorem for multiplication of complex numbers (**Art. 117**) are equal, the result is the nth power of $r(\cos \theta + i \sin \theta)$. Hence $[r(\cos \theta + i \sin \theta)]^n = r^n(\cos n\theta + i \sin n\theta)$.

This result is known as DeMoivre's Theorem, discovered by Abraham DeMoivre (1667–1754), who was French by birth but lived in England after the age of seventeen.

Note that the theorem has been established when n is a positive integer only.

Example 1.—$[r(\cos \theta + i \sin \theta)]^3 = r^3(\cos 3\theta + i \sin 3\theta)$.

Example 2.—$[2(\cos 40° + i \sin 40°)]^6 = 2^6(\cos 240° + i \sin 240°)$

$$= 64(-\tfrac{1}{2} - \tfrac{1}{2}\sqrt{3}i) = -32 - 32\sqrt{3}i.$$

EXERCISES

Simplify the following and express the results in the rectangular form. Plot in Exercises 1 to 6.

1. $[3(\cos 15° + i \sin 15°)]^6$. $Ans.$ $729i$.

2. $[2(\cos 50° + i \sin 50)]^6$. $Ans.$ $32 - 32\sqrt{3}i$.

3. $[2(\cos 120° + i \sin 120°)]^4$. $Ans.$ $-8 + 8\sqrt{3}i$.

4. $[2(\cos 315° + i \sin 315°)]^4$. $Ans.$ -16.

5. $(\tfrac{1}{2}\sqrt{2} + \tfrac{1}{2}\sqrt{2}i)^4$. $Ans.$ -1.

6. $(\tfrac{1}{2}\sqrt{3} - \tfrac{1}{2}i)^5$. $Ans.$ $-\tfrac{1}{2}\sqrt{3} - \tfrac{1}{2}i$.

7. $(\tfrac{1}{2}\sqrt{2} - \tfrac{1}{2}\sqrt{2}i)^{100}$. $Ans.$ -1.

8. $(\tfrac{1}{2}\sqrt{3} + \tfrac{1}{2}i)^{500}$. $Ans.$ $-\tfrac{1}{2} - \tfrac{1}{2}\sqrt{3}i$.

9. $(-\tfrac{1}{2} + \tfrac{1}{2}\sqrt{3}i)^{1000}$. $Ans.$ $-\tfrac{1}{2} + \tfrac{1}{2}\sqrt{3}i$.

10. $[\tfrac{1}{2}\sqrt{2}(-1 - i)]^{200}$. $Ans.$ 1.

In Exercises 11 to 15, raise the right-hand side to the indicated power by the binomial theorem, simplify, and then apply Theorem II of **Art. 112**.

11. $\cos 2\theta + i \sin 2\theta = (\cos \theta + i \sin \theta)^2$.

12. $\cos 3\theta + i \sin 3\theta = (\cos \theta + i \sin \theta)^3$.

13. $\cos 4\theta + i \sin 4\theta = (\cos \theta + i \sin \theta)^4$.

14. $\cos 5\theta + i \sin 5\theta = (\cos \theta + i \sin \theta)^5$.

15. $\cos 6\theta + i \sin 6\theta = (\cos \theta + i \sin \theta)^6$.

16. Using the results of Exercise 12, express $\tan 3\theta$ in terms of $\tan \theta$.

17. Using the results of Exercise 13, express $\tan 4\theta$ in terms of $\tan \theta$.

122. DeMoivre's theorem for negative and fractional exponents.—DeMoivre's theorem is also true when n is not a positive integer.

CASE I.—*When n is a positive rational number.*

Let $n = \dfrac{p}{q}$ and let $\theta = q\varphi$.

Then $[r(\cos \theta + i \sin \theta)]^n = [r(\cos \theta + i \sin \theta)]^{\frac{p}{q}}$

$$= [r(\cos q\varphi + i \sin q\varphi)]^{\frac{p}{q}} = [r(\cos \varphi + i \sin \varphi)^q]^{\frac{p}{q}}$$

$$= r^{\frac{p}{q}}(\cos \varphi + i \sin \varphi)^p = r^{\frac{p}{q}}(\cos p\varphi + i \sin p\varphi)$$

$$= r^n(\cos \frac{p}{q}\theta + i \sin \frac{p}{q}\theta) = r^n(\cos n\theta + i \sin n\theta).$$

CASE II.—*When n is a negative rational number.*

Let $n = -m$, where m is a positive integer or fraction.

Then $[r(\cos \theta + i \sin \theta)]^n = [r(\cos \theta + i \sin \theta)]^{-m}$

$$= \frac{1}{[r(\cos \theta + i \sin \theta)]^m} = \frac{1}{r^m(\cos m\theta + i \sin m\theta)}$$

$$= \frac{1(\cos 0° + i \sin 0°)}{r^m(\cos m\theta + i \sin m\theta)} = r^{-m}[\cos (-m\theta) + i \sin (-m\theta)]$$

$$= r^n(\cos n\theta + i \sin n\theta).$$

Hence DeMoivre's theorem is true when n is any rational number. The theorem can also be proved for irrational values of n.

123. Evolution of complex numbers.—By means of DeMoivre's theorem, all the nth roots of a complex number can be found. It will be seen that, in order to get all the roots, it will be necessary to use the complete polar form of the complex number. Thus,

$$\sqrt[n]{r(\cos \theta + i \sin \theta)} = [r(\cos \theta + i \sin \theta)]^{\frac{1}{n}}$$

$$= \{r[\cos (\theta + 2k\pi) + i \sin (\theta + 2k\pi)]\}^{\frac{1}{n}}$$

$$= r^{\frac{1}{n}}\left(\cos \frac{\theta + 2k\pi}{n} + i \sin \frac{\theta + 2k\pi}{n}\right).$$

By $r^{\frac{1}{n}}$ is meant the arithmetical value of $\sqrt[n]{r}$. Giving k the values 0, 1, 2, $\cdots n - 1$, in succession, all the nth roots of the complex number can be found.

Example 1.—Find all the cube roots of $1 - i$ in polar form. Plot.

Solution.—Plot $1 - i$ and find r and θ by inspection or computation.

$$1 - i = \sqrt{2}[\cos (315° + k \cdot 360°) + i \sin (315° + k \cdot 360°)].$$

$$\sqrt[3]{1 - i} = \{\sqrt{2}[\cos (315° + k \cdot 360°) + i \sin (315° + k \cdot 360°)]\}^{\frac{1}{3}}$$

$$= \sqrt[6]{2}\left(\cos \frac{315° + k \cdot 360°}{3} + i \sin \frac{315° + k \cdot 360°}{3}\right)$$

$$= \sqrt[6]{2}[\cos (105° + k \cdot 120°) + i \sin (105° + k \cdot 120°)].$$

Giving k in succession the values 0, 1, 2, the required cube roots are found. Representing them by z_1, z_2, and z_3, they are

$$z_1 = \sqrt[6]{2}(\cos 105° + i \sin 105°),$$
$$z_2 = \sqrt[6]{2}(\cos 225° + i \sin 225°),$$
$$z_3 = \sqrt[6]{2}(\cos 345° + i \sin 345°).$$

These are all the cube roots, for, if k should be given values greater than 2, no new cube roots would be found, as every root so found would be either z_1, z_2, or z_3. The plotting is shown in Fig. 113.

The three cube roots can be changed to the rectangular form by using logarithms to express approximately in decimals the products indicated. This gives the following:

$$z_1 = -0.2905 + 1.084i.$$
$$z_2 = -0.7937 - 0.7937i.$$
$$z_3 = 1.084 - 0.2905i.$$

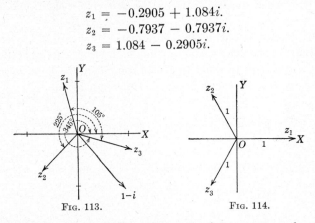

FIG. 113.   FIG. 114.

Example 2.—Find all the cube roots of 1 in rectangular form. Plot.

Solution.—The modulus of 1 is 1 and its amplitude is 0°.

Then $1 = 1[\cos (0° + k \cdot 360°) + i \sin (0° + k \cdot 360°)]$
        $= \cos (k \cdot 360°) + i \sin (k \cdot 360°).$

Hence $\sqrt[3]{1} = [\cos (k \cdot 360°) + i \sin (k \cdot 360°)]^{\frac{1}{3}}$
        $= \cos (k \cdot 120°) + i \sin (k \cdot 120°).$

Giving k in succession the values 0, 1, 2, the three cube roots of 1 are as follows:

$$z_1 = \cos 0° + i \sin 0°.$$
$$z_2 = \cos 120° + i \sin 120°.$$
$$z_3 = \cos 240° + i \sin 240°.$$

Changing these to the rectangular form,

$$z_1 = 1, z_2 = -\tfrac{1}{2} + \tfrac{1}{2}\sqrt{3}i, z_3 = -\tfrac{1}{2} - \tfrac{1}{2}\sqrt{3}i.$$

The plotting is shown in Fig. 114.

Note that in Examples 1 and 2 each of the cube roots lies at a vertex of an equilateral triangle whose center is at the origin.

The triangle in each case is inscribed in a circle of radius equal to the common modulus of the roots.

Example 3.—Find all the fourth roots of -1 in rectangular form.

Solution.—The modulus of -1 is 1 and its amplitude is $180°$. Then $-1 = 1[\cos (180° + k \cdot 360°) + i \sin (180° + k \cdot 360°)]$.

$$\sqrt[4]{-1} = \cos (45° + k \cdot 90°) + i \sin (45° + k \cdot 90°).$$

Giving k in succession the values 0, 1, 2, 3, the four fourth roots of -1 are as follows:

$$z_1 = \cos \ 45° + i \sin \ 45° = \ \ \tfrac{1}{2}\sqrt{2} + \tfrac{1}{2}\sqrt{2}i.$$
$$z_2 = \cos 135° + i \sin 135° = -\tfrac{1}{2}\sqrt{2} + \tfrac{1}{2}\sqrt{2}i.$$
$$z_3 = \cos 225° + i \sin 225° = -\tfrac{1}{2}\sqrt{2} - \tfrac{1}{2}\sqrt{2}i.$$
$$z_4 = \cos 315° + i \sin 315° = \ \ \tfrac{1}{2}\sqrt{2} - \tfrac{1}{2}\sqrt{2}i.$$

These results, if plotted, would lie at the vertices of a square.

Finding the nth roots of a complex number, $a + bi$, is equivalent to solving the equation $x^n - (a + bi) = 0$. Therefore, DeMoivre's theorem gives a means of solving the general binomial equation. For example, the three roots of Example 1 are the three roots of the cubic equation $x^3 - 1 + i = 0$. The three roots of Example 2 are the solutions of the equation $x^3 - 1 = 0$.

As already pointed out, the n distinct nth roots of a complex number lie at the vertices of a regular n-gon whose center is at the origin, and whose vertices lie on a circle whose radius is r, the common modulus of the roots. This is immediately apparent from the general form of the nth root. Whence it is seen that all the nth roots have the same modulus and hence all lie at the same distance from the origin. Also their amplitudes differ by the constant angle $\dfrac{2\pi}{n}$, as k is given in succession the values 0, 1, 2, $\cdots n - 1$. Therefore, the points representing the roots are equally spaced around a circle.

EXERCISES

Find all the roots in Exercises 1 to 14 and express in polar form.

1. $x^4 = 1 - i$.

2. $x^3 = 1 - i$.

3. $x^3 = -1 - i$.

4. $x^3 = \tfrac{1}{2}\sqrt{3} + \tfrac{1}{2}i$.

5. $x^3 = \tfrac{1}{2}\sqrt{3} - \tfrac{1}{2}i$.

6. $x^5 = i$.

7. $x^5 = -1$.

8. $x^2 = \cos 20° + i \sin 20°$.

9. $x^2 = \cos 140° + i \sin 140°$.

10. $x^3 = \cos 105° + i \sin 105°$.

11. $x^3 = \cos 300° + i \sin 300°$.

12. $x^5 = -32$.

13. $x^4 = 8 + 8\sqrt{3}i$.

14. $x^4 = -8 - 8\sqrt{3}i$.

Find all the roots in Exercises 15 to 22 in rectangular form and represent them graphically.

15. $x^3 = -1$.   **19.** $x^4 = -1$.

16. $x^3 = -8$.   **20.** $x^6 = -i$.

17. $x^3 = i$.   **21.** $x^5 = 32 \ (\cos 150° + i \sin 150°)$.

18. $x^3 = -i$.   **22.** $x^4 = \cos 120 + i \sin 120$.

Solve the following equations, express the roots in rectangular form, and represent them graphically:

23. $x^3 - 1 = 0$.   **28.** $x^5 + 32 = 0$.

24. $x^4 - 1 = 0$.   **29.** $x^4 - i = 0$.

25. $x^5 - 1 = 0$.   **30.** $x^4 + i = 0$.

26. $x^6 - 64 = 0$.   **31.** $x^5 - \sqrt{-32} = 0$.

27. $x^2 + 1 = 0$.   **32.** $x^5 - \sqrt{-243} = 0$.

TRIGONOMETRIC SERIES

124. Expansion of sin $n\theta$ and cos $n\theta$.—By DeMoivre's theorem and the binomial theorem,

$$(1) \quad \cos n\theta + i \sin n\theta = (\cos \theta + i \sin \theta)^n = \cos^n \theta + ni \cos^{n-1} \theta \cdot \sin \theta$$

$$- \frac{n(n-1)}{2!} \cos^{n-2} \theta \sin^2 \theta - \frac{in(n-1)(n-2)}{3!} \cos^{n-3} \theta \sin^3 \theta$$

$$+ \frac{n(n-1)(n-2)(n-3)}{4!} \cos^{n-4} \theta \sin^4 \theta$$

$$+ \frac{in(n-1)(n-2)(n-3)(n-4)}{5!} \cos^{n-5} \theta \sin^5 \theta - \cdots .\text{*}$$

Equating the real parts,

$$\cos n\theta = \cos^n \theta - \frac{n(n-1)}{2!} \cos^{n-2} \theta \sin^2 \theta$$

$$+ \frac{n(n-1)(n-2)(n-3)}{4!} \cos^{n-4} \theta \sin^4 \theta + \cdots .$$

Let $\alpha = n\theta$, then $\theta = \dfrac{\alpha}{n}$ and $n = \dfrac{\alpha}{\theta}$, where α is to be held constant while n and θ are to vary. Substituting these values,

* The symbol $n!$, or $\lfloor n$, is used to denote the product $1 \cdot 2 \cdot 3 \cdots n$, and is read "factorial n."

$$\cos \alpha = \cos^n \theta - \frac{\frac{\alpha}{\theta}\left(\frac{\alpha}{\theta} - 1\right)}{2!} \cos^{n-2} \theta \sin^2 \theta$$

$$+ \frac{\frac{\alpha}{\theta}\left(\frac{\alpha}{\theta} - 1\right)\left(\frac{\alpha}{\theta} - 2\right)\left(\frac{\alpha}{\theta} - 3\right)}{4!} \cos^{n-4} \theta \sin^4 \theta + \cdots.$$

$$= \cos^n \theta - \frac{\alpha(\alpha - \theta)}{2!} \cos^{n-2} \theta \left(\frac{\sin \theta}{\theta}\right)^2$$

$$+ \frac{\alpha(\alpha - \theta)(\alpha - 2\theta)(\alpha - 3\theta)}{4!} \cos^{n-4} \theta \left(\frac{\sin \theta}{\theta}\right)^4 \cdots.$$

Now, as n becomes infinite $\frac{\alpha}{n} = \theta$ approaches zero, $\cos \theta \to 1$,

$\frac{\sin \theta}{\theta} \to 1$, and $\alpha - \theta \to \alpha$.   Therefore,

$$(2) \qquad \cos \alpha = 1 - \frac{\alpha^2}{2!} + \frac{\alpha^4}{4!} - \frac{\alpha^6}{6!} + \cdots.$$

Equating the coefficients of the imaginary parts of (1),

$$\sin n\theta = n \cos^{n-1} \theta \sin \theta - \frac{n(n-1)(n-2)}{3!} \cos^{n-3} \theta \sin^3 \theta$$

$$+ \frac{n(n-1)(n-2)(n-3)(n-4)}{5!} \cos^{n-5} \theta \sin^5 \theta - \cdots$$

Making the substitutions for θ and n,

$$\sin \alpha = \alpha \cos^{n-1} \theta \left(\frac{\sin \theta}{\theta}\right) - \frac{\alpha(\alpha - \theta)(\alpha - 2\theta)}{3!} \cos^{n-3} \theta \left(\frac{\sin \theta}{\theta}\right)^3$$

$$+ \frac{\alpha(\alpha - \theta)(\alpha - 2\theta)(\alpha - 3\theta)(\alpha - 4\theta)}{5!} \cos^{n-5} \theta \left(\frac{\sin \theta}{\theta}\right)^5 - \cdots.$$

Then when n becomes infinite

$$(3) \qquad \sin \alpha = \alpha - \frac{\alpha^3}{3!} + \frac{\alpha^5}{5!} - \frac{\alpha^7}{7!} + \cdots.$$

In (2) and (3), α is in radians.

If we divide (3) by (2), we get

$$\tan \alpha = \frac{\sin \alpha}{\cos \alpha} = \frac{\alpha - \dfrac{\alpha^3}{3!} + \dfrac{\alpha^5}{5!} - \dfrac{\alpha^7}{7!} \cdots}{1 - \dfrac{\alpha^2}{2!} + \dfrac{\alpha^4}{4!} - \dfrac{\alpha^6}{6!} \cdots} = \alpha + \frac{\alpha^3}{3} + \frac{2\alpha^5}{15} + \cdots.$$

125. Computation of trigonometric functions.—Formulas (2) and (3) may be used to compute the functions of angles. Thus,

let $\qquad\qquad\qquad \alpha = 10° = \frac{1}{18}\pi.$

Then

$$\sin\frac{1}{18}\pi = \frac{1}{18}\pi - \frac{\left(\frac{1}{18}\pi\right)^3}{3!} + \frac{\left(\frac{1}{18}\pi\right)^5}{5!} - \cdots = a - b + c - \cdots ,$$

where $a, b, c, \ldots$ may be computed as follows:

$$\begin{aligned}
\log \pi &= 0.49715 & 3 \log \pi &= 1.49145 \\
\log 18 &= 1.25527 & \text{colog } 18^3 &= 6.23419 - 10 \\
\overline{\log a} &= 9.24188 - 10 & \text{colog } 3! &= 9.22185 - 10 \\
a &= 0.17453 & \overline{\log b} &= 6.94749 - 10 \\
& & b &= 0.000886
\end{aligned}$$

$$\begin{aligned}
5 \log \pi &= 2.48575 \\
\text{colog } 18^5 &= 3.72365 - 10 \\
\text{colog } 5! &= 7.92082 - 10 \\
\overline{\log c} &= 4.13022 - 10 \\
c &= 0.000001349 \\
\end{aligned}$$

$$\sin 10° = a - b = 0.17453 - 0.000886 = 0.17364.$$

From the table of natural functions, $\sin 10° = 0.17365$. By means of (2), $\cos 10°$ may be computed.

EXERCISES

Compute the following functions correct to the fourth decimal place and compare with the tables:

1. $\sin 20°$.   **3.** $\tan 30°$.
2. $\cos 25°$.   **4.** $\sin 45°$.

126. Exponential values of sin θ, cos θ, and tan θ.—In algebra it is proved that if e is the base of the natural system of logarithms, then

$$(1) \qquad e^x = 1 + x + \frac{x^2}{2!} + \frac{x^3}{3!} + \frac{x^4}{4!} + \cdots .$$

Now if $i\theta$ is substituted for x, where $i = \sqrt{-1}$,

$$e^{i\theta} = 1 + i\theta + \frac{i^2\theta^2}{2!} + \frac{i^3\theta^3}{3!} + \frac{i^4\theta^4}{4!} + \cdots$$

$$= \left(1 - \frac{\theta^2}{2!} + \frac{\theta^4}{4!} - \frac{\theta^6}{6!} + \cdots\right) + i\left(\theta - \frac{\theta^3}{3!} + \frac{\theta^5}{5!} - \frac{\theta^7}{7!} + \cdots\right).$$

But, by **Art. 124,** the expressions in the first and second parentheses are equal to $\cos \theta$ and $\sin \theta$, respectively.

(2) $\qquad \therefore e^{i\theta} = \cos \theta + i \sin \theta.$

Substituting $x = -i\theta$ in (1) and reducing as before, we have

(3) $\qquad e^{-i\theta} = \cos \theta - i \sin \theta.$

Subtracting (3) from (2),

(4) $\qquad \sin \theta = \dfrac{e^{i\theta} - e^{-i\theta}}{2i}.$

Adding (2) and (3),

(5) $\qquad \cos \theta = \dfrac{e^{i\theta} + e^{-i\theta}}{2}.$

Dividing (4) by (5),

(6) $\qquad \tan \theta = \dfrac{e^{i\theta} - e^{-i\theta}}{i(e^{i\theta} + e^{-i\theta})}.$

Note.—The expressions for $\sin \theta$, $\cos \theta$, and $\tan \theta$, given in (4), (5), and (6), are called *exponential values* of these functions. They are also called *Euler's Equations* after Euler their discoverer. Euler (1707–1783) was one of the greatest of the physicists, astronomers, and mathematicians of the eighteenth century.

EXERCISES

By means of the exponential values prove the following identities:

1. $\sin^2 \theta + \cos^2 \theta = 1.$ $\qquad$ **3.** $1 + \cot^2 \theta = \csc^2 \theta.$

2. $1 + \tan^2 \theta = \sec^2 \theta.$ $\qquad$ **4.** $\sin 2\theta = 2 \sin \theta \cos \theta.$

5. $\cos 2\theta = \cos^2 \theta - \sin^2 \theta = 2 \cos^2 \theta - 1 = 1 - 2 \sin^2 \theta.$

6. $\cos 3\theta = 4 \cos^3 \theta - 3 \cos \theta.$

127. Series for $\sin^n \theta$ and $\cos^n \theta$ in terms of sines or cosines of multiples of θ.—From (4) of Art. **126,**

$$2i \sin \theta = e^{i\theta} - e^{-i\theta}.$$

Expanding by the binomial theorem,

$$(2i \sin \theta)^n = (e^{i\theta} - e^{-i\theta})^n$$

$$= (e^{i\theta})^n + n(e^{i\theta})^{n-1}(-e^{-i\theta}) + \frac{n(n-1)}{2!}(e^{i\theta})^{n-2}(-e^{-i\theta})^2$$

$$+ \cdots + \frac{n(n-1)}{2!}(e^{i\theta})^2(-e^{-i\theta})^{n-2} + ne^{i\theta}(-e^{-i\theta})^{n-1} + (-e^{-i\theta})^n.$$

When n is *odd*, the number of terms in the series is *even*, and when n is *even*, the number of terms is *odd*. Therefore, when n is odd, the terms can be grouped in pairs, the first with the last, the second with the last but one, etc. But, when n is even, there will be a certain number of pairs and one extra term, which is the middle term of the series.

From this series, general formulas can be derived for expressing $\sin^n \theta$ as a series of sines or cosines of multiples of θ.

By using (5) of **Art. 126,** $\cos^n \theta$ can be dealt with in a similar manner.

Here special cases only will be given. From these and other special cases, however, laws can easily be discovered that will determine the coefficients, and multiples of the angles.

Example 1.—Express $\sin^5 \theta$ in sines of multiples of θ.

Since $\sin \theta = \dfrac{e^{i\theta} - e^{-i\theta}}{2i}$,

$$\sin^5 \theta = \frac{1}{2^4}\left[\frac{e^{i5\theta} - 5e^{i3\theta} + 10e^{i\theta} - 10e^{-i\theta} + 5e^{-i3\theta} - e^{-i5\theta}}{2i}\right].$$

Grouping in pairs, the first with the last, the second with the last but one, etc.,

$$\sin^5 \theta = \frac{1}{2^4}\left[\frac{e^{i5\theta} - e^{-i5\theta}}{2i} - 5\frac{e^{i3\theta} - e^{-i3\theta}}{2i} + 10\frac{e^{i\theta} - e^{-i\theta}}{2i}\right].$$

$$\therefore \sin^5 \theta = \tfrac{1}{16}(\sin 5\theta - 5 \sin 3\theta + 10 \sin \theta).$$

Example 2.—Express $\sin^6 \theta$ in cosines of multiples of θ.

Since $\qquad\qquad \sin \theta = \dfrac{e^{i\theta} - e^{-i\theta}}{2i}$,

$$\sin^6 \theta = -\frac{1}{2^5}\left[\frac{e^{i6\theta} - 6e^{i4\theta} + 15e^{i2\theta} - 20 + 15e^{-i2\theta} - 6e^{-i4\theta} + e^{-i6\theta}}{2}\right].$$

Grouping in pairs,

$$\sin^6 \theta = -\frac{1}{2^5}\left[\frac{e^{i6\theta} + e^{-i6\theta}}{2} - 6\frac{e^{i4\theta} + e^{-i4\theta}}{2} + 15\frac{e^{i2\theta} + e^{-i2\theta}}{2} - 10\right].$$

$$\therefore \sin^6 \theta = -\tfrac{1}{32}(\cos 6\theta - 6 \cos 4\theta + 15 \cos 2\theta - 10).$$

Example 3.—Express $\cos^3 \theta$ in cosines of multiples of θ.

Since $\qquad\qquad \cos \theta = \dfrac{e^{i\theta} + e^{-i\theta}}{2}$,

$$\cos^3 \theta = \frac{1}{4}\left[\frac{e^{i3\theta} + 3e^{i\theta} + 3e^{-i\theta} + e^{-i3\theta}}{2}\right]$$

$$= \frac{1}{4}\left[\frac{e^{i3\theta} + e^{-i3\theta}}{2} + 3\frac{e^{i\theta} + e^{-i\theta}}{2}\right].$$

$$\therefore \cos^3 \theta = \tfrac{1}{4}[\cos 3\theta + 3 \cos \theta].$$

Example 4.—Express $\cos^4 \theta$ in cosines of multiples of θ

Since
$$\cos \theta = \frac{e^{i\theta} + e^{-i\theta}}{2},$$

$$\cos^4 \theta = \frac{1}{8}\left[\frac{e^{i4\theta} + 4e^{i2\theta} + 6 + 4e^{-i2\theta} + e^{-i4\theta}}{2}\right]$$

$$= \frac{1}{8}\left[\frac{e^{i4\theta} + e^{-i4\theta}}{2} + 4\frac{e^{i2\theta} + e^{-i2\theta}}{2} + 3\right].$$

$$\therefore \cos^4 \theta = \tfrac{1}{8}(\cos 4\theta + 4 \cos 2\theta + 3).$$

EXERCISES

Prove the following identities:
1. $\sin^4 \theta = \tfrac{1}{8}(\cos 4\theta - 4 \cos 2\theta + 3)$.
2. $\cos^7 \theta = \tfrac{1}{64}(\cos 7\theta + 7 \cos 5\theta + 21 \cos 3\theta + 35 \cos \theta)$.
3. $128 \cos^8 \theta = \cos 8\theta + 8 \cos 6\theta + 28 \cos 4\theta + 56 \cos 2\theta + 35$.
4. $64 \sin^7 \theta = 35 \sin \theta - 21 \sin 3\theta + 7 \sin 5\theta - \sin 7\theta$.
5. $\sin^6 \theta + \cos^6 \theta = \tfrac{1}{8}(\cos 4\theta - 4 \cos 2\theta + 3)$.

128. Hyperbolic functions.—In **Art. 56,** the trigonometric functions were called circular functions because of their relation to the arc of a circle. There is another set of functions whose properties are very similar to the properties of the trigonometric functions. Because of their relation to the hyperbola, they are called **hyperbolic functions.** They are defined as follows:

(1) Hyperbolic sine x (written $\sinh x$) $= \dfrac{e^x - e^{-x}}{2}.$

(2) Hyperbolic cosine x (written $\cosh x$) $= \dfrac{e^x + e^{-x}}{2}.$

(3) Hyperbolic tangent x (written $\tanh x$) $= \dfrac{e^x - e^{-x}}{e^x + e^{-x}}.$

(4) Hyperbolic cotangent x (written $\coth x$) $= \dfrac{e^x + e^{-x}}{e^x - e^{-x}}.$

(5) Hyperbolic secant x (written $\operatorname{sech} x$) $= \dfrac{2}{e^x + e^{-x}}.$

(6) Hyperbolic cosecant x (written $\operatorname{csch} x$) $= \dfrac{2}{e^x - e^{-x}}.$

In these formulas e is the base of the Napierian system of logarithms, and so stands for the number $2.7182818 \cdots$.

From the definitions, the following relations are evident:

$$\tanh x = \frac{\sinh x}{\cosh x}, \quad \tanh x = \frac{1}{\coth x}, \quad \operatorname{sech} x = \frac{1}{\cosh x}.$$

129. Relations between the hyperbolic functions.—Squaring (1) and (2) and subtracting the second from the first,

$$\cosh^2 x - \sinh^2 x = \frac{e^{2x} + 2 + e^{-2x}}{4} - \frac{e^{2x} - 2 + e^{-2x}}{4} = 1.$$

$$\therefore \cosh^2 x - \sinh^2 x = 1.$$

By analogy, from (1) we may write

$$\sinh(x + y) = \frac{e^{x+y} - e^{-(x+y)}}{2}.$$

Also, $\sinh x \cosh y = \dfrac{e^x - e^{-x}}{2} \cdot \dfrac{e^y + e^{-y}}{2}$

$$= \tfrac{1}{4}[e^{x+y} - e^{-x}e^y + e^x e^{-y} - e^{-(x+y)}].$$

And $\cosh x \sinh y = \dfrac{e^x + e^{-x}}{2} \cdot \dfrac{e^y - e^{-y}}{2}$

$$= \tfrac{1}{4}[e^{x+y} + e^{-x}e^y - e^x e^{-y} - e^{-(x+y)}].$$

Adding the last two,

$$\sinh x \cosh y + \cosh x \sinh y = \tfrac{1}{2}[e^{x+y} - e^{-(x+y)}].$$

Comparing this with the first,

$$\sinh(x + y) = \sinh x \cosh y + \cosh x \sinh y.$$

EXERCISES

Prove the following identities:
1. $\operatorname{sech}^2 x + \tanh^2 x = 1$.
2. $\coth^2 x - \operatorname{csch}^2 x = 1$.
3. $\sinh(-x) = -\sinh x$.
4. $\cosh(-x) = \cosh x$.
5. $\sinh(x - y) = \sinh x \cosh y - \cosh x \sinh y$.
6. $\cosh(x + y) = \cosh x \cosh y - \sinh x \sinh y$.
7. $\cosh(x - y) = \cosh x \cosh y + \sinh x \sinh y$.
8. $\tanh(x + y) = \dfrac{\tanh x + \tanh y}{1 + \tanh x \tanh y}$.
9. $\sinh 2x = 2 \sinh x \cosh x$.
10. $\cosh 2x = \cosh^2 x + \sinh^2 x$.

130. Relations between the trigonometric and hyperbolic functions.—If in (4) of **Art. 126** we substitute $i\theta$ for θ,

$$i \sin i\theta = \tfrac{1}{2}[e^{i(i\theta)} - e^{-i(i\theta)}] = -\tfrac{1}{2}[e^\theta - e^{-\theta}] = -\sinh \theta.$$

(1) $\therefore$ **sin** $i\theta = i$ **sinh** θ.

Substituting $i\theta$ for θ in (5) of **Art. 126,**

$$\cos i\theta = \tfrac{1}{2}[e^{i(i\theta)} + e^{-i(i\theta)}] = \tfrac{1}{2}[e^\theta + e^{-\theta}] = \cosh \theta.$$

(2) $\therefore$ **cos** $i\theta$ = **cosh** θ.

Dividing (1) by (2),

(3) $\tan i\theta = i \tanh \theta.$

131. Expression of sinh x and cosh x in a series. Computation.—By definition and by (1) of **Art. 126,**

$$\sinh x = \tfrac{1}{2}[e^x - e^{-x}]$$

$$= \frac{1}{2}\left[\left(1 + x + \frac{x^2}{2!} + \frac{x^3}{3!} + \cdots\right) - \left(1 - x + \frac{x}{2!} - \frac{x^3}{3!} + \cdots\right)\right]$$

$$= \frac{1}{2}\left[2x + \frac{2x^3}{3!} + \frac{2x^5}{5!} + \cdots\right] = x + \frac{x^3}{3!} + \frac{x^5}{5!} + \cdots .$$

(1) $\therefore \sinh x = x + \dfrac{x^3}{3!} + \dfrac{x^5}{5!} + \cdots .$

Also, $\cosh x = \tfrac{1}{2}[e^x + e^{-x}]$

$$= \frac{1}{2}\left[\left(1 + x + \frac{x^2}{2!} + \frac{x^3}{3!} + \cdots\right) + \left(1 - x + \frac{x^2}{2!} - \frac{x^3}{3!} + \cdots\right)\right]$$

$$= \frac{1}{2}\left[2 + \frac{2x^2}{2!} + \frac{2x^4}{4!} + \cdots\right] = 1 + \frac{x^2}{2!} + \frac{x^4}{4!} + \cdots .$$

(2) $\therefore \cosh x = 1 + \dfrac{x^2}{2!} + \dfrac{x^4}{4!} + \dfrac{x^6}{6!} + \cdots .$

Series (1) and (2) for sinh x and cosh x are convergent for all real values of x. Therefore, for any real value of x the hyperbolic functions of x can be computed.

131'. Forces and velocities represented as complex numbers.—Since forces and velocities, to be completely defined, must be known in magnitude and direction, they are vectors and may be expressed in the complex number notation. In Fig. *A*, *OP* represents to scale a force of F lb., making an angle θ with the *x*-axis. By **Art. 113**

$$OP = F(\cos \theta + i \sin \theta). \qquad [1]$$

Since *OP* locates the point P with polar coordinates (F, θ), it suggests the following notation: Force (F, θ) represents a force of magnitude or modulus F lb., with direction or amplitude θ. Force $(5, 0°)$ defines point A in Fig. *B*, and is *OA*. Force $(5, 135°)$ locates point P and is *OB*.

Example 1.—Locate the following:

Force $(10, \ 90°)$; Force $(\ 8, 180°)$;
Force $(10, 240°)$; Force $(15, 300°)$.

Similarly, velocity (20 miles, 45°) means that a body is moving 20 miles per hour in a northeasterly direction, as the x-axis will be taken as the East and West line.

Equation (1) may be written

$$OP = F \cos \theta + iF \sin \theta = x + yi$$

where x and y are the rectangular components of OP.

If the problem is to find the resultant or sum of several concurrent forces, first express each of the forces in the rectangular form. Then by **Art. 115,** these complex numbers may be added

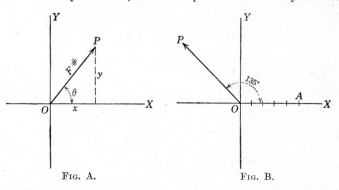

FIG. A.   FIG. B.

algebraically. Their sum is a complex number with the x component equal to the sum of the x's of the forces, and the y component equal to the sum of the y's.

Example 2.—Find the resultant of the forces in Example 1.

Force (10, 90°) $= 0 + 10i$.

Force (8, 180°) $= -8 + 0i$.

Force (10, 240°) $= -5 - 8.66i$.

Force (15, 300°) $= 7.5 - 13i$.

Force $(F, \theta) = (0 - 8 - 5 + 7.5) + (10 + 0 - 8.66 - 13)i$.

$$= -5.5 - 11.66i$$

Then $F = \sqrt{(-5.5)^2 + (-11.66)^2}$,

$$= 12.8$$

and $\theta = \tan^{-1}\left(\dfrac{-11.66}{-5.5}\right)$

$$= 180° + 64° 44.8' = 244° 44.8'$$

Force (12.8, 244° 44.8′) is the resultant. Notice that the angle θ is in the third quadrant since both components are negative.

Example 3.—The current in a river flowing due south causes a boat to drift three miles per hour. At the same time a wind from the southwest causes the boat to drift to the northeast at the rate of six miles per hour. Find the resultant velocity of the boat both in magnitude and direction.

Solution.—

$$\text{Velocity (3 miles, } 270°) = 0 - 3i.$$
$$\text{Velocity (6 miles, } 45°) = 4.24 + 4.24i.$$
$$\text{Velocity } (V, \theta) = 4.24 + 1.24i.$$
$$V = \sqrt{(4.24)^2 + (1.24)^2}$$
$$= 4.32 \text{ miles per hour}$$
$$\theta = \tan^{-1} \frac{1.24}{4.24}$$
$$= 16° \ 18.1'.$$

Therefore, the boat moves with a velocity of 4.32 miles per hour in a direction E 16° 18.1′ N.

If a set of concurrent forces are in equilibrium, their resultant must equal zero; that is, $x + yi = 0$. But this can be true when, and only when, $x = 0$ and $y = 0$. The sum of all the x-components of the forces will equal zero. Similarly, the summation of y-components equals zero. This leads to two equations which can be solved simultaneously.

For other problems the student is asked to solve Nos. 1, 2, 3, 4, 5, 6, 9, 11, 12 of **Art. 69,** by the theory of complex numbers. Also 35, 36, 37, 38, 39, 40 of General Exercises at the end of Chapter IX.

ANSWERS TO EXERCISES

Page 170

1. $9 - 5i.$ **4.** $8 - 9i.$ **7.** $\frac{1}{5}(7 - 6i).$

2. $-2 - 3i.$ **5.** $-7 + 17i.$ **8.** $\frac{1}{25}(23 - 14i).$

3. $10 + 3i.$ **6.** $11 - 3i.$ **9.** $\frac{3}{10}(3 - i).$

10. $\frac{2}{5}(2 + 9i).$

11. $\frac{1}{3}(-2\sqrt{2} + 5i).$

12. $\frac{1}{13}(6 - \sqrt{2}) - \frac{1}{13}(\sqrt{3} + 2\sqrt{6})i.$

13. $\frac{1}{5}(2\sqrt{2} - 3\sqrt{3}) + \frac{1}{5}(2\sqrt{3} + 3\sqrt{2})i.$

14. $\sqrt{2} - \sqrt{3}i$ **17.** $1 - \frac{1}{5}\sqrt{5}i.$ **20.** $-2 + 2i.$

15. $-7 - 6i.$ **18.** $\frac{1}{2} + \frac{1}{2}i.$ **21.** $-7 - 24i.$

16. $\frac{1}{5}(3 - i).$ **19.** $-2i.$ **22.** $-3\sqrt{3} - 7\sqrt{2}i.$

23. $1.$ **24.** $-1.$ **25.** $\dfrac{a + b + 2\sqrt{ab}}{a - b},$

26. $2a^2 - 1 + 2ai\sqrt{1 - a^2}.$

27. $a^2 - \sqrt{1 - a^4} + ai(\sqrt{1 - a^2} + \sqrt{1 + a^2}).$ **28.** $0.$ **29.** $1.$

30. i.   **31.** $\dfrac{8}{a^6} - 3 + \left(\dfrac{6\sqrt{2}}{a^3} - \dfrac{\sqrt{2}a^3}{4} \right)i$.

32. $\dfrac{\sqrt{3}a^3}{9} - \dfrac{3\sqrt{3}}{a} + \left(\sqrt{3}a - \dfrac{3\sqrt{3}}{a^3} \right)i$.   **34.** $-17 + 12i$.

35. 42.

Page 174

6. $2\sqrt{3}(\cos 300° + i \sin 300°)$.

8. $2^{\frac{3}{8}}(\cos 135° + i \sin 135°)$.

10. $2\sqrt{2}(\cos 60° + i \sin 60°)$.

12. $2\sqrt{7}(\cos 150° + i \sin 150°)$.

14. $4(\cos 90° + i \sin 90°)$.

16. $6(\cos 270° + i \sin 270°)$.

18. $\cos 270° + i \sin 270°$.

20. $\cos 180° + i \sin 180°$.

22. $\sqrt{3}(\cos 90° + i \sin 90°)$.

24. $3(\cos 270° + i \sin 270°)$.

26. $2\sqrt{5}(\cos 333° \ 26' + i \sin 333° \ 26')$.

34. $3\sqrt{2}[\cos (45° + k \cdot 360°) + i \sin (45° + k \cdot 360°)]$.

37. $3[\cos (90° + k \cdot 360°) + i \sin (90° + k \cdot 360°)]$.

38. $\frac{3}{2}\sqrt{3} + \frac{3}{2}i$.

43. $-2\sqrt{3} - 2i$.

47. $-\sqrt{3} + i$.

Page 181

1. $\sqrt[8]{2}(\cos 78° \ 45' + i \sin 78° \ 45')$.

$\sqrt[8]{2}(\cos 168° \ 45' + i \sin 168° \ 45')$.

$\sqrt[8]{2}(\cos 258° \ 45' + i \sin 258° \ 45')$.

$\sqrt[8]{2}(\cos 348° \ 45' + i \sin 348° \ 45')$.

4. $\cos 10° + i \sin 10°$;   **11.** $\cos 100° + i \sin 100°$;
$\cos 130° + i \sin 130°$; $\cos 220° + i \sin 220°$;
$\cos 250° + i \sin 250°$. $\cos 340° + i \sin 340°$.

16. $1 + \sqrt{3}i$;
$1 - \sqrt{3}i$;
-2.

20. $0.7071 + 0.7071i$.   **30.** $0.3827 + 0.9239i$.
$-0.2588 + 0.9659i$. $-0.9239 + 0.3827i$.
$-0.9659 + 0.2588i$. $-0.3827 - 0.9239i$.
$-0.7071 - 0.7071i$. $0.9239 - 0.3827i$.
$0.2588 - 0.9659i$.
$0.9659 - 0.2588i$.

CHAPTER XII

SPHERICAL TRIGONOMETRY

132. Spherical trigonometry investigates the relations that exist between the parts of a spherical triangle.

For convenience, a few of the definitions and theorems of spherical geometry are stated here.

The section of the surface of a sphere made by a plane is a **great circle** if the plane passes through the center of the sphere, and a **small circle** if the plane does not pass through the center of the sphere.

The diameter of a sphere perpendicular to the plane of a circle of the sphere is called the **axis** of that circle. The points where the axis of a circle of a sphere intersects the surface of the sphere are called the **poles** of the circle.

133. Spherical triangle.—A **spherical triangle** is the figure on the surface of a sphere bounded by three arcs of great circles. The three arcs are the sides of the triangle, and the angles formed by the arcs at the points where they meet are the angles of the triangle.

The angle between two intersecting arcs is measured by the angle between the tangents drawn to the arcs at the point of intersection.

If a trihedral angle is placed with its vertex at the center of a sphere, the face planes intersect the surface of the sphere in arcs of great circles

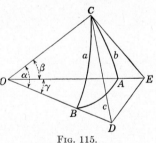

FIG. 115.

which form a spherical triangle. The sides of the spherical triangle measure the face angles of the trihedral angle, and the angles of the triangle are equal to the dihedral angles of the trihedral angle.

In Fig. 115, O is the center of a sphere. $O\text{-}ABC$ is a trihedral angle. AB, BC, and CA are arcs of great circles. ABC is a spherical triangle. Arcs a, b, and c are the measures of α, β, and γ

respectively. $\angle BCA$ and D^-OC^-E are measured by the same plane angle, as also are $\angle ABC$ and E^-OD^-C, and $\angle CAB$ and C^-OE^-D.

The sum of the sides of a spherical triangle is less than 360°.

The sum of the angles of a spherical triangle is greater than 180° and less than 540°.

It is evident that the sides and angles of a spherical triangle can be greater than 180°; however, to simplify the subject, it is agreed to consider only those spherical triangles in which the sides and angles are each less than 180°.

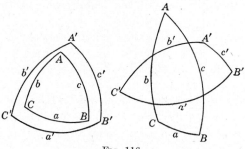

Fig. 116.

134. Polar triangles.—If the vertices of a spherical triangle are used as poles and great circles drawn, another triangle is formed called the **polar triangle** of the first.

Thus in Fig. 116, A is the pole of a', B the pole of b', C the pole of c', and $A'B'C'$ is the polar triangle of ABC.

It is evident that, in general, the great circles drawn as stated will intersect so as to form eight triangles. The one of these is the polar triangle in which A and A', B and B', C and C' lie on the same side of a', b', and c' respectively.

If one triangle is the polar of another, then the latter is the polar triangle of the former.

The sides and the angles of a spherical triangle are the supplements, respectively, of the angles and the sides opposite in the polar triangle, and, conversely.

Thus in Fig. 116, $A' = \pi - a$, $B' = \pi - b$, $C' = \pi - c$,
$$a' = \pi - A, b' = \pi - B, c' = \pi - C.$$

These relations are of great importance, for, if any general theorem be proved with respect to the sides and angles of any spherical triangle, it can at once be applied to the polar triangle. Thus, any theorem of a spherical triangle may be at once transformed into another by replacing each side, or angle, by the supplement of its opposite angle, or side, in the polar triangle.

Since the side of a spherical triangle and the corresponding face angle of the trihedral angle have the same numerical measure, the plane trigonometric functions may be taken of the arcs as well as of the plane angles. Hence the identities of plane trigonometry are true for the sides of a spherical triangle.

A **right spherical** triangle is one which has an angle equal to 90°. A **birectangular** triangle is one which has two right

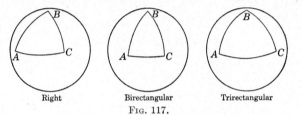

| Right | Birectangular | Trirectangular |

Fig. 117.

angles. A **trirectangular** triangle is one which has three right angles.

RIGHT SPHERICAL TRIANGLES

135. In a spherical triangle there are six parts, three sides and three angles, besides the radius of the sphere which is supposed known. In general, *if three of these parts are given the other parts can be found*. If the triangle is a right spherical triangle, two given parts in addition to the right angle are sufficient to solve the triangle.

Since there are three unknowns to be found in solving a right triangle, it is necessary to have any two given parts combined with the remaining three in three independent relations or formulas. Now, since the five parts taken three at a time form *ten* combinations, *ten* formulas are necessary and sufficient to solve all right spherical triangles.

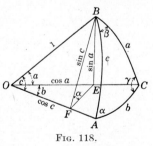

Fig. 118.

If a, b, c, α, and β are the five parts of the triangle, omitting the right angle, then the ten combinations of these taken three at a time are abc, $ab\alpha$, $ab\beta$, $ac\alpha$, $ac\beta$, $a\alpha\beta$, $bc\alpha$, $bc\beta$, $ba\beta$, and $c\alpha\beta$. It is necessary to derive a formula connecting the parts in each of these combinations.

136. Derivation of formulas for the solution of right spherical triangles.—Let O be the center of a sphere of unit radius, and ABC a right spherical triangle, with γ the right angle, formed by the intersection of the three planes AOB, AOC, and COB with the surface of the sphere. Pass the plane BFE through B perpendicular to OA. Then the plane angle BFE measures α, and a, b, and c have, respectively, the same measures as angles COB, AOC, and AOB. Further, $EB = \sin a$, $FB = \sin c$, $OF = \cos c$, and $OE = \cos a$.

Then
$$FE = EB \cot \alpha = \sin a \cot \alpha. \qquad (a)$$
$$FE = FB \cos \alpha = \sin c \cos \alpha. \qquad (b)$$
$$FE = OE \sin b = \cos a \sin b. \qquad (c)$$
$$FE = OF \tan b = \cos c \tan b. \qquad (d)$$

From (a) and (b), $\sin a \cot \alpha = \sin c \cos \alpha$.

$$\sin a = \sin c \, \frac{\cos \alpha}{\cot \alpha}, \text{ or}$$

(1) $$\sin a = \sin \alpha \sin c. \qquad (ac\alpha)$$

By analogy, interchanging a and b, α and β,

(2) $$\sin b = \sin \beta \sin c. \qquad (bc\beta)$$

From (a) and (c), $\sin a \cot \alpha = \cos a \sin b$.

$$\therefore \sin b = \frac{\sin a}{\cos a} \cot \alpha, \text{ or}$$

(3) $$\sin b = \tan a \cot \alpha. \qquad (ab\alpha)$$
(4) By analogy, $$\sin a = \tan b \cot \beta. \qquad (ab\beta)$$

From (a) and (d), $\sin a \cot \alpha = \cos c \tan b$.

$$\therefore \cos c = \frac{\sin a \cot \alpha}{\tan b} = \frac{\tan b \cot \beta \cot \alpha}{\tan b}, \text{ or}$$

(5) $$\cos c = \cot \alpha \cot \beta. \qquad (c\alpha\beta)$$

From (b) and (c), $\sin c \cos \alpha = \cos a \sin b$.

$$\therefore \cos \alpha = \frac{\cos a \sin b}{\sin c} = \frac{\cos a \sin c \sin \beta}{\sin c}, \text{ or}$$

(6) $$\cos \alpha = \sin \beta \cos a. \qquad (a\alpha\beta)$$
(7) By analogy, $$\cos \beta = \sin \alpha \cos b. \qquad (b\alpha\beta)$$

From (b) and (d), $\sin c \cos \alpha = \cos c \tan b$.

$$\therefore \cos \alpha = \frac{\cos c}{\sin c} \tan b, \text{ or}$$

(8) $$\cos \alpha = \tan b \cot c. \qquad (bc\alpha)$$
(9) By analogy, $$\cos \beta = \tan a \cot c. \qquad (ac\beta)$$

From (c) and (d), $\cos a \sin b = \cos c \tan b$.

$$\therefore \cos c = \frac{\cos a \sin b}{\tan b}, \text{ or}$$

(10) $$\cos c = \cos a \cos b. \qquad (abc)$$

137. Napier's rules of circular parts.—The preceding ten formulas for the solution of right spherical triangles are included in a theorem first stated and proved by Napier. The theorem is usually stated as two rules known as "Napier's rules of circular parts."

In the right spherical triangle ABC, omit the right angle at C and consider the sides a and b, and the complements of α, β, and c. Call these the circular parts of the triangle and designate them as a, b, co-α, co-β, and co-c.

In the triangle or the circular scheme shown in the figure, any one of these five parts may be selected and called the mid-

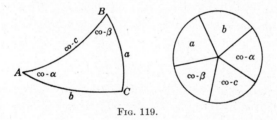

Fig. 119.

dle part; then the two parts next to it are called **adjacent parts**, and the other two parts the **opposite parts**. For example, if b is chosen as the middle part, then co-α and a are the adjacent parts and co-c and co-β are the opposite parts. Napier's rules are then stated as follows:

(1) *The sine of a middle part equals the product of the* **tangents** *of the* **adjacent** *parts.*

(2) *The sine of a middle part equals the product of the* **cosines** *of the* **opposite** *parts.*

It may assist in remembering the rules to notice the repetition of a in (1) and of o in (2).

Napier's rules may be verified by showing that they give the ten formulas of **Art. 136**. A demonstration of the theorem as given by Napier may be found in Todhunter and Leathem's "Spherical Trigonometry."

Example.—Use co-α as the middle part and apply rule (1).

$$\sin (\text{co-}\alpha) = \tan b \tan (\text{co-}c).$$
$$\therefore \cos \alpha = \tan b \cot c, \text{ which is formula (8).}$$

Exercise.—Verify all the ten formulas by Napier's rules.

Napier's rules thus furnish a very convenient way for the determination of the formulas for the solution of right spherical triangles.

138. Species.—Two angular quantities are said to be of the **same species** when they are both in the same quadrant, and of **different species** when they are in different quadrants.

Since any or all the parts of a right spherical triangle may be less than or greater than 90°, it is necessary to have a method for the determination of the species of the parts. The following rules will be found to cover all cases:

(1) *An oblique angle and its opposite side are always of the same species.*

(2) *If the hypotenuse is less than* 90°, *the two oblique angles and therefore the two sides of the triangle are of the same species; if the hypotenuse is greater than* 90°, *the two oblique angles, and therefore the two sides, are of opposite species.*

These rules are here verified in two cases. As an exercise, the student is asked to verify them in other cases.

Example 1.—By formula (5) (**Art. 136**), $\cos c = \cot \alpha \cot \beta$. If $c < 90°$, $\cos c$ is $+$. Then the product $\cot \alpha \cot \beta$ must be $+$, and this will be true if $\cot \alpha$ and $\cot \beta$ are both $+$ or both $-$; that is, if α and β are both in the same quadrant.

If $c > 90°$, $\cos c$ is $-$. Then the product $\cot \alpha \cot \beta$ must be $-$; that is, $\cot \alpha$ and $\cot \beta$ must be opposite in sign, and therefore α and β must be in different quadrants. This verifies rule (2).

Example 2.—From formula (7) (**Art. 136**), $\sin \alpha = \dfrac{\cos \beta}{\cos b}$.

Since $\sin \alpha$ is always $+$, $\cos \beta$ and $\cos b$ must both be $+$ or both $-$. Therefore, both β and b are in the same quadrant. This verifies rule (1).

139. Solution of right spherical triangles.—As stated before, when any two parts other than the right angle are given, the remaining parts of the right spherical triangle can be found. The necessary formulas can be obtained by taking each of the unknown parts in turn with the two known parts, and then applying Napier's rules. Or the formulas can be chosen from **Art. 136.**

The quadrant in which the unknown part belongs is determined by the rules of species.

The work may be checked by applying Napier's rules to the three parts obtained by the solution of the triangle.

Example 1.—Given $\alpha = 30° 51.2'$, $\beta = 71° 36'$; find a, b, and c, using Napier's rules.

<table>
<tr><td>*Formulas*</td><td>*Construction*</td></tr>
</table>

To find a, co-α is the middle part, a and co-β the opposite parts. Then sin (co-α) = cos a cos (co-β), or cos α = cos a sin β.

$$\therefore \cos a = \frac{\cos \alpha}{\sin \beta}.$$

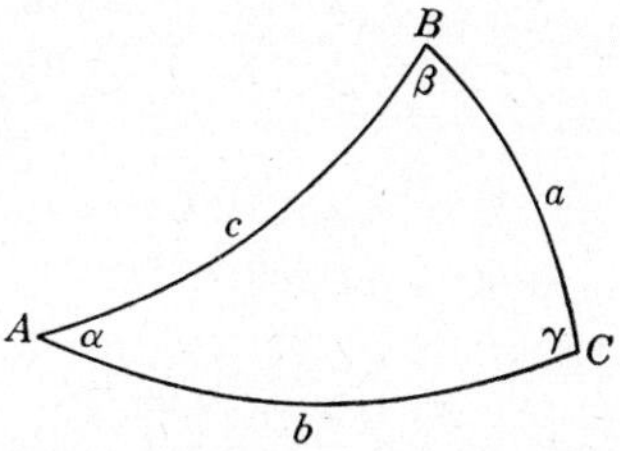

Fig. 120.

To find b, co-β is the middle part, co-α and b the opposite parts. Then sin (co-β) = cos (co-α) cos b, or cos β = sin α cos b.

$$\therefore \cos b = \frac{\cos \beta}{\sin \alpha}.$$

To find c, co-c is the middle part and co-α and co-β are the adjacent parts. Then sin (co-c) = tan (co-α) tan (co-β).

$$\therefore \cos c = \cot \alpha \cot \beta.$$

To check, use co-c as the middle part with a and b as the opposite parts. Then sin (co-c) = cos a cos b, or cos c = cos a cos b.

Computation

log cos α = 9.93373	log cos β = 9.49920
log sin β = 9.77721	log sin α = 9.70998
log cos a = 9.95652	log cos b = 9.78922
a = 25° 12.8'	b = 52° 0.8'
log cot α = 0.22375	*Check*
log cot β = 9.52200	log cos a = 9.95652
log cos c = 9.74575	log cos b = 9.78922
c = 56°9.6'	log cos c = 9.74574

Note.—The formulas used in this solution could have been taken from **Art. 136,** by selecting the formulas for the combinations ($a\alpha\beta$), ($b\alpha\beta$), and ($c\alpha\beta$).

Example 2 (ambiguous case).—Given $a = 24°\,8'$, $\alpha = 32°\,10'$; find β, b, and c, using Napier's rules.

<table>
<tr><td align="center">*Formulas*</td><td align="center">*Construction*</td></tr>
</table>

To find β. $\sin (\text{co-}\alpha) = \cos a \cos (\text{co-}\beta)$.

$$\therefore \sin \beta = \frac{\cos \alpha}{\cos a}.$$

To find b. $\sin b = \tan a \tan (\text{co-}\alpha)$.

$$\therefore \sin b = \tan a \cot \alpha.$$

To find c. $\sin a = \cos (\text{co-}\alpha) \cos (\text{co-}c)$.

$$\therefore \sin c = \frac{\sin a}{\sin \alpha}.$$

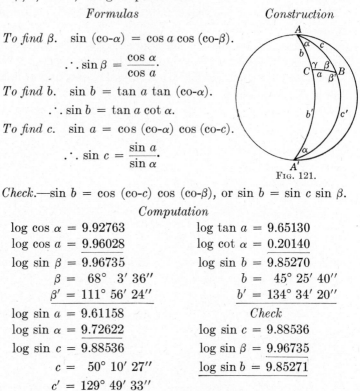

Fig. 121.

Check.—$\sin b = \cos (\text{co-}c) \cos (\text{co-}\beta)$, or $\sin b = \sin c \sin \beta$.

Computation

$\log \cos \alpha = 9.92763$	$\log \tan a = 9.65130$
$\log \cos a = 9.96028$	$\log \cot \alpha = 0.20140$
$\log \sin \beta = 9.96735$	$\log \sin b = 9.85270$
$\beta = 68°\,3'\,36''$	$b = 45°\,25'\,40''$
$\beta' = 111°\,56'\,24''$	$b' = 134°\,34'\,20''$
$\log \sin a = 9.61158$	*Check*
$\log \sin \alpha = 9.72622$	$\log \sin c = 9.88536$
$\log \sin c = 9.88536$	$\log \sin \beta = 9.96735$
$c = 50°\,10'\,27''$	$\log \sin b = 9.85271$
$c' = 129°\,49'\,33''$	

Since each of the unknown parts is determined from the sine, there are two values of each unknown part. For this reason it is called the ambiguous case. The proper grouping of the parts may be determined from the rules for species.

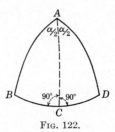

Fig. 122.

By rule (2), when $c < 90°$, α and β must be in the same quadrant. By rule (1), b and β must be in the same quadrant.

$\therefore a$, b, c, α, and β are the parts of one right spherical triangle.

Again by rule (2), when $c > 90°$, α and β are of opposite species.

$\therefore a$, b', c', α and β' are the parts of a right spherical triangle.

140. Isosceles spherical triangles.—When two sides of a spherical triangle are equal, it is said to be **isosceles.**

By dropping a perpendicular from the vertex of the triangle to the base, the triangle is divided into two symmetrical right triangles, as ACD and ACB in the figure.

The solution of the isosceles spherical triangle is, therefore, made to depend upon the solution of two right spherical triangles.

141. Quadrantal triangles.—When one side of a spherical triangle is equal to 90°, the triangle is called a **quadrantal triangle.**

By taking the polar triangle of a quadrantal triangle a right triangle is obtained, and this can be solved. The supplements of the parts of the right triangle will give the corresponding parts of the quadrantal triangle.

EXERCISES

1. Given $c = 69° 25' 11''$, $\beta = 63° 25' 3''$;
find $a = 50° 0' 0''$, $b = 56° 50' 52''$, $\alpha = 54° 54' 42''$.

2. Given $c = 78° 53' 20''$, $\alpha = 83° 56' 40''$;
find $a = 77° 21' 40''$, $b = 28° 14' 34''$, $\beta = 28° 49' 54''$.

3. Given $c = 61° 4' 56''$, $a = 40° 31' 20''$;
find $b = 50° 29' 48''$, $\beta = 61° 49' 23''$, $\alpha = 47° 55' 35''$.

4. Given $c = 70° 23' 42''$, $b = 48° 39' 16''$;
find $a = 59° 28' 30''$, $\alpha = 66° 7' 22''$, $\beta = 52° 50' 18''$.

5. Given $\alpha = 27° 28' 38''$, $\beta = 73° 27' 11''$;
find $c = 55° 9' 40''$, $a = 22° 15' 10''$, $b = 51° 53' 0''$.

6. Given $\alpha = 83° 56' 40''$, $\beta = 151° 10' 3''$;
find $a = 77° 21' 50''$, $b = 151° 45' 29''$, $c = 101° 6' 40''$.

7. Given $a = 25° 12' 48''$, $b = 52° 0' 45''$;
find $c = 56° 9' 38''$, $\alpha = 30° 51' 16''$, $\beta = 71° 36' 0''$.

8. Given $a = 100°$, $b = 98° 20'$;
find $c = 88° 33.5'$, $\alpha = 99° 53.8'$, $\beta = 98° 12.5'$.

9. Given $\alpha = 92° 8' 23''$, $b = 49° 59' 58''$;
find $a = 92° 47' 34''$, $c = 91° 47' 55''$, $\beta = 50° 2' 0''$.

10. Given $\beta = 54° 35' 17''$, $a = 15° 16' 50''$;
find $b = 20° 20' 20''$, $c = 25° 14' 38''$, $\alpha = 38° 10' 0''$.

11. Given $\beta = 83° 56' 40''$, $b = 77° 21' 40''$;
find $a = 28° 14' 34''$, $c = 78° 53' 20''$, $\alpha = 28° 49' 54''$;
$a' = 151° 45' 29''$, $c' = 101° 6' 40''$, $\alpha' = 151° 10' 3''$.

12. Given $\alpha = 66° 7' 20''$, $a = 59° 28' 27''$;
find $b = 48° 39' 16''$, $c = 70° 23' 42''$, $\beta = 52° 50' 20''$;
$b' = 131° 20' 44''$, $c' = 109° 36' 18''$, $\beta' = 127° 9' 40''$.

13. Solve the isosceles spherical triangle in which the equal sides are each 34° 45.6', and their included angle 112° 44.6'.

Ans. Equal angles = 38° 59.6'; side = 56° 41'.

14. Solve the isosceles triangle in which the equal angles are each 102° 6.4', and the base 115° 18'.

Ans. Equal sides = 97° 34'; included angle = 116° 54.5'.

15. In a quadrantal triangle, $c = 90°$, $a = 116° 44' 48''$, $b = 44° 26' 21''$;
find $\alpha = 130° 0' 4''$, $\beta = 36° 54' 48''$, $\gamma = 59° 4' 26''$.

16. In a quadrantal triangle, $c = 90°$, $\alpha = 121°\ 20'$, $\beta = 42°\ 1'$; find $a = 112°\ 10'\ 20''$, $b = 46°\ 31'\ 36''$, $\gamma = 67°\ 16'\ 22''$.

OBLIQUE SPHERICAL TRIANGLES

142. Sine theorem (law of sines).—*In any spherical triangle, the sines of the angles are proportional to the sines of the opposite sides.*

Proof.—Let ABC (Fig. 123) be a spherical triangle. Construct the great circle arc CD, forming the two right spherical triangles CBD and CAD. Represent the arc CD by h.

By (1) of **Art. 136.**

$$\sin \alpha = \frac{\sin h}{\sin b}, \text{ and } \sin \beta = \frac{\sin h}{\sin a}.$$

By division, $\dfrac{\sin \alpha}{\sin \beta} = \dfrac{\sin a}{\sin b}$, or $\dfrac{\sin \alpha}{\sin a} = \dfrac{\sin \beta}{\sin b}.$

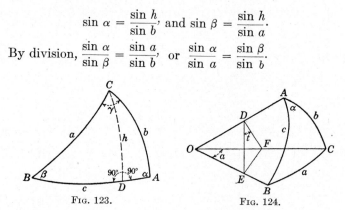

Fig. 123.   Fig. 124.

In a similar manner it may be proved that

$$\frac{\sin \alpha}{\sin \gamma} = \frac{\sin a}{\sin c}, \text{ or } \frac{\sin \alpha}{\sin a} = \frac{\sin \gamma}{\sin c}.$$

[44] $$\therefore \frac{\sin \alpha}{\sin a} = \frac{\sin \beta}{\sin b} = \frac{\sin \gamma}{\sin c}.$$

Formula **[44]** is useful in solving a spherical triangle when two angles and a side opposite one of them are given, or when two sides and an angle opposite one are given.

Note.—While, in the figure, D falls between A and B, the theorem can be as readily proved if D does not fall between A and B.

143. Cosine theorem (law of cosines).—*In any spherical triangle, the cosine of any side is equal to the product of the cosines of the two other sides, increased by the product of the sines of these sides times the cosine of their included angle.*

Proof.—Let ABC (Fig. 124) be a spherical triangle cut from the surface of a sphere, with center O, and radius OA chosen as unity. At any point D in OA, draw a plane EDF perpendicular to the edge OA and meeting the faces of the trihedral angle in DE, DF, and EF. Then $\angle EDF = t$ is the measure of α.

In the triangle DEF, $\overline{EF}^2 = \overline{ED}^2 + \overline{FD}^2 - 2ED \cdot FD \cos t$.

Also, in triangle EOF, $\overline{EF}^2 = \overline{OE}^2 + \overline{OF}^2 - 2OE \cdot OF \cos a$.

Equating these values of $\overline{EF}^2$,

$\overline{OE}^2 + OF - 2OE \cdot OF \cos a = \overline{ED}^2 + \overline{FD}^2 - 2ED \cdot FD \cos t$.

Or $2OE \cdot OF \cos a = \overline{OE}^2 - \overline{ED}^2 + \overline{OF}^2 - \overline{FD}^2 + 2ED \cdot FD \cos t$.

But OED and OFD are right triangles, then

$$\overline{OE}^2 - \overline{ED}^2 = \overline{OD}^2 \text{ and } \overline{OF}^2 - \overline{FD}^2 = \overline{OD}^2.$$

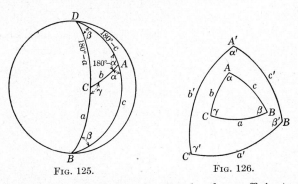

FIG. 125.　　　　　FIG. 126.

Making these substitutions, dividing by the coefficient *of* $\cos a$, and arranging the factors, there results

$$\cos a = \frac{OD}{ED} \cdot \frac{OD}{OF} + \frac{ED}{OE} \cdot \frac{FD}{OF} \cos t.$$

[45₁]　　　$\therefore \cos a = \cos b \cos c + \sin b \sin c \cos \alpha$.

Similarly,

[45₂]　　　$\cos b = \cos a \cos c + \sin a \sin c \cos \beta$.

[45₃]　　　$\cos c = \cos a \cos b + \sin a \sin b \cos \gamma$.

In Fig. 124, both b and c are less than $90°$, while no restriction is placed upon α or a. The resulting formulas are true, however, in general, as may easily be shown.

In Fig. 125, let ABC be a spherical triangle with $c > 90°$ and $b < 90°$. Complete the great circle arcs to form the triangle DCA, in which $AD = (180° - c) < 90°$. The parts of DCA are $180° - c$, $180° - \alpha$, $180° - a$, β, and b. Then by [45₁],

$\cos(180° - a) = \cos b \cos(180° - c) + \sin b \sin(180° - c) \cos(180° - \alpha)$.

$\therefore \cos a = \cos b \cos c + \sin b \sin c \cos \alpha$.

Exercise.—Draw a spherical triangle in which the two sides b and c are each greater than $90°$, and verify formula [45_1].

144. Theorem.—*The cosine of any angle of a spherical triangle is equal to the product of the sines of the two other angles multiplied by the cosine of their included side, diminished by the product of the cosines of the two other angles.*

Let ABC be the spherical triangle of which $A'B'C'$ is the polar triangle. Then $a = 180° - \alpha'$, $b = 180° - \beta'$, $c = 180° - \gamma'$, and $\alpha = 180° - a'$.

Substituting these values in [45_1] and simplifying,

$$\cos \alpha' = -\cos \beta' \cos \gamma' + \sin \beta' \sin \gamma' \cos a'.$$

This formula expresses a relation between the parts of a polar triangle. But the relation is true for any triangle, since for every spherical triangle there is a polar triangle and conversely.

[46_1] $\therefore \cos \alpha = -\cos \beta \cos \gamma + \sin \beta \sin \gamma \cos a.$

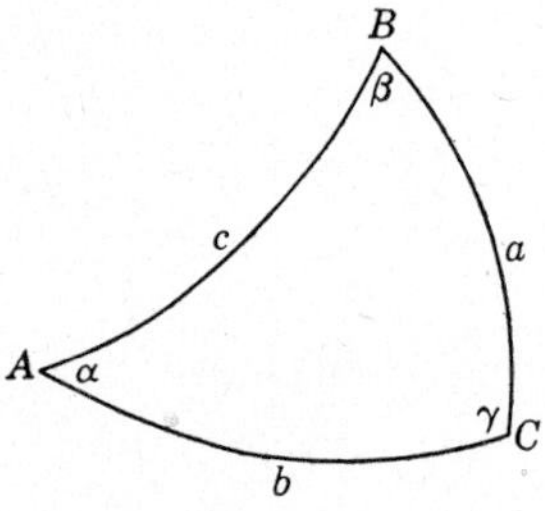

FIG. 127.

Similarly

[46_2] $\cos \beta = -\cos \alpha \cos \gamma + \sin \alpha \sin \gamma \cos b.$

[46_3] $\cos \gamma = -\cos \alpha \cos \beta + \sin \alpha \sin \beta \cos c.$

145. Given the three sides to find the angles.—Let ABC be a spherical triangle with given sides a, b, and c.

From [45_1],

$$\cos \alpha = \frac{\cos a - \cos b \cos c}{\sin b \sin c}. \tag{a}$$

In order to adapt this formula to logarithmic computation, proceed as follows:

(1) Subtracting each member of formula (a) from unity,

$$1 - \cos \alpha = 1 - \frac{\cos a - \cos b \cos c}{\sin b \sin c}.$$

Then $2 \sin^2 \frac{1}{2}\alpha = \frac{\cos (b - c) - \cos a}{\sin b \sin c}.$

But $\cos (b - c) - \cos a = -2 \sin \frac{1}{2}(b - c + a) \sin \frac{1}{2}(b - c - a)$ by [28]. Also $\sin \frac{1}{2}(b - c - a) = -\sin \frac{1}{2}(a - b + c)$.

$$\therefore \sin^2 \frac{1}{2}\alpha = \frac{\sin \frac{1}{2}(a + b - c) \sin \frac{1}{2}(a - b + c)}{\sin b \sin c}.$$

Now let $a + b + c = 2s.$

Then $a + b - c = 2(s - c),$

and $a - b + c = 2(s - b).$

[47₁] $\therefore \sin \frac{1}{2}\alpha = \sqrt{\dfrac{\sin (s - b) \sin (s - c)}{\sin b \sin c}}.$

In like manner the following are obtained:

[47₂] $\sin \frac{1}{2}\beta = \sqrt{\dfrac{\sin (s - a) \sin (s - c)}{\sin a \sin c}}.$

[47₃] $\sin \frac{1}{2}\gamma = \sqrt{\dfrac{\sin (s - a) \sin (s - b)}{\sin a \sin b}}.$

(2) By adding each member of formula (a) to unity, and carrying out the work in a similar manner to that in (1), the following are obtained:

[48₁] $\cos \frac{1}{2}\alpha = \sqrt{\dfrac{\sin s \sin (s - a)}{\sin b \sin c}}.$

[48₂] $\cos \frac{1}{2}\beta = \sqrt{\dfrac{\sin s \sin (s - b)}{\sin a \sin c}}.$

[48₃] $\cos \frac{1}{2}\gamma = \sqrt{\dfrac{\sin s \sin (s - c)}{\sin a \sin b}}.$

(3) By dividing [48₁] by [48₁],

$\tan \frac{1}{2}\alpha = \sqrt{\dfrac{\sin (s-b) \sin (s-c)}{\sin s \sin (s-a)}} = \sqrt{\dfrac{\sin (s-a) \sin (s-b) \sin (s-c)}{\sin s \sin^2 (s-a)}}.$

By writing $r = \sqrt{\dfrac{\sin (s - a) \sin (s - b) \sin (s - c)}{\sin s}},$

[49₁] $\tan \frac{1}{2}\alpha = \dfrac{r}{\sin (s - a)}.$

In a like manner the following are obtained:

[49₂] $\tan \frac{1}{2}\beta = \dfrac{r}{\sin (s - b)}.$

[49₃] $\tan \frac{1}{2}\gamma = \dfrac{r}{\sin (s - c)}.$

146. Given the three angles to find the sides.—If in the formulas [47] and [48] the parts of the spherical triangle be replaced by their values in terms of the parts of the polar triangle, the following formulas are obtained, where $S = \frac{1}{2}(\alpha + \beta + \gamma)$:

[50_1] $\cos \dfrac{1}{2}a = \sqrt{\dfrac{\cos (S - \beta) \cos (S - \gamma)}{\sin \beta \sin \gamma}}.$

[50_2] $\cos \dfrac{1}{2}b = \sqrt{\dfrac{\cos (S - \alpha) \cos (S - \gamma)}{\sin \alpha \sin \gamma}}.$

[50_3] $\cos \dfrac{1}{2}c = \sqrt{\dfrac{\cos (S - \alpha) \cos (S - \beta)}{\sin \alpha \sin \beta}}.$

[51_1] $\sin \dfrac{1}{2}a = \sqrt{-\dfrac{\cos S \cos (S - \alpha)}{\sin \beta \sin \gamma}}.$

[51_2] $\sin \dfrac{1}{2}b = \sqrt{-\dfrac{\cos S \cos (S - \beta)}{\sin \alpha \sin \gamma}}.$

[51_3] $\sin \dfrac{1}{2}c = \sqrt{-\dfrac{\cos S \cos (S - \gamma)}{\sin \alpha \sin \beta}}.$

Dividing [51_1] by [50_1],

$$\tan \frac{1}{2}a = \sqrt{\frac{-\cos S \cos (S - \alpha)}{\cos (S - \beta) \cos (S - \gamma)}}$$

$$= \cos (S - \alpha)\sqrt{\frac{-\cos S}{\cos (S - \alpha) \cos (S - \beta) \cos (S - \gamma)}}.$$

By writing $R = \sqrt{\dfrac{-\cos S}{\cos (S - \alpha) \cos (S - \beta) \cos (S - \gamma)}},$

[52_1] $\tan \frac{1}{2}a = R \cos (S - \alpha).$

In like manner the following are obtained:

[52_2] $\tan \frac{1}{2}b = R \cos (S - \beta).$

[52_3] $\tan \frac{1}{2}c = R \cos (S - \gamma).$

Note.—Since $90° < S < 270°$, $\cos S$ is negative. Also, since, in the polar triangle, any side is less than the sum of the two others,

$$\pi - \alpha < (\pi - \beta) + (\pi - \gamma), \text{ or } \beta + \gamma - \alpha < \pi.$$

Further, $\beta + \gamma - \alpha > -\pi.$

$$\therefore \; -\tfrac{1}{2}\pi < S - \alpha < \tfrac{1}{2}\pi, \text{ and } \cos (S - \alpha) \text{ is positive.}$$

Similarly, it can be shown that $\cos (S - \beta)$ and $\cos (S - \gamma)$ are each positive.

This makes the radical expressions of this article real.

Further, the positive sign must be given to the radicals in each case, for $\frac{1}{2}a$, $\frac{1}{2}b$, and $\frac{1}{2}c$ are each less than 90°.

147. Napier's analogies.—Dividing [49_1] by [49_2],

$$\frac{\tan \frac{1}{2}\alpha}{\tan \frac{1}{2}\beta} = \frac{\sin (s - b)}{\sin (s - a)}$$

Taking this proportion by composition and division,

$$\frac{\tan \tfrac{1}{2}\alpha + \tan \tfrac{1}{2}\beta}{\tan \tfrac{1}{2}\alpha - \tan \tfrac{1}{2}\beta} = \frac{\sin (s - b) + \sin (s - a)}{\sin (s - b) - \sin (s - a)}. \qquad (1)$$

But
$$\frac{\tan \tfrac{1}{2}\alpha + \tan \tfrac{1}{2}\beta}{\tan \tfrac{1}{2}\alpha - \tan \tfrac{1}{2}\beta} = \frac{\sin \tfrac{1}{2}(\alpha + \beta)}{\sin \tfrac{1}{2}(\alpha - \beta)}.$$

Also
$$\frac{\sin (s - b) + \sin (s - a)}{\sin (s - b) - \sin (s - a)} = \frac{2 \sin \tfrac{1}{2}(2s - a - b) \cos \tfrac{1}{2}(a - b)}{2 \cos \tfrac{1}{2}(2s - a - b) \sin \tfrac{1}{2}(a - b)}$$

$$= \frac{\tan \tfrac{1}{2}c}{\tan \tfrac{1}{2}(a - b)}.$$

Substituting these values in formula (1), there results

[53]
$$\frac{\tan \tfrac{1}{2}(a - b)}{\tan \tfrac{1}{2}c} = \frac{\sin \tfrac{1}{2}(\alpha - \beta)}{\sin \tfrac{1}{2}(\alpha + \beta)}.$$

Replacing a, b, c, α, and β by their values in terms of the parts of the polar triangle, [53] becomes

[54]
$$\frac{\tan \tfrac{1}{2}(\alpha - \beta)}{\cot \tfrac{1}{2}\gamma} = \frac{\sin \tfrac{1}{2}(a - b)}{\sin \tfrac{1}{2}(a + b)}.$$

Again, multiplying [49₁] by [49₂],

$$\frac{\tan \tfrac{1}{2}\alpha \tan \tfrac{1}{2}\beta}{1} = \frac{\sin (s - c)}{\sin s}.$$

Taking this proportion by composition and division,

$$\frac{1 + \tan \tfrac{1}{2}\alpha \tan \tfrac{1}{2}\beta}{1 - \tan \tfrac{1}{2}\alpha \tan \tfrac{1}{2}\beta} = \frac{\sin s + \sin (s - c)}{\sin s - \sin (s - c)}. \qquad (2)$$

But

$$\frac{1 + \tan \tfrac{1}{2}\alpha \tan \tfrac{1}{2}\beta}{1 - \tan \tfrac{1}{2}\alpha \tan \tfrac{1}{2}\beta} = \frac{\cos \tfrac{1}{2}\alpha \cos \tfrac{1}{2}\beta + \sin \tfrac{1}{2}\alpha \sin \tfrac{1}{2}\beta}{\cos \tfrac{1}{2}\alpha \cos \tfrac{1}{2}\beta - \sin \tfrac{1}{2}\alpha \sin \tfrac{1}{2}\beta} = \frac{\cos \tfrac{1}{2}(\alpha - \beta)}{\cos \tfrac{1}{2}(\alpha + \beta)}.$$

Also
$$\frac{\sin s + \sin (s - c)}{\sin s - \sin (s - c)} = \frac{2 \sin \tfrac{1}{2}(2s - c) \cos \tfrac{1}{2}c}{2 \cos \tfrac{1}{2}(2s - c) \sin \tfrac{1}{2}c} = \frac{\tan \tfrac{1}{2}(a + b)}{\tan \tfrac{1}{2}c}.$$

Substituting these values in formula (2), there results

[55]
$$\frac{\tan \tfrac{1}{2}(a + b)}{\tan \tfrac{1}{2}c} = \frac{\cos \tfrac{1}{2}(\alpha - \beta)}{\cos \tfrac{1}{2}(\alpha + \beta)}.$$

Replacing a, b, c, α, and β by their values in terms of the parts of the polar triangle, [55] becomes

[56]
$$\frac{\tan \tfrac{1}{2}(\alpha + \beta)}{\cot \tfrac{1}{2}\gamma} = \frac{\cos \tfrac{1}{2}(a - b)}{\cos \tfrac{1}{2}(a + b)}.$$

Equations [53], [54], [55], and [56] are known as **Napier's analogies.**

By making the proper changes in a, b, c, α, β, and γ, the corresponding formulas may be written for the other parts of the triangle.

148. Gauss's equations.—Taking the values of $\sin \frac{1}{2}\alpha$, $\cos \frac{1}{2}\alpha$, $\sin \frac{1}{2}\beta$, and $\cos \frac{1}{2}\beta$, and combining the functions of $\frac{1}{2}\alpha$ with those of $\frac{1}{2}\beta$, there result the four following forms:

$$\sin \tfrac{1}{2}\alpha \cos \tfrac{1}{2}\beta = \sqrt{\frac{\sin (s-b) \sin (s-c)}{\sin b \sin c}} \sqrt{\frac{\sin s \sin (s-b)}{\sin a \sin c}}$$

$$= \frac{\sin (s-b)}{\sin c} \sqrt{\frac{\sin s \sin (s-c)}{\sin a \sin b}} = \frac{\sin (s-b)}{\sin c} \cos \tfrac{1}{2}\gamma. \quad (1)$$

$$\cos \tfrac{1}{2}\alpha \sin \tfrac{1}{2}\beta = \sqrt{\frac{\sin s \sin (s-a)}{\sin b \sin c}} \sqrt{\frac{\sin (s-a) \sin (s-c)}{\sin a \sin c}}$$

$$= \frac{\sin (s-a)}{\sin c} \sqrt{\frac{\sin s \sin (s-c)}{\sin a \sin b}} = \frac{\sin (s-a)}{\sin c} \cos \tfrac{1}{2}\gamma. \quad (2)$$

$$\cos \tfrac{1}{2}\alpha \cos \tfrac{1}{2}\beta = \sqrt{\frac{\sin s \sin (s-a)}{\sin b \sin c}} \sqrt{\frac{\sin s \sin (s-b)}{\sin a \sin c}}$$

$$= \frac{\sin s}{\sin c} \sqrt{\frac{\sin (s-a) \sin (s-b)}{\sin a \sin b}} = \frac{\sin s}{\sin c} \sin \tfrac{1}{2}\gamma. \quad (3)$$

$$\sin \tfrac{1}{2}\alpha \sin \tfrac{1}{2}\beta = \sqrt{\frac{\sin (s-b) \sin (s-c)}{\sin b \sin c}} \sqrt{\frac{\sin (s-a) \sin (s-c)}{\sin a \sin c}}$$

$$= \frac{\sin (s-c)}{\sin c} \sqrt{\frac{\sin (s-a) \sin (s-b)}{\sin a \sin b}} = \frac{\sin (s-c)}{\sin c} \sin \tfrac{1}{2}\gamma. \quad (4)$$

Adding (1) and (2), there results

$$\sin \tfrac{1}{2}(\alpha + \beta) = \frac{\cos \tfrac{1}{2}\gamma}{\sin c}[\sin (s-b) + \sin (s-a)]$$

$$= \frac{\cos \tfrac{1}{2}\gamma}{2 \sin \tfrac{1}{2}c \cos \tfrac{1}{2}c} 2 \sin \tfrac{1}{2}[2s - (a+b)] \cos \tfrac{1}{2}(a-b).$$

But $\sin \frac{1}{2}[2s - (a+b)] = \sin \frac{1}{2}c$.

[57] $\therefore \cos \frac{1}{2}c \sin \frac{1}{2}(\alpha + \beta) = \cos \frac{1}{2}\gamma \cos \frac{1}{2}(a - b).$

Subtracting (4) from (3), there results

$$\cos \tfrac{1}{2}(\alpha + \beta) = \frac{\sin \tfrac{1}{2}\gamma}{\sin c}[\sin s - \sin (s-c)]$$

$$= \frac{\sin \tfrac{1}{2}\gamma}{2 \sin \tfrac{1}{2}c \cos \tfrac{1}{2}c} 2 \cos \tfrac{1}{2}(2s - c) \sin \tfrac{1}{2}c.$$

But $\cos \frac{1}{2}(2s - c) = \cos \frac{1}{2}(a + b)$.

[58] $\therefore \cos \frac{1}{2}c \cos \frac{1}{2}(\alpha + \beta) = \sin \frac{1}{2}\gamma \cos \frac{1}{2}(a + b).$

Subtracting (2) from (1), there results

$$\sin \tfrac{1}{2}(\alpha - \beta) = \frac{\cos \tfrac{1}{2}\gamma}{\sin c}[\sin (s - b) - \sin (s - a)]$$

$$= \frac{\cos \tfrac{1}{2}\gamma}{2 \sin \tfrac{1}{2}c \cos \tfrac{1}{2}c} 2 \cos \tfrac{1}{2}[2s - (a + b)] \sin \tfrac{1}{2}(a - b).$$

[59] $\therefore \sin \tfrac{1}{2}c \sin \tfrac{1}{2}(\alpha - \beta) = \cos \tfrac{1}{2}\gamma \sin \tfrac{1}{2}(a - b).$

Adding (3) to (4), there results

$$\cos \tfrac{1}{2}(\alpha - \beta) = \frac{\sin \tfrac{1}{2}\gamma}{\sin c}[\sin s + \sin (s - c)]$$

$$= \frac{\sin \tfrac{1}{2}\gamma}{2 \sin \tfrac{1}{2}c \cos \tfrac{1}{2}c} 2 \sin \tfrac{1}{2}(2s - c) \cos \tfrac{1}{2}c.$$

[60] $\therefore \sin \tfrac{1}{2}c \cos \tfrac{1}{2}(\alpha - \beta) = \sin \tfrac{1}{2}\gamma \sin \tfrac{1}{2}(a + b).$

Equations [57], [58], [59], and [60] are known as **Gauss's equations**, or **Delambre's analogies**. Geometric proofs of Gauss's equations and Napier's analogies can be found in Todhunter and Leathem's "Spherical Trigonometry."

Exercise.—Derive [60] from [57] by using the parts of the polar triangle.

149. Rules for species in oblique spherical triangles.—(1) *If a side (or an angle) differs from 90° by a larger number of degrees than another side (or angle) in the triangle, it is of the same species as its opposite angle (or side).*

Since all angles and sides of a spherical triangle are each less than 180°, in order to verify this rule, it is necessary to show that $\cos a$ and $\cos \alpha$, for example, have the same sign when

$$| a - 90° | > | b - 90° |.$$

From [45₁], $\cos a = \cos b \cos c + \sin b \sin c \cos \alpha.$

$$\therefore \cos \alpha = \frac{\cos a - \cos b \cos c}{\sin b \sin c}.$$

Since $| a - 90° | > | b - 90° |$, a is nearer 0 or 180° than b, and therefore $| \cos a | > | \cos b |$, and, since $\cos c$ cannot exceed unity,

$$\therefore | \cos a | > | \cos b \cos c |.$$

Further, the denominator will always be positive.

Then the sign of $\cos \alpha$ is the sign of the numerator of the fraction. That is, $\cos \alpha$ has the same sign as $\cos a$; therefore a and α are in the same quadrant.

For example, suppose $a = 120°$, $b = 70°$, $c = 130°$. Since $|\,120° - 90°\,| > |\,90° - 70°\,|$, α is in the second quadrant with a. Also, since $|\,130° - 90°\,| > |\,90° - 70°\,|$, γ is in the second quadrant with c. This leaves β undetermined in quadrant. It is determined by the second rule, which follows.

(2) *Half the sum of two sides of a spherical triangle must be of the same species as half the sum of the two opposite angles.*

From]55], $\tan \dfrac{1}{2}(a + b) = \tan \dfrac{1}{2}c\,\dfrac{\cos \frac{1}{2}(\alpha - \beta)}{\cos \frac{1}{2}(\alpha + \beta)}$.

Since $\frac{1}{2}c < 90°$, $\tan \frac{1}{2}c > 0$. Also, since $(\alpha - \beta) < 180°$, $\cos \frac{1}{2}(\alpha - \beta) > 0$. Therefore, $\tan \frac{1}{2}(a + b)$ and $\cos \frac{1}{2}(\alpha + \beta)$ are of the same sign. But $a + b$ and $\alpha + \beta$ must each be less than $360°$, and, therefore, $\frac{1}{2}(a + b)$ and $\frac{1}{2}(\alpha + \beta)$ must each be less than $180°$. Then $\frac{1}{2}(a + b)$ and $\frac{1}{2}(\alpha + \beta)$ must both be in the first quadrant or both be in the second quadrant, since $\tan \frac{1}{2}(a + b)$ and $\cos \frac{1}{2}(\alpha + \beta)$ are of the same sign.

150. Cases.—In the solution of oblique spherical triangles, the six following cases arise:

Case I.   *Given the three sides.*

Case II.   *Given the three angles.*

Case III.   *Given two sides and the included angle.*

Case IV.   *Given two angles and the included side.*

Case V.   *Given two sides and an angle opposite one of them.*

Case VI.   *Given two angles and a side opposite one of them.*

Any oblique spherical triangle can be solved by the formulas derived in the previous articles. In selecting a formula choose one which includes the parts given and the one to be found. The following list of formulas, together with the corresponding formulas for other parts, is sufficient for solving any spherical triangle:

$$\frac{\sin a}{\sin \alpha} = \frac{\sin b}{\sin \beta} = \frac{\sin c}{\sin \gamma}. \tag{1}$$

$$\tan \frac{1}{2}\alpha = \frac{r}{\sin (s - a)},$$

where

$$r = \sqrt{\frac{\sin (s - a)\, \sin (s - b)\, \sin (s - c)}{\sin s}}. \tag{2}$$

$$\tan \tfrac{1}{2}a = R \cos (S - \alpha),$$

where

$$R = \sqrt{\frac{-\cos S}{\cos (S - \alpha)\, \cos (S - \beta)\, \cos (S - \gamma)}} \tag{3}$$

$$\frac{\tan \frac{1}{2}(a - b)}{\tan \frac{1}{2}c} = \frac{\sin \frac{1}{2}(\alpha - \beta)}{\sin \frac{1}{2}(\alpha + \beta)}. \tag{4}$$

$$\frac{\tan \frac{1}{2}(a + b)}{\tan \frac{1}{2}c} = \frac{\cos \frac{1}{2}(\alpha_. - \beta)}{\cos \frac{1}{2}(\alpha + \beta)}. \tag{5}$$

$$\frac{\tan \frac{1}{2}(\alpha - \beta)}{\cot \frac{1}{2}\gamma} = \frac{\sin \frac{1}{2}(a - b)}{\sin \frac{1}{2}(a + b)}. \tag{6}$$

$$\frac{\tan \frac{1}{2}(\alpha + \beta)}{\cot \frac{1}{2}\gamma} = \frac{\cos \frac{1}{2}(a - b)}{\cos \frac{1}{2}(a + b)}. \tag{7}$$

151. Case I. Given the three sides to find the three angles.
Example.—Given $a = 46° 20' 45''$, $b = 65° 18' 15''$, $c = 90° 31' 46''$; to find α, β, and γ. ·

Formulas   *Construction*

$$\tan \frac{1}{2}\alpha = \frac{r}{\sin (s - a)}.$$

$$\tan \frac{1}{2}\beta = \frac{r}{\sin (s - b)}.$$

$$\tan \frac{1}{2}\gamma = \frac{r}{\sin (s - c)}.$$

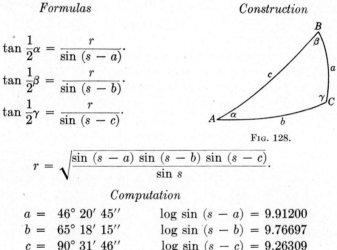

Fig. 128.

$$r = \sqrt{\frac{\sin (s - a) \sin (s - b) \sin (s - c)}{\sin s}}.$$

Computation

$a = \ \ 46° 20' 45''$	$\log \sin (s - a) = 9.91200$
$b = \ \ 65° 18' 15''$	$\log \sin (s - b) = 9.76697$
$c = \ \ 90° 31' 46''$	$\log \sin (s - c) = 9.26309$
$2s = \overline{202° 10' 46''}$	$\text{colog} \sin s = \underline{0.00819}$
$s = 101° \ \ 5' 23''$	$\log r^2 = 8.95025$
$s - a = \ \ 54° 44' 38''$	$\log r = 9.47513$
$s - b = \ \ 35° 47' \ \ 8''$	$\log \tan \frac{1}{2}\alpha = 9.56313$
$s - c = \ \ 10° 33' 37''$	$\therefore \frac{1}{2}\alpha = 20° \ \ 5' 15''$
$2s = \overline{202° 10' 46''}$	$\log \tan \frac{1}{2}\beta = 9.70816$
A check	$\therefore \frac{1}{2}\beta = 27° \ \ 3' 12''$
	$\log \tan \frac{1}{2}\gamma = 0.21204$
	$\therefore \frac{1}{2}\gamma = 58° 27' 45''$

Check by the sine law.

EXERCISES

1. Given $a = 68° 45'$, $b = 53° 15'$, $c = 46° 30'$;
find $\alpha = 94° 52' 40''$, $\beta = 58° 56' 10''$, $\gamma = 50° 50' 52''$.

2. Given $a = 70° 14' 20''$, $b = 49° 24' 10''$, $c = 38° 46' 10''$;
find $\alpha = 110° 51' 16''$, $\beta = 48° 56' 4''$, $\gamma = 38° 26' 48''$.
3. Given $a = 50° 12.1'$, $b = 116° 44.8'$, $c = 129° 11.7'$;
find $\alpha = 59° 4.4'$, $\beta = 94° 23.2'$, $\gamma = 120° 4.8'$.
4. Given $a = 68° 20.4'$, $b = 52° 18.3'$, $c = 96° 20.7'$;
find $\alpha = 56° 16.3'$, $\beta = 45° 4.7'$, $\gamma = 117° 12.3'$.
5. Given $a = 96° 24' 30''$, $b = 68° 27' 26''$, $c = 87° 31' 37''$;
find $\alpha = 97° 53' 0''$, $\beta = 67° 59' 39''$, $\gamma = 84° 46' 40''$.
6. Given $a = 31° 9' 13''$, $b = 84° 18' 28''$, $c = 115° 10' 0''$;
find $\alpha = 4° 23' 35''$, $\beta = 8° 28' 20''$, $\gamma = 172° 17' 56''$.

152. Case II.   Given the three angles to find the three sides.—
For the solution, use $\tan \frac{1}{2}a = R \cos (S - \alpha)$ and the corresponding forms, and proceed as in Case I.

EXERCISES

1. Given $\alpha = 129° 5' 28''$, $\beta = 142° 12' 42''$, $\gamma = 105° 8' 10''$;
find $a = 135° 49' 20''$, $b = 146° 37' 15''$, $c = 60° 4' 54''$.
2. Given $\alpha = 59° 4' 28''$, $\beta = 94° 23' 12''$, $\gamma = 120° 4' 52''$;
find $a = 50° 12' 4''$, $b = 116° 44' 48''$, $c = 129° 11' 42''$.
3. Given $\alpha = 107° 33' 20''$, $\beta = 127° 22' 0''$, $\gamma = 128° 41' 49''$;
find $a = 82° 47' 34''$, $b = 124° 12' 31''$, $c = 125° 41' 43''$.
4. Given $\alpha = 102° 14' 12''$, $\beta = 54° 32' 24''$, $\gamma = 89° 5' 46''$;
find $a = 104° 25' 8''$, $b = 53° 49' 25''$, $c = 97° 44', 18''$.

153. Case III.   Given two sides and the included angle.—
The sum and the difference of the two unknown angles can be found by [**54**] and [**56**].   The unknown side can be found by either [**53**] or [**55**]; together, they furnish a check on the work.

Example.—Given $a = 103° 44.7'$, $b = 64° 12.3'$, $\gamma = 98° 33.8'$; find α, β, and c.

<table>
<tr><td>Formulas</td><td>Construction</td></tr>
</table>

From [**54**],
$$\tan \frac{1}{2}(\alpha - \beta) = \cot \frac{1}{2}\gamma \frac{\sin \frac{1}{2}(a - b)}{\sin \frac{1}{2}(a + b)}.$$

From [**56**],
$$\tan \frac{1}{2}(\alpha + \beta) = \cot \frac{1}{2}\gamma \frac{\cos \frac{1}{2}(a - b)}{\cos \frac{1}{2}(a + b)}.$$

From [**53**],
$$\tan \frac{1}{2}c = \tan \frac{1}{2}(a - b) \frac{\sin \frac{1}{2}(\alpha + \beta)}{\sin \frac{1}{2}(\alpha - \beta)}.$$

From [**55**],
$$\tan \frac{1}{2}c = \tan \frac{1}{2}(a + b) \frac{\cos \frac{1}{2}(\alpha + \beta)}{\cos \frac{1}{2}(\alpha - \beta)}.$$

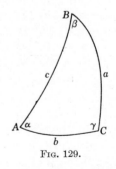

Fig. 129.

Computation

$$a = 103° \ 44.7'$$
$$b = 64° \ 12.3'$$
$$\tfrac{1}{2}(a + b) = \overline{83° \ 58.5'}$$
$$\tfrac{1}{2}(a - b) = 19° \ 46.2'$$
$$\tfrac{1}{2}\gamma = 49° \ 16.9'$$
$$\alpha = 98° \ 55.9'$$
$$\beta = 66° \ 18'$$

$$\log \cot \tfrac{1}{2}\gamma = 9.93485$$
$$\log \sin \tfrac{1}{2}(a - b) = 9.52923$$
$$\text{colog } \sin \tfrac{1}{2}(a + b) = 0.00241$$
$$\log \tan \tfrac{1}{2}(\alpha - \beta) = \overline{9.46649}$$
$$\therefore \tfrac{1}{2}(\alpha - \beta) = 16° \ 19'$$
$$\log \cot \tfrac{1}{2}\gamma = 9.93485$$
$$\log \cos \tfrac{1}{2}(a - b) = 9.97360$$
$$\text{colog } \cos \tfrac{1}{2}(a + b) = 0.97897$$
$$\log \tan \tfrac{1}{2}(\alpha + \beta) = \overline{0.88742}$$
$$\therefore \tfrac{1}{2}(\alpha + \beta) = 82° \ 37'$$

$$\log \tan \tfrac{1}{2}(a - b) = 9.55562$$
$$\log \sin \tfrac{1}{2}(\alpha + \beta) = 9.99638$$
$$\text{colog } \sin \tfrac{1}{2}(\alpha - \beta) = 0.55138$$
$$\log \tan \tfrac{1}{2}c = \overline{0.10338}$$
$$\therefore \tfrac{1}{2}c = 51° \ 45.3'$$

$$\log \tan \tfrac{1}{2}(\alpha + \beta) = 0.97657$$
$$\log \cos \tfrac{1}{2}(\alpha + \beta) = 9.10893$$
$$\text{colog } \cos \tfrac{1}{2}(\alpha - \beta) = 0.01785$$
$$\log \tan \tfrac{1}{2}c = \overline{0.10335}$$
$$\therefore \tfrac{1}{2}c = 51° \ 45.3'$$

EXERCISES

1. Given $b = 99° \ 40' \ 48''$, $c = 64° \ 23' \ 15''$, $\alpha = 97° \ 26' \ 29''$;
find $\quad a = 100° \ 49' \ 30''$, $\beta = 95° \ 38' \ 4''$, $\gamma = 65° \ 33' \ 10''$.

2. Given $a = 88° \ 21' \ 20''$, $b = 124° \ 7' \ 17''$, $\gamma = 50° \ 2' \ 1''$;
find $\quad \alpha = 63° \ 22' \ 56''$, $\beta = 132° \ 13' \ 58''$, $c = 58° \ 58' \ 24''$.

3. Given $b = 156° \ 12.2'$, $c = 112° \ 48.6'$, $\alpha = 76° \ 32.4'$;
find $\quad a = 63° \ 48.7'$, $\beta = 154° \ 4.1'$, $\gamma = 87° \ 27.1'$.

4. Given $a = 70° \ 20' \ 50''$, $b = 38° \ 28'$, $\gamma = 52° \ 29' \ 45''$;
find $\quad \alpha = 107° \ 47' \ 7''$, $\beta = 38° \ 58' \ 27''$, $c = 51° \ 40' \ 54''$.

5. Given $a = 135° \ 49' \ 20''$, $c = 60° \ 4' \ 54''$, $\beta = 142° \ 12' \ 42''$;
find $\quad \alpha = 129° \ 5' \ 28''$, $\gamma = 105° \ 8' \ 10''$, $b = 146° \ 37' \ 15''$.

154. Case IV. Given two angles and the included side.—
This case, like the preceding, is to be solved by Napier's analogies, using the four forms in a similar manner.

EXERCISES

1. Given $\alpha = 59° \ 4' \ 25''$, $\beta = 88° \ 12' \ 24''$, $c = 47° \ 42' \ 1''$;
find $\quad a = 50° \ 2' \ 1''$, $b = 63° \ 15' \ 15''$, $\gamma = 55° \ 52' \ 42''$.

2. Given $\alpha = 63° \ 45.6'$, $\beta = 95° \ 56.7'$, $c = 52° \ 27.8'$;
find $\quad a = 61° \ 41.3'$, $b = 77° \ 29.4'$, $\gamma = 53° \ 53.5'$.

3. Given $\alpha = 125° \ 41' \ 44''$, $\gamma = 82° \ 47' \ 35''$, $b = 52° \ 37' \ 57''$;
find $\quad a = 128° \ 41' \ 46''$, $c = 107° \ 33' \ 20''$, $\beta = 55° \ 47' \ 40''$.

4. Given $\beta = 34° \ 29' \ 30''$, $\gamma = 36° \ 6' \ 50''$, $a = 85° \ 59' \ 0''$;
find $\quad b = 47° \ 29' \ 20''$, $c = 50° \ 6' \ 20''$, $\alpha = 129° \ 58' \ 30''$.

155. Case V. Given two sides and the angle opposite one of them.—In this case the angle opposite the other side can be found by the sine law, when the other side and angle can be found by Napier's analogies. For example, given a, b, and α, to find c, β, and γ, use the following formulas:

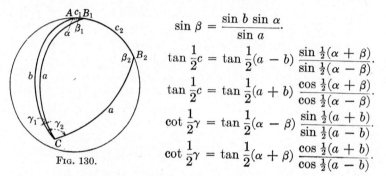

$$\sin \beta = \frac{\sin b \sin \alpha}{\sin a}.$$

$$\tan \frac{1}{2}c = \tan \frac{1}{2}(a - b) \frac{\sin \frac{1}{2}(\alpha + \beta)}{\sin \frac{1}{2}(\alpha - \beta)}.$$

$$\tan \frac{1}{2}c = \tan \frac{1}{2}(a + b) \frac{\cos \frac{1}{2}(\alpha + \beta)}{\cos \frac{1}{2}(\alpha - \beta)}.$$

$$\cot \frac{1}{2}\gamma = \tan \frac{1}{2}(\alpha - \beta) \frac{\sin \frac{1}{2}(a + b)}{\sin \frac{1}{2}(a - b)}.$$

$$\cot \frac{1}{2}\gamma = \tan \frac{1}{2}(\alpha + \beta) \frac{\cos \frac{1}{2}(a + b)}{\cos \frac{1}{2}(a - b)}.$$

Fig. 130.

A check is obtained by the agreement in the values of $\frac{1}{2}c$ and $\frac{1}{2}\gamma$ from the different formulas.

Since β is determined from $\sin \beta$, there will be two values of β less than $180°$, both of which may enter into a triangle. By the first rule for species (**Art. 149**), if $|\,90° - b\,| > |\,90° - a\,|$, b and β must be the same species. This definitely determines β. Otherwise, both values of β may be admissible. The application of the second rule for species will show whether or not two triangles are possible.

Example.—Given $a = 148° \ 34' \ 24''$, $b = 142° \ 11' \ 36''$, and $\alpha = 153° \ 17' \ 36''$; find c, β, and γ.

$$\sin \beta = \frac{\sin b \sin \alpha}{\sin a}.$$

$$\log \sin 142° \ 11' \ 36'' = 9.78746$$
$$\log \sin 153° \ 17' \ 36'' = 9.65265$$
$$\text{colog} \sin 148° \ 34' \ 24'' = 0.28282$$
$$\log \sin \beta = \overline{9.72293}$$
$$\beta_1 = 31° \ 53' \ 42''$$
$$\beta_2 = 148° \ 6' \ 18''$$

Here, since $|\,90° - 142° \ 11' \ 36''\,| < |\,90° - 148° \ 34' \ 24''\,|$, both values of β may be admissible. Since $\frac{1}{2}(a + b) = 145° \ 23'$ is in the second quadrant, as also are $\frac{1}{2}(\alpha + \beta_1) = 90° \ 35' \ 36''$ and $\frac{1}{2}(\alpha + \beta_2) = 150° \ 42'$, they are of the same species by the second rule for species. Hence, both β_1 and β_2 are admissible values to use.

The student can complete the solution and find the following values:

$$c_1 = \quad 7° \, 18' \, 24''. \qquad\qquad \gamma_1 = \quad 6° \, 17' \, 36''.$$
$$c_2 = 62° \quad 8' \, 36''. \qquad\qquad \gamma_2 = 130° \, 21' \, 12''.$$

This case is the *ambiguous case* in oblique spherical triangles, and is analogous to the ambiguous case in plane trigonometry. In practical applications, some facts about the general shape of the triangle may be known which will determine the values to be chosen without having recourse to the rules for species. A complete discussion of the ambiguous case may be found in Todhunter and Leathem's "Spherical Trigonometry," pages 80 to 85.

EXERCISES

1. Given $a = 46° \, 20' \, 45''$, $b = 65° \, 18' \, 15''$, $\alpha = 40° \, 10' \, 30''$;
find $c_1 = 90° \, 31' \, 46''$, $\beta_1 = 54° \, 6' \, 19''$, $\gamma_1 = 116° \, 55' \, 26''$;
$c_2 = 27° \, 23' \, 14''$, $\beta_2 = 125° \, 53' \, 41''$, $\gamma_2 = 24° \, 12' \, 53''$.

2. Given $a = 99° \, 40' \, 48''$, $b = 64° \, 23' \, 15''$, $\alpha = 95° \, 38' \, 4''$;
find $c = 100° \, 49' \, 30''$, $\beta = 65° \, 33' \, 10''$, $\gamma = 97° \, 26' \, 29''$.

3. Solve and check, $a = 31° \, 40' \, 25''$, $b = 32° \, 30'$, $\alpha = 88° \, 20'$.

4. Solve and check, $a = 149°$, $b = 133°$, $\alpha = 146°$.

5. Given $a = 62° \, 15' \, 24''$, $b = 103° \, 18' \, 47''$, $\alpha = 53° \, 42' \, 38''$;
find $c_1 = 153° \, 9' \, 36''$, $\beta_1 = 62° \, 24' \, 25''$, $\gamma_1 = 155° \, 43' \, 11''$;
$c_2 = 70° \, 25' \, 26''$, $\beta_2 = 117° \, 35' \, 35''$, $\gamma_2 = 59° \, 6' \, 50''$.

156. Case VI. Given two angles and the side opposite one of them.—In this case use the same formulas as in Case V, and apply the rules for species when there is any question as to the number of solutions.

EXERCISES

1. Given $\alpha = 29° \, 2' \, 55''$, $\beta = 45° \, 44' \, 6''$, $a = 35° \, 37' \, 18''$
find $b_1 = 59° \, 12' \, 16''$, $c_1 = 82° \, 17' \, 5''$, $\gamma_1 = 124° \, 17' \, 52''$;
$b_2 = 120° \, 47' \, 44''$, $c_2 = 150° \, 50' \, 51''$, $\gamma_2 = 156° \, 2' \, 24''$.

2. Given $\alpha = 73° \, 11' \, 18''$, $\beta = 61° \, 18' \, 12''$, $a = 46° \, 45' \, 30''$;
find $b = 41° \, 52' \, 35''$, $c = 41° \, 35' \, 4''$, $\gamma = 60° \, 42' \, 47''$.

3. Solve and check, $\alpha = 122°$, $\beta = 71°$, $a = 81°$.

4. Solve and check, $\alpha = 37° \, 42'$, $\beta = 47° \, 20'$, $b = 41° \, 50'$.

5. Given $\alpha = 36° \, 20' \, 20''$, $\beta = 46° \, 30' \, 40''$, $a = 42° \, 15' \, 20''$;
find $b_1 = 55° \, 25' \, 2''$, $c_1 = 81° \, 27' \, 26''$, $\gamma_1 = 119° \, 22' \, 28''$;
$b_2 = 124° \, 34' \, 58''$, $c_2 = 162° \, 34' \, 27''$, $\gamma_2 = 164° \, 41' \, 55''$.

157. Area of a spherical triangle.—Let r be the radius of the sphere on which the triangle is situated, Δ the area of the triangle, and E the spherical excess.

By spherical geometry, the areas of any two spherical triangles are to each other as their spherical excesses. Now the area of a trirectangular triangle is $\frac{1}{2}\pi r^2$, and its spherical excess is $90°$.

Then $$\Delta : \tfrac{1}{2}\pi r^2 = E : 90°.$$

[61] $$\therefore \Delta = \frac{\pi r^2 E}{180°}.$$

When all the angles of the triangle are known, the spherical excess and, therefore, the area are easily computed. If the angles are not all given, but enough data are known for the solution of the triangle, the angles may be found by Napier's analogies, and then the area may be computed by the above formula.

158. L'Huilier's formula.—This is a formula for determining the spherical excess directly in terms of the sides. It may be derived as follows: Since $E = \alpha + \beta + \gamma - 180°$,

$$\tan \frac{1}{4}E = \frac{\sin \frac{1}{4}(\alpha + \beta + \gamma - 180°)}{\cos \frac{1}{4}(\alpha + \beta + \gamma - 180°)}$$

$$= \frac{2 \sin \frac{1}{4}(\alpha + \beta + \gamma - 180°) \cos \frac{1}{4}(\alpha + \beta - \gamma + 180°)}{2 \cos \frac{1}{4}(\alpha + \beta + \gamma - 180°) \cos \frac{1}{4}(\alpha + \beta - \gamma + 180°)}$$

$$= \frac{\sin \frac{1}{2}(\alpha + \beta) - \cos \frac{1}{2}\gamma}{\cos \frac{1}{2}(\alpha + \beta) + \sin \frac{1}{2}\gamma}, \text{ by [29] and [31].}$$

By [57], $\sin \frac{1}{2}(\alpha + \beta) = \dfrac{\cos \frac{1}{2}\gamma \cos \frac{1}{2}(a - b)}{\cos \frac{1}{2}c}.$

By [58], $\cos \frac{1}{2}(\alpha + \beta) = \dfrac{\sin \frac{1}{2}\gamma \cos \frac{1}{2}(a + b)}{\cos \frac{1}{2}c}.$

By making these substitutions,

$$\tan \frac{1}{4}E = \left(\frac{\cos \frac{1}{2}(a - b) - \cos \frac{1}{2}c}{\cos \frac{1}{2}(a + b) + \cos \frac{1}{2}c}\right) \cot \frac{1}{2}\gamma$$

$$= \left(\frac{-2 \sin \frac{1}{4}(a - b + c) \sin \frac{1}{4}(a - b - c)}{2 \cos \frac{1}{4}(a + b + c) \cos \frac{1}{4}(a + b - c)}\right) \cot \frac{1}{2}\gamma$$

$$= \frac{\sin \frac{1}{2}(s - b) \sin \frac{1}{2}(s - a)}{\cos \frac{1}{2}s \cos \frac{1}{2}(s - c)} \sqrt{\frac{\sin s \sin (s - c)}{\sin (s - a) \sin (s - b)}}.$$

[62] $\therefore \tan \frac{1}{4}E = \sqrt{\tan \frac{1}{2}s \tan \frac{1}{2}(s - a) \tan \frac{1}{2}(s - b) \tan \frac{1}{2}(s - c)}.$

EXERCISES

1. On a sphere of radius 6 in., $\alpha = 87° 20' 45''$, $\beta = 32° 40' 56''$, and $\gamma = 77° 45' 32''$. Find the area of the triangle.   *Ans.* 11.176 sq. in.

2. Given $a = 56° 37'$, $b = 108° 14'$, $c = 75° 29'$; find E.
Ans. $E = 48° 32' 35''$.

3. Given $a = 47° 18'$, $b = 53° 26'$, $c = 63° 54'$; find E.
Ans. $E = 24° 29' 50''$.

4. Given $\alpha = 110° 10'$, $b = 33° 1' 45''$, $c = 155° 5' 18''$; find E.
Ans. $E = 133° 48' 53''$.

5. Given $a = b = c = 60°$, on a sphere of 12-in. radius; find the area of the triangle.   *Ans.* 79.38 sq. in.

6. Given $\alpha = 49° 50'$, $\beta = 67° 30'$, $\gamma = 74° 40'$, on a sphere of 10-in. radius; find the area of the triangle. *Ans.* 20.94 sq. in.

7. Given $\alpha = 110°$, $\beta = 94°$, $c = 44°$, on a sphere of 10-ft. radius; find the area of the triangle. *Ans.* 128.15 sq. ft.

8. Given $a = 15° 22' 44''$, $c = 44° 27' 40''$, $\beta = 167° 42' 27''$, on a sphere of radius 100 ft.; find the area of the triangle. *Ans.* 248.32 sq. ft.

9. Find the area of a triangle having sides of 1° each on the surface of the earth. *Ans.* 2070 sq. miles.

APPLICATIONS OF SPHERICAL TRIGONOMETRY

159. Definitions and notations.—In all the applications of spherical trigonometry to the measurements of arcs of great circles on the surface of the earth, and to problems of astronomy, the earth will be treated as a sphere of radius 3956 miles.

A **meridian** is a great circle of the earth drawn through the poles N and S. The meridian NGS passing through Greenwich, England, is called the **principal meridian.**

The **longitude** of any point P on the earth's surface is the angle between the principal meridian NGS and the meridian NPS through P. It is measured by the great circle arc, CA, of the equator between the points where the meridians cut the equator.

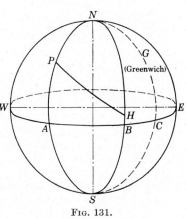

Fig. 131.

If a point on the surface of the earth is west of the principal meridian, its longitude is *positive*. If east, it is *negative*. A point 70° west of the principal meridian is usually designated as in "longitude 70° W." "Longitude 70° E." means in 70° east longitude. The letter θ is used to designate longitude.

The **latitude** of a point on the surface of the earth is the number of degrees it is north or south of the equator, measured along a meridian. Latitude is *positive* when measured north of the equator, and *negative* when south. The letter ϕ is used to designate latitude.

160. The terrestrial triangle.—Given two points on the earth's surface, H with latitude ϕ_1 and longitude θ_1, and P with latitude ϕ_2 and longitude θ_2; then the arcs $HN = 90° - \phi_1$, $PN = 90° - \phi_2$, and HP, which represents the distance between

the points, form a spherical triangle called the **terrestrial triangle.**
The angle $HNP = \theta_2 - \theta_1$, the difference of the longitudes, is
known, as are also the arcs HN and PN. Two sides and the
included angle of the triangle HPN are then known and the triangle can be solved for the distance HP and for the *bearing* of one
point from the other.

The angle NHP is the **bearing** of P from H, and angle NPH the
bearing of H from P. The bearing will be represented by γ.
The bearing of a line is usually the smallest angle which the line
or path makes with the meridian through the point.

A complete solution of the terrestrial triangle by Napier's analogies and the sine law will furnish the bearings of any two points
and their distance apart.

EXERCISES

1. Find the shortest distance, in statute miles, between New York, 40°
45′ N., 73° 58′ W., and Chicago, 41° 50′ N., 87° 35′ W.   *Ans.* 710 miles.

2. Find the shortest distance, in statute miles, between Chicago, 41° 50′
N., 87° 35′ W., and San Francisco, 37° 40′ N., 122° 28′ W.

Ans. 1859 miles.

Find the shortest distance between the following places, and find the
bearing of each from the other:

3. New York, 40° 45′ N., 73° 58′ W., and Rio Janeiro, 22° 54′ S., 43° 10′ W.
  Ans. Distance = 69° 47.8′ = 4187.8 geographic miles.
  Bearing of New York from Rio Janeiro, N. 24° 24.9′ W.
  Bearing of Rio Janeiro from New York, S. 30° 10.5′ E.

4. San Francisco, 37° 48′ N., 122° 28′ W., and Manila, 14° 36′ N., 121° 5′ E.
  Ans. Distance = 100° 43.5′ = 6043 geographic miles.
  Bearing of San Francisco from Manila, N. 46° 3.4′ E.
  Bearing of Manila from San Francisco, N. 61° 51.7′ W.

Find the shortest distance in statute miles between the following places
and check the work:

5. Chicago, 41° 50′ N., 87° 35′ W., and Manila, 14° 36′ N., 121° 5′ E.

6. Greenwich, 51° 29′ N., and Valparaiso, 33° 2′ S., 71° 42′ W.

7. Paris, 48° 50′ N., 2° 20′ E., and Calcutta, 22° 35′ N., 88° 27′ E.

8. From a point at 40° N., 8° 15.6′ W. a ship sails on the arc of a great
circle a distance of 3000 statute miles, starting in the direction S. 61° 15′ W·
Find its latitude and longitude.   *Ans.* 12° 18.5′ N., 46° 22.0′ W.

9. What is the shortest distance on the surface of the earth from a point
A, 45° N., 74° W., and a point B which is 2000 miles directly west from A?

Ans. 1978 miles.

161. Applications to astronomy.—The daily rotation of the
earth about its axis, from west to east, causes the stars to appear
to rotate daily from east to west. They move as if attached to
the surface of an immense sphere rotating about an axis through

its center. This sphere is called the **celestial sphere,** and the center of the earth is taken as its center.

The location of a star, or any heavenly body, is the point where a line drawn from the observer through the star pierces the celestial sphere. The location of one heavenly body with reference to another is thus seen to depend upon the arcs of great circles and spherical angles.

162. Fundamental points, circles of reference, and systems of coordinates.—The **north pole** P and the **south pole** Q of the celestial sphere (Fig. 132) are the points where the earth's axis produced pierces the surface of the sphere.

The **horizon** of any point on the earth is the great circle cut from the celestial sphere by a horizontal plane through the point. Thus HAH' is the horizon.

If at any point on the earth a perpendicular is erected to the horizon at that point, the point where it pierces the celestial sphere above the plane is called the **zenith** of the point, while the piercing point below the plane is called the **nadir** of the point. Thus, Z is the zenith and N the nadir of the point O.

The intersection of the plane of the earth's equator with the celestial sphere is called the **celestial equator.** Thus, EAW is the celestial equator.

The great circle through the north pole and a star is called the **hour circle** of the star. Thus, PSI is the hour circle of the star at S.

The hour circle through the zenith is called the **celestial meridian,** or simply the meridian. Thus, $PZEH$ is the celestial meridian.

The **hour angle** of a star is the angle at the pole between the meridian and the hour circle of the star. Thus, angle SPZ is the hour angle of S. The hour angle is usually expressed as so many hours, minutes, and seconds before or after noon. An hour angle of 1 hr. is $\frac{1}{24}$ of 360°, or 15°.

The **declination** of a star is its angular distance north or south of the equator. The declination of the star S is IS.

The **altitude** of a star is its angular distance above the horizon measured on the great circle through the zenith and the star. The altitude of the star S is MS.

From the definition of latitude in **Art. 159,** it is easily seen that the meridian arc EZ from the equator toward the zenith is the latitude of the point on the earth's surface.

The triangle *ZPS* is called the **astronomical triangle.** *ZP* is the colatitude of the observer, *SZ* is the coaltitude of the star, *SP* is the codeclination of the star, and the angle *SPZ* is the hour angle of the star. The answers to many practical problems of astronomy are obtained by solving the astronomical triangle. The determination of correct time, when the declination and altitude of the sun and the latitude of the observer are

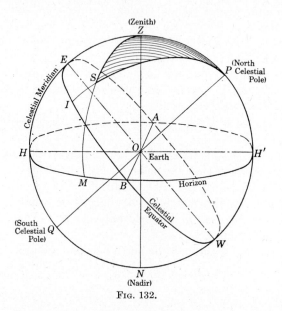

Fig. 132.

known, is obtained by solving for angle *SPZ*. The time of sunrise, neglecting refraction, may be found from the determination of angle *SPZ* when the altitude is zero. We then have a quadrantal triangle, and its polar triangle is a right spherical triangle.

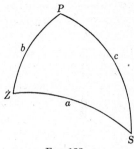

Fig. 133.

Example 1.—The latitude of Boston is 42° 20′ N. A forenoon observation showed the altitude of the sun to be 25° 30′. If the declination of the sun is 15° 50′ N., find the time of observation.

Solution.—In the triangle *PZS*,

$$PS = 90° - \text{Decl.} = 74° 10′.$$
$$PZ = 90° - \text{Lat.} = 47° 40′.$$
$$ZS = 90° - \text{Alt.} = 64° 30′.$$

To determine $\angle P$, use [49$_1$],

$$\tan \frac{1}{2}P = \sqrt{\frac{\sin (s - b) \sin (s - c)}{\sin s \sin (s - a)}}.$$

$a = 64° 30'$	log sin 45° 30' = 9.85324
$b = 47° 40'$	log sin 19° = 9.51264
$c = 74° 10'$	colog sin 93° 10' = 0.00066
$2s = 186° 20'$	colog sin 28° 40' = 0.31902
$s = 93° 10'$	log tan² $\frac{1}{2}P$ = 9.68556
$s - a = 28° 40'$	log tan $\frac{1}{2}P$ = 9.84278
$s - b = 45° 30'$	$\frac{1}{2}P$ = 34° 50' 55''
$s - c = 19°$	P = 69° 41' 50''

$\therefore \angle P$ in hours = 4 hr. 38 min. 47 sec.

Therefore, the time is 7 hr. 21 min. 13 sec. A.M.

Example 2.—Find the time of sunset for a place, latitude 32° 15' N., when the declination is 17° 38' N.

Solution.—In the triangle ZPS,

$PS = 90° - 17° 38' = 72° 22'.$
$PZ = 90° - 32° 15' = 57° 45'.$
$ZS = 90°.$

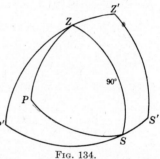

Fig. 134.

Triangle ZPS is then a quadrantal triangle which may be solved by Napier's analogies. A better method, however, is to solve the polar triangle and from that obtain the required parts of the given triangle.

In the polar triangle $P'Z'S'$, $\angle P' = 90°$. $\angle S' = 180° - PZ$, and $\angle Z' = 180° - PS$.

By Napier's rules or by (5) (**Art. 136**),

$\cos S'Z' = \cot S' \cot Z'.$
$\cos S'Z' = \cot (180° - 57° 45') \cot (180° - 72° 22')$
$\qquad = \tan 32° 15' \tan 17° 38'.$

log tan 32° 15' = 9.80000
log tan 17° 38' = 9.50223
log cos $S'Z'$ = 9.30223
$\therefore S'Z' = 78° 25' 50''$
$\therefore \angle P = 180° - 78° 25' 50'' = 101° 34' 10''.$

And $\angle P$ in hours = 6 hr. 46 min. 17 sec.

Therefore the sun sets at 6 hr. 46 min. 17 sec. P.M.

EXERCISES

1. A forenoon observation on the sun showed the altitude to be 41°. If the latitude of the observer is 40° N. and the sun's declination is 20° N., find the time of observation. *Ans.* 8 hr. 29 min. 20 sec.

2. Find the time of sunset at a place, latitude 45° 30′ N., if the declination of the sun is 18° N. *Ans.* 7 hr. 17 min. 14 sec.

3. Find the altitude of the sun at 3 P.M. for a place, latitude 19° 25′ N. when the declination of the sun is 8° 23′ N. *Ans.* 45° 5′.

4. If the latitude of an observer is 8° 57′ N., and the sun's declination is 23° 2′ S., find the time of sunrise. *Ans.* 6 hr. 15 min. 21.6 sec. A.M.

5. Find the time of sunrise at Chicago, latitude 41° 50′, on June 21, when the sun's declination is 23° 30′. *Ans.* 4 hr. 28 min. 23 sec. A.M.

FORMULAS

[1] $\sin^2 \theta + \cos^2 \theta = 1$.

[2] $1 + \tan^2 \theta = \sec^2 \theta$.

[3] $1 + \cot^2 \theta = \csc^2 \theta$.

[4] $\sin \theta = \dfrac{1}{\csc \theta}$ and $\csc \theta = \dfrac{1}{\sin \theta}$.

[5] $\cos \theta = \dfrac{1}{\sec \theta}$ and $\sec \theta = \dfrac{1}{\cos \theta}$.

[6] $\tan \theta = \dfrac{1}{\cot \theta}$ and $\cot \theta = \dfrac{1}{\tan \theta}$.

[7] $\tan \theta = \dfrac{\sin \theta}{\cos \theta}$.

[8] $\cot \theta = \dfrac{\cos \theta}{\sin \theta}$.

[9] $x = l \cos \theta$. (Projection on x-axis.)

[10] $y = l \sin \theta$. (Projection on y-axis.)

[11] $G = \frac{1}{2} r^2 (\theta - \sin \theta)$. (Area of segment.)

[12] $\sin \theta < \theta < \tan \theta$. $\lim\limits_{\theta \to 0} \left[\dfrac{\theta}{\sin \theta} \right] = 1$.

[13] $\sin (\alpha + \beta) = \sin \alpha \cos \beta + \cos \alpha \sin \beta$.

[14] $\cos (\alpha + \beta) = \cos \alpha \cos \beta - \sin \alpha \sin \beta$.

[15] $\sin (\alpha - \beta) = \sin \alpha \cos \beta - \cos \alpha \sin \beta$.

[16] $\cos (\alpha - \beta) = \cos \alpha \cos \beta + \sin \alpha \sin \beta$.

[17] $\tan (\alpha + \beta) = \dfrac{\tan \alpha + \tan \beta}{1 - \tan \alpha \tan \beta}$.

[18] $\tan (\alpha - \beta) = \dfrac{\tan \alpha - \tan \beta}{1 + \tan \alpha \tan \beta}$.

[19] $\sin 2\theta = 2 \sin \theta \cos \theta$.

[20] $\cos 2\theta = \cos^2 \theta - \sin^2 \theta = 1 - 2 \sin^2 \theta = 2 \cos^2 \theta - 1$.

[21] $\tan 2\theta = \dfrac{2 \tan \theta}{1 - \tan^2 \theta}.$

[22] $\sin \dfrac{1}{2}\theta = \pm\sqrt{\dfrac{1 - \cos \theta}{2}}.$

[23] $\cos \dfrac{1}{2}\theta = \pm\sqrt{\dfrac{1 + \cos \theta}{2}}.$

[24] $\tan \dfrac{1}{2}\theta = \pm\sqrt{\dfrac{1 - \cos \theta}{1 + \cos \theta}} = \dfrac{1 - \cos \theta}{\sin \theta} = \dfrac{\sin \theta}{1 + \cos \theta}.$

[25] $\sin \alpha + \sin \beta = 2 \sin \frac{1}{2}(\alpha + \beta) \cos \frac{1}{2}(\alpha - \beta).$

[26] $\sin \alpha - \sin \beta = 2 \cos \frac{1}{2}(\alpha + \beta) \sin \frac{1}{2}(\alpha - \beta).$

[27] $\cos \alpha + \cos \beta = 2 \cos \frac{1}{2}(\alpha + \beta) \cos \frac{1}{2}(\alpha - \beta).$

[28] $\cos \alpha - \cos \beta = -2 \sin \frac{1}{2}(\alpha + \beta) \sin \frac{1}{2}(\alpha - \beta).$

[29] $\sin \alpha \cos \beta = \frac{1}{2} \sin (\alpha + \beta) + \frac{1}{2} \sin (\alpha - \beta).$

[30] $\cos \alpha \sin \beta = \frac{1}{2} \sin (\alpha + \beta) - \frac{1}{2} \sin (\alpha - \beta).$

[31] $\cos \alpha \cos \beta = \frac{1}{2} \cos (\alpha + \beta) + \frac{1}{2} \cos (\alpha - \beta).$

[32] $\sin \alpha \sin \beta = -\frac{1}{2} \cos (\alpha + \beta) + \frac{1}{2} \cos (\alpha - \beta).$

[33] $\dfrac{a}{\sin \alpha} = \dfrac{b}{\sin \beta} = \dfrac{c}{\sin \gamma}.$ (Law of sines.)

[34] $a^2 = b^2 + c^2 - 2bc \cos \alpha.$ (Law of cosines.)

[35] $K = \dfrac{b^2 \sin \alpha \sin \gamma}{2 \sin \beta}.$

[36] $K = \frac{1}{2}ab \sin \gamma.$

[37] $\dfrac{a + b}{a - b} = \dfrac{\tan \frac{1}{2}(\alpha + \beta)}{\tan \frac{1}{2}(\alpha - \beta)}.$

[38] $\tan \dfrac{1}{2}(\alpha - \beta) = \dfrac{a - b}{a + b} \cot \dfrac{1}{2}\gamma.$

[39] $\sin \dfrac{1}{2}\alpha = \sqrt{\dfrac{(s - b)(s - c)}{bc}}.$

[40] $\cos \dfrac{1}{2}\alpha = \sqrt{\dfrac{s(s - a)}{bc}}.$

[41] $\tan \dfrac{1}{2}\alpha = \sqrt{\dfrac{(s - b)(s - c)}{s(s - a)}}.$

[42] $\tan \dfrac{1}{2}\alpha = \dfrac{r}{s - a},$ where $r = \sqrt{\dfrac{(s - a)(s - b)(s - c)}{s}}.$

[43] $K = \sqrt{s(s - a)(s - b)(s - c)}.$

[44] $\dfrac{\sin \alpha}{\sin a} = \dfrac{\sin \beta}{\sin b} = \dfrac{\sin \gamma}{\sin c}.$

[45] $\cos a = \cos b \cos c + \sin b \sin c \cos \alpha.$

[46] $\cos \alpha = -\cos \beta \cos \gamma + \sin \beta \sin \gamma \cos a.$

[47] $\sin\frac{1}{2}\alpha = \sqrt{\dfrac{\sin(s-b)\sin(s-c)}{\sin b\sin c}}$, where $s = \frac{1}{2}(a+b+c)$.

[48] $\cos\frac{1}{2}\alpha = \sqrt{\dfrac{\sin s\sin(s-a)}{\sin b\sin c}}$.

[49] $\tan\frac{1}{2}\alpha = \dfrac{r}{\sin(s-a)}$, where

$$r = \sqrt{\dfrac{\sin(s-a)\sin(s-b)\sin(s-c)}{\sin s}}.$$

[50] $\cos\frac{1}{2}a = \sqrt{\dfrac{\cos(S-\beta)\cos(S-\gamma)}{\sin\beta\sin\gamma}}$,

where $S = \frac{1}{2}(\alpha+\beta+\gamma)$.

[51] $\sin\frac{1}{2}a = \sqrt{-\dfrac{\cos S\cos(S-\alpha)}{\sin\beta\sin\gamma}}$.

[52] $\tan\frac{1}{2}a = R\cos(S-\alpha)$, where

$$R = \sqrt{\dfrac{-\cos S}{\cos(S-\alpha)\cos(S-\beta)\cos(S-\gamma)}}.$$

[53] $\dfrac{\tan\frac{1}{2}(a-b)}{\tan\frac{1}{2}c} = \dfrac{\sin\frac{1}{2}(\alpha-\beta)}{\sin\frac{1}{2}(\alpha+\beta)}$.

[54] $\dfrac{\tan\frac{1}{2}(\alpha-\beta)}{\cot\frac{1}{2}\gamma} = \dfrac{\sin\frac{1}{2}(a-b)}{\sin\frac{1}{2}(a+b)}$.

[55] $\dfrac{\tan\frac{1}{2}(a+b)}{\tan\frac{1}{2}c} = \dfrac{\cos\frac{1}{2}(\alpha-\beta)}{\cos\frac{1}{2}(\alpha+\beta)}$.

[56] $\dfrac{\tan\frac{1}{2}(\alpha+\beta)}{\cot\frac{1}{2}\gamma} = \dfrac{\cos\frac{1}{2}(a-b)}{\cos\frac{1}{2}(a+b)}$.

[57] $\cos\frac{1}{2}c\sin\frac{1}{2}(\alpha+\beta) = \cos\frac{1}{2}\gamma\cos\frac{1}{2}(a-b)$.

[58] $\cos\frac{1}{2}c\cos\frac{1}{2}(\alpha+\beta) = \sin\frac{1}{2}\gamma\cos\frac{1}{2}(a+b)$.

[59] $\sin\frac{1}{2}c\sin\frac{1}{2}(\alpha-\beta) = \cos\frac{1}{2}\gamma\sin\frac{1}{2}(a-b)$.

[60] $\sin\frac{1}{2}c\cos\frac{1}{2}(\alpha-\beta) = \sin\frac{1}{2}\gamma\sin\frac{1}{2}(a+b)$.

[61] $\Delta = \dfrac{\pi r^2 E}{180°}$.

[62] $\tan\frac{1}{4}E = \sqrt{\tan\frac{1}{2}s\tan\frac{1}{2}(s-a)\tan\frac{1}{2}(s-b)\tan\frac{1}{2}(s-c)}$

[63] $[r(\cos\theta + i\sin\theta)]^n = r^n[\cos n\theta + i\sin n\theta]$.

(DeMoivre's theorem, **Art. 121.**)

[64] $\sin\alpha = \alpha - \dfrac{\alpha^3}{|3} + \dfrac{\alpha^5}{|5} - \dfrac{\alpha^7}{|7} + \cdots$.

[65] $\cos\alpha = 1 - \dfrac{\alpha^2}{|2} + \dfrac{\alpha^4}{|4} - \dfrac{\alpha^6}{|6} + \cdots$.

[66] $\tan\alpha = \alpha + \dfrac{\alpha^3}{3} + \dfrac{2\alpha^5}{15} + \cdots$.

USEFUL CONSTANTS

1 cu. ft. of water weighs 62.5 lb. = 1000 oz.   (Approx.)

1 gal. of water weighs $8\frac{1}{3}$ lb.   (Approx.)

1 gal. = 231 cu. in. (by law of Congress).

1 bu. = 2150.42 cu. in. (by law of Congress).

1 bu. = 1.2446 — cu. ft. = $\frac{5}{4}$ cu. ft.   (Approx.)

1 cu. ft. = $7\frac{1}{2}$ gal.   (Approx.)

1 bbl. = 4.211 — cu. ft.

1 m. = 39.37 in. (by law of Congress).

1 in. = 25.4 mm.

1 ft. = 30.4801 cm.

1 kg. = 2.20462 lb.

1 g. = 15.432 gr.

1 lb. (avoirdupois) = 453.5924277 g. = 0.45359 + kg.

1 lb. (avoirdupois) = 7000 gr. (by law of Congress).

1 lb. (apothecaries) = 5760 gr. (by law of Congress).

1 l. = 1.05668 qt. (liquid) = 0.90808 qt. (dry).

1 qt. (liquid) = 946.358 cc. = 0.946358 l., or cu. dm.

1 qt. (dry) = 1101.228 cc. = 1.101228 l., or cu. dm.

π = 3.14159265358979 = 3.1416 = $\frac{355}{113}$ = $3\frac{1}{7}$.   (All approx.)

1 radian = 57° 17′ 44.8″ = 57.2957795° +.

1° = 0.01745329 + radian.

e = 2.718281828 +, the base of the Napierian logarithms.

INDEX

227